HISTORY OF THE OFFICE OF
SCIENTIFIC RESEARCH AND DEVELOPMENT

A summary of the activities of the entire organization in the development of improved weapons of warfare has been published as *Scientists Against Time* by James Phinney Baxter, 3rd. Details about the different parts of the organization are presented in a series of volumes with the common title, *Science in World War II,* which has been prepared under authority from:

Vannevar Bush, President, Carnegie Institution of Washington
Director, Office of Scientific Research and Development

James B. Conant, President, Harvard University
Chairman, National Defense Research Committee

Alfred N. Richards, Vice-President in charge of Medical Affairs, University of Pennsylvania
Chairman, Committee on Medical Research

Karl T. Compton, President, Massachusetts Institute of Technology
Chief, Office of Field Service

Science in World War II

NEW WEAPONS FOR AIR WARFARE
DIVISIONS 4, 5, AND 7 OF NDRC; SECTION T, OSRD

COMBAT SCIENTISTS
OFFICE OF FIELD SERVICE; NALOC; DOLOC

ADVANCES IN MILITARY MEDICINE
COMMITTEE ON MEDICAL RESEARCH

ROCKETS, GUNS, AND TARGETS
DIVISIONS 1, 2, AND 3 OF NDRC

CHEMISTRY
DIVISIONS 8, 9, 10, 11, 19 AND TDAC OF NDRC

APPLIED PHYSICS: ELECTRONICS; OPTICS; METALLURGY
DIVISIONS 13, 15, 16, 17, 18 AND COMMITTEE ON
PROPAGATION OF NDRC

ORGANIZING SCIENTIFIC RESEARCH FOR WAR
ADMINISTRATIVE FRAMEWORK OF OSRD

COMBAT SCIENTISTS

Scourge of the Pacific

Suicide Attacks were a major problem. Could the scientists create counter-weapons in time?

SCIENCE IN WORLD WAR II

Office of Scientific Research and Development

Combat Scientists

by LINCOLN R. THIESMEYER

and JOHN E. BURCHARD

VOLUME EDITOR

Alan T. Waterman

FOREWORD BY

Karl T. Compton

With Illustrations

An Atlantic Monthly Press Book

Little, Brown and Company • Boston

1947

FIRST EDITION

Published September 1947

ATLANTIC–LITTLE, BROWN BOOKS
ARE PUBLISHED BY
LITTLE, BROWN AND COMPANY
IN ASSOCIATION WITH
THE ATLANTIC MONTHLY PRESS

Published simultaneously
in Canada by McClelland and Stewart Limited

PRINTED IN THE UNITED STATES OF AMERICA

THE AUTHORS

Lincoln R. Thiesmeyer, the author of the history of the Office of Field Service, which forms Part One of this volume, was Head Technical Aide of that Office. He is now Executive Assistant to the Director of the Brookhaven National Laboratory.

John E. Burchard, the author of Part Two of this volume, which deals with the story of NALOC and DOLOC, served as Chairman of both those special committees of NDRC, in addition to holding other appointments within OSRD. He is now Director of Libraries at Massachusetts Institute of Technology.

Alan T. Waterman, the editor of the volume, was appointed Deputy Director of the Office of Field Service when it was organized, and its Director after July 1945. He is now Deputy Chief and Chief Scientist of the Office of Naval Research.

Karl T. Compton, the author of the Foreword, was a Member of the National Defense Research Committee throughout its period of existence and also the first Director of the Office of Field Service, from October 15, 1943, to July 31, 1945. He is President of the Massachusetts Institute of Technology.

PUBLISHER'S NOTE

Under the terms of the contract for the publication of *Combat Scientists* and of the other volumes in the long history of the activities of the Office of Scientific Research and Development, entitled *Science in World War II,* the publisher has agreed to waive its right under the copyright of each separate volume after ten years from the date of its publication. Thereafter the volume in question will be in the public domain and dedicated to the public.

This history of OSRD is intended to be a survey of the way in which certain weapons were developed, improved, or brought into use, not a complete documentary record of the making of the inventions that happen to be mentioned in it.

The authors and editor of this volume do not receive any royalty from its sale.

FOREWORD

THE term "combat scientists" first appeared in a letter from a member of the Office of Field Service in charge of a detachment of scientists operating in one of the war theaters, who had observed their successes and disappointments and the way in which they reacted to discomfort and difficulty. Describing these observations, he wrote: "To my mind there are two types of scientists, just as there are two kinds of soldiers — 'limited service' and 'combat.' Scientists to work with the armed forces in the field must be 'combat scientists,' — those who can do their job with little appreciation shown and often against odds."

Two different scientists, both excellent men, reported several months apart on their experiences on missions which happened to take them over about the same route in the Far Pacific. One of them was critical, disillusioned, and almost resentful over his experiences. He had struggled with red tape at every turn. He had had the greatest difficulty making arrangements to travel from one island to another. He felt that he had been continually slighted by the officers with whom he tried to deal, and attributed this to the fact that his "assimilated" officer's rank was not high enough to command respect. Nobody seemed to care whether he was there or not, or to wish his help. It was a sad and discouraging story.

The other man came back full of enthusiasm over both his accomplishment and his treatment. In view of the story of his predecessor on this route, he was asked whether he had ever been bothered by red tape and whether he ever had any difficulty in making travel arrangements. He seemed surprised at the question and said, "No, we never ran into any red tape. Whenever we wanted to go any place, we went down to the airport and asked if someone there would give us a lift, and everybody was always most co-operative." He said that he had had a "swell time," that everybody had seemed interested, and that he had succeeded in accomplishing everything which he had hoped for, and more.

Both of these men were competent laboratory scientists. The second was a combat scientist; the first was not. Fortunately, there were few in the ranks of the Office of Field Service who were not excellent combat scientists. Of course, to be exact one should say "combat scientists-engineers," for the engineers and scientists worked so closely together in field-service activities as well as in the development of new devices that for the most part the two were indistinguishable. As the war progressed the usefulness of this service became generally appreciated, its prestige grew, the difficulties diminished, and the opportunities were enhanced.

The idea of field service, to be rendered by research and development scientists, developed gradually during the war. It was one of the things not clearly envisaged at the beginning, when the whole scientific objective was to develop new instrumentalities of warfare or new medicines by scientific work in the laboratories. Soon, however, it was recognized that a certain amount of salesmanship was necessary if these valuable new devices were to be accepted, produced, and used. Before long, situations arose in which the laboratories had to undertake pilot plant construction of "crash program" equipment in order to take maximum advantage of the opportunities for its use while the large production by manufacturing companies was getting under way. Ultimately many of the scientists were spending a large portion of their time in co-operation with the manufacturers or with the branches of the Army and Navy charged with procurement.

Finally, when these new devices went into the field, it was usually found necessary to send with them some of the scientists who had been involved in their production, in order in the early stages to assist in their maintenance, to train the troops in their use, and even to advise the High Command regarding their tactical possibilities. It was even found necessary to establish branch laboratories in or near the active war theaters for the purpose of making quick repairs or new modifications to meet special tactical requirements. Scientific groups were established to analyze the performance of new equipment and, on the basis of actual records of such performance, they were able to advise regarding its most advantageous disposition or use or further modification.

By the early part of 1943 a considerable number of scientists had been dispatched to the European theater on various scientific missions as emissaries of the various Divisions of the Office of Scientific Research and Development. While in Europe they operated under the general supervision of the London office of OSRD. But later that year two large permanent groups were set up in England — the British Branch of the Radiation Laboratory under Division 14 and the American Branch Laboratory of Division 15, dealing respectively with radar and radar countermeasures.

Obviously the most efficient use of scientific talent for the purpose of winning the war would be achieved if scientists were shifted at an appropriate rate from their laboratories to the field. It was recognized, however, that the laboratories at home would continue to have a very important function right up to the end in supplying their representatives in the theaters with information, equipment, and from time to time with additional personnel. Consequently, the actual ultimate objective was an active field service in the theaters, backed up by adequate laboratory strength at home.

As a result of these considerations, Dr. Vannevar Bush, Director of OSRD, established the Office of Field Service by a directive dated October 15, 1943, and I was appointed Chief of this office. My first and best move was immediately to associate with me, as Deputy Chief, Professor Alan T. Waterman, and from this beginning, aided by the competent personnel subsequently attached to the office and with the finest of support from the Director of OSRD and personnel of all the Divisions of the National Defense Research Committee and the Committee on Medical Research, the program of the Office of Field Service developed as described in the following chapters.

One important decision was made very early, namely, that the Office of Field Service would not undertake to manage those field-service activities in the European theater which were already efficient, going concerns under the joint administration of their respective NDRC divisions at home and the London office of OSRD. The program of OFS was directed primarily to the Pacific where, because of the higher priority of the European war up to that time, the OSRD influence had as yet scarcely been felt. Consequently, all field-service activities in the Pacific were eventually developed and operated under OFS. There were, however, some special missions to the European theater — one organized by OFS in connection with scientific intelligence, several also on the utilization of new radar devices, especially in the urgent days just preceding the Normandy invasion. Also, the formal administration of the Operational Research Group in the Navy was transferred from Division 6, NDRC, to OFS.

Here let me pay tribute to a few of the many great combat scientists in OFS — Dr. George R. Harrison, Dr. Paul E. Klopsteg, and Dr. H. Kirk Stephenson, who successively headed the work of the Office of Field Service in the Southwest Pacific, and to Dr. Lauriston C. Marshall, who headed the Operational Research Section organized under Lieutenant General Robert C. Richardson in the Central Pacific. Their ability and good judgment won the recognition and support of the overburdened officers of this area, and their sense of humor enabled them to survive the inevitable difficulties in launching an activity without military precedent. Dr. Philip M. Morse, who directed a large operations research group for the Navy, was rarely in active theaters, but he had and used the attributes of the combat scientist in his daily negotiations with naval officers of all ranks. The contributions made by all these men and their associates in the many projects of OFS constitute an impressive record.

The New Developments Division of the Army and the Office of the Co-ordinator of Research and Development of the Navy were our Service partners in establishing this co-operative civilian-military activity. Without their sincere interest and support, it is doubtful if the effort at field service in the Pacific could have succeeded in any substantial way.

There was a steady development in the techniques, the opportunities, and the magnitude of the operations of the Office of Field Service during the twenty-three months from its establishment to the end of the Japanese war. The climax of its achievements was the establishment of the Pacific Branch, OSRD, under General MacArthur's command in Manila, with substations in other regions of the Pacific. This PBOSRD was a recognized operating unit in the organization of the Pacific theater; its director reported directly to General MacArthur's Chief of Staff; it had full advantage of military status. Nevertheless, its members retained civilian privileges essential to effective scientific work. It had free communication on all technical matters with the Office of

Field Service and with the supporting OSRD laboratories, and received from them its staff and equipment.

While the war happily ended before this organization got into full operation, the plans were complete, the steps had been authorized, and there is general agreement that it represented the peak of achievement in developing methods for field service by combat scientists. It could well be the starting model for field service in the event of any future war emergency.

KARL T. COMPTON

July 1, 1946

PREFACE

O NE of the broad problems encountered by the Office of Scientific Research and Development was that of providing the Army and Navy with expert scientific advice in field operations on the employment of new weapons, devices, and techniques. The purpose of this volume is to give an account of the many forms this assistance took and something of its scope, together with a glimpse of the manner in which this phase of OSRD activity was organized and operated.

Part One of this volume deals with the activities of the Office of Field Service, in which after 1943 were concentrated the field activities of OSRD. For the authorship of this Part OSRD was fortunate indeed in securing the services of Dr. Lincoln R. Thiesmeyer, who served as Head Technical Aide throughout the existence of the OFS. Dr. Thiesmeyer, well known as geologist and educator, came to the OFS at its establishment. From the very outset his ability, enthusiasm, and tireless energy proved a major factor in development of the OFS program. No happier choice for the writing of the OFS history could have been made, and it is indeed a pleasure to make here a most appreciative acknowledgment of his major contributions to the permanent record of OFS.

Part Two contains chapters devoted to studies conducted by two special committees under the National Defense Research Committee, dealing with landing operations in their navigational and demolition aspects, respectively. The author of these chapters, Professor John E. Burchard, formerly Professor of Architecture at the Massachusetts Institute of Technology and currently Director of Libraries at the same institution, was chairman of both committees. He had a varied and distinguished career during the war. At the outset he was Chairman of the Committee on Passive Protection Against Bombing under the National Research Council, then Chief of Division 2 of NDRC, concerned with "Effects of Impact and Explosion." In 1944 he joined the staff of the Office of Field Service, OSRD, on special mission to Army

Headquarters, Central Pacific Area, from which he returned to serve as Assistant Chief and later Deputy Chief of OFS, and finally, after V-J Day, as Chairman of the OSRD Committee on Publications. It is with pleasure and gratitude that acknowledgment is made here of his authoritative account of the interesting and important work of his committees.

Grateful mention should be made also of the more indirect contributions of Dr. David M. Delo, Technical Aide of OFS, whose final report included extremely valuable summaries and analyses of OFS activities useful to the historian, and of Dr. Howard W. Troyer, consultant to OFS, whose critical survey of projects and recorded interviews with returning field personnel have likewise been helpful. Especial thanks are also due Mrs. Mildred A. Mooney, secretary to Dr. Thiesmeyer, for her loyal and efficient assistance in the typing and arranging of the manuscript, and to Mrs. Margaret C. Hopkins and Miss Mary E. Jorgensen for similar assistance to Professor Burchard.

Finally, a tribute should here be paid to the entire staff of OFS, whose wholehearted co-operation and loyal support under the inspiring leadership of Dr. Karl T. Compton, Chief of the Office of Field Service throughout most of its history, made possible the operations described herein. The firm backing provided at critical times by Dr. Vannevar Bush, Director of OSRD, and the generous assistance of administrative officers in all its research and development branches and its central staff were essential ingredients in the success of OFS. It has been an inspiration to have been associated with so capable and loyal a group.

ALAN T. WATERMAN
Chief, Office of Field Service

July 1, 1946

CONTENTS

ILLUSTRATIONS

PART ONE

History of the Office
of Field Service

by

LINCOLN R. THIESMEYER

CHAPTER I

BLUEPRINT FOR FIELD SERVICE

THE CIVILIAN SPECIALIST GOES UP FRONT

THE SCIENTIST closed his eyes for a moment as the needles sank repeatedly into the flesh of his upper arm. Then the Army nurse entered the date — December 17, 1943 — on the long white cards opposite each of the shots he had just taken. Smallpox, typhoid, tetanus, typhus, and cholera — the whole series.

The Army had waived the customary rule that immunizations be completed before departure. He could get the second and third sets of inoculations en route and in the combat areas. The military could always set aside such regulations when a matter seemed urgent enough. And they had asked that he be prepared to leave in less than three days.

Meanwhile in other offices of the Pentagon and in the Navy Building machinery was already in motion to provide the documents and credentials needed to get him off speedily and introduce him to the foremost commanding officers of both Army and Navy at Pacific outposts. Red tape was cut and papers were moving swiftly from office to office. The traveler was an outstanding man of American science, Dr. Karl T. Compton, one of the famous Compton brothers, President of Massachusetts Institute of Technology and a leading figure in the Office of Scientific Research and Development. This was OSRD, the Government's war agency that had done such amazing work in helping to create new secret weapons for our side — radar, rockets, bazookas, DUKW's, and a lot of others.

All week Dr. Compton had spent most of his time in sessions at the topmost levels in Washington — with the Secretary of War's Office, with a score of admirals and generals of the Allied High Command, with Dr. Vannevar Bush, Director of OSRD, and with his scientific colleagues who planned and supervised the work of its many subdivisions. As Chief of the newly-established Office of Field Service (OFS) in OSRD, Compton was asked to confer with Admiral Nimitz and Lieutenant General Richardson in Hawaii, with Lieutenant General Harmon in Nouméa, with General MacArthur in Australia, and with the highest officers of their staffs. These men commanded the three major areas in which the Pacific war was then being fought. Both the military and civilian scientific organizations at home wanted to know in detail and at first hand what critical problems our forces were encountering in the use of the many new devices and implements of combat that now were pouring from the production lines, what countermeasures might be contrived to render the secret weapons of the Japanese less effective, and, more specifically, if civilian specialists were sent directly to the combat areas from the laboratories and war plants, how they could help to solve these problems. Wartime communications by courier letter, teletype, or radio could never be a substitute for on-the-spot discussions between an expert familiar with the behavior of a contrivance and men who knew its effectiveness in combat.

Dr. Compton had been chosen for this assignment because of his familiarity with the whole war research and development effort of American science. As an original member of the National Defense Research Committee (NDRC), master planning group in the OSRD, which had organized comprehensive war research in university and industrial laboratories all over the country, he had an intimate knowledge of the manifold applications of science and engineering to a war that was becoming increasingly a contest for technological supremacy. The institution he headed had become the chief center for the development of radar, and this was only one of the many marvelous instruments devised by the powerful corps of scientists assembled there. Moreover, he knew quite well how necessary it is that specialists go into the field with new equipment to help in teaching troops to use it properly, to diagnose the difficulties when it does not work as was expected, and to keep the laboratories at home informed of changes that might adapt it to uses in the field that were not foreseen in its original design. The Radiation Laboratory of M.I.T. had even established a British Branch (BBRL) in England to provide such services closer to the front lines of Europe. And the Radio Research Laboratory at Harvard, likewise an OSRD-supported activity, had set up a Branch Laboratory (ABL-15) in England to serve the same purposes in the use of countermeasures to Germany's radar.

In the days preceding this trip Dr. Compton's schedule had been an

exhausting round of activities. It was probably not much more demanding than his customary program as head of one of the nation's
most active centers of war research and special technical education,
nor than the preceding two months had been when his Office of Field
Service was swinging into operation. In addition to the usual list of
conferences, however, it was filled with a multitude of items relating
to his personal comfort, safety, and effectiveness on the long Pacific
journey. Moreover he had to confer with the heads of OSRD units
that worked on rockets, medicine, underwater devices, chemical warfare, metallurgy, and special weapons, with Australian representatives
of the British Commonwealth Scientific Office (BCSO), with a radar
subcommittee set up by the Joint Chiefs of Staff, and with representatives of both Army and Navy technical branches. At Cambridge,
Massachusetts, in the remaining two days there were further talks
with OSRD leaders in radar, radar countermeasures, guided missiles,
and optical devices; sessions with his administrative aides at M.I.T.;
a radio broadcast; an officers' Christmas ball; and last-minute packing.

On Sunday evening, December 19, Dr. Compton stepped aboard a
plane at the Boston Airport, headed for California. His locked briefcase contained pages and pages of questions from the Divisions of
NDRC and from the Army and Navy, questions for which he was
to find the answers in conversations with officers in the Pacific: how
were the new weapons working out; what were the most troublesome
technical problems in those areas; what had the officers heard about
new techniques in medicine; what sort of help from the research organizations would they welcome? He was dressed as an officer, but
he wore no insignia of rank for he was still a civilian. In his pocket
was a card from the Adjutant General's Office (AGO) which identified
him as an Expert Consultant to the Secretary of War and a noncombatant. It specified that if he were captured the enemy should
treat him as they would a Colonel in our regular Army.

Traveling on a Priority # 1 from Boston, he would have gone straight
through to the Coast and been out over the Pacific in less than two days.
But weather grounded the plane in Winslow, Arizona, and he rode
all night in a bus to Los Angeles. This was typical of the delays that
upset the plans of travelers on urgent war business.

Arriving in San Francisco, he checked in at the Air Transport Command (ATC) and then, completely fagged, sank into eleven hours of sleep. The next day there were more shots in the arm — second typhus and second cholera — then the lecture about ditching procedure that the ATC supplies for its patrons at ports of aerial embarkation. What to do if the gas runs out, or the engines fail, or the plane is mortally hit by flak.

The next morning a huge, greenish-gray dragonfly with a white star on its flanks crawled out of the hangar. In a few moments its wings were spread over the Pacific. It carried the highest-ranking scientific emissary OSRD had yet sent westward. Dr. Karl T. Compton, Chief of OFS, was off on a circuit which might be the most significant trip of his thirty-odd years as a national figure in American life.

In the European theater of war scientists from OSRD had been working closely with the military forces for many months. Some were attached at high staff levels as special advisors to the commanding officers. Others were providing field service in the installation and maintenance of new devices, studying their use in operations, improvising changes that would lead to better performance. Retaining their status as civilians but wearing the uniform of the Service to which they were assigned, they worked at command posts, aboard battleships, and in headquarters offices throughout the theater.

Hundreds of new weapons created or perfected by OSRD were already in use. Since the Allied High Command considered the campaign against Germany of first importance, most of the newer materiel had been allocated to the forces preparing for the invasion of Europe. Operating more and more specialized editions of these items to fullest advantage called for hundreds of experts. The Army and Navy had undertaken a stupendous task of mass technical education. But there just was not time to turn a farmhand or a grocery clerk, for instance, into a competent radar or rocket technician and then keep him abreast of the latest models. Under such conditions the effectiveness of our newest weapons in bombers over Africa and on cruisers in the Atlantic fell far short of what specialists had predicted from unrealistic tests at home. Consequently the Armed Forces urged that OSRD laboratories send their representatives to military positions overseas along with this new equipment to help teach the troops how best to use it.

In London OSRD had established a Liaison Office two years earlier to encourage and co-ordinate the exchange of scientific information with Allied governments. This office had acquired a small staff of specialists in various fields of science. In effect, this represented a growing pool of especially competent technical men close to the front, already processed for overseas service, ready to go into action at once. As the pace of the war in Europe accelerated, these men were repeatedly called forward to counsel with commanders about the new, ingenious, and complicated contraptions which their colleagues in America had designed. Thereby, the London office really formed an advance center of information from which officers could get pertinent details about the latest devices placed in their hands or under development in this country. Its channels of communication to OSRD laboratories were direct. Its civilian scientists, relatively unhampered by military restrictions, could travel freely back to the States to bring to the laboratories, in turn, detailed descriptions of the performance of weapons OSRD had developed. In short, OSRD was well known in the European and Mediterranean areas. A continual stream of its specialists was circulating among the troops; its inventions were supporting the mounting offensive.

At this stage in the war the situation in the Pacific was far different. The campaign was spread over a much larger area, supply lines were long, and communications slow. The military operations were sporadic and involved smaller numbers of men, munitions, and equipment. The new creations of science that were proving so effective against the Nazis were only beginning to filter in limited quantities into the island areas. Transportation was at a premium and few agents from OSRD had traveled through Pacific theaters acquainting officers with the potentialities of scientific aid up front. The military operations themselves presented wholly different problems because of the terrain, the climate, and the tactics of the enemy. Weapons that were devastating in the open, arid stretches of Africa might be almost useless in the dank and thickly forested defiles of New Guinea. Vehicles that had raced across the sandy beaches of the Mediterranean might bog down quickly on the coral atolls of the Marshalls.

Nowhere in the millions of square miles of the Pacific which we still held was there an OSRD office like the one in London that could keep the combat units posted about our progress with secret weapons and their potency in the growing battle on the other side of the globe. There were no OSRD scientists attached as consultants to aid in planning the operations, no groups of special counselors working with the troops. Channels of communication were exasperatingly slow. On many occasions information sent out from laboratories or technical branches of the Armed Services never got to the right parties in the field; and operational information from the field was misdirected or buried before it reached the proper agencies at home. With such a meager flow of technical intelligence the laboratories could not find out quickly how their products were being employed, how they should be modified to meet better the needs of a local situation, or what new ones should be devised.

MacArthur's headquarters was still located in Australia; yet the exchange of scientific information with our allies that could bring about a co-ordinated impact of both American and Australian science on Pacific problems had to be carried out at long range through British offices in Washington or London. The Australian technical men were closer to those problems. They were doing splendid work on aspects of jungle fighting that were almost beyond the ken of American researchers. We had much to gain from collaboration with them.

Only a few representatives from OSRD had previously been in the Pacific. Invitations for others to come out were infrequent. Having no established experience with the commands in that area to guide them and with no well-connected and efficient liaison office like the one in London to introduce and steer them, the OSRD pioneers who had been in that area had only intuition to govern their dealings with the complicated military organizations they encountered. Despite such handicaps some of these emissaries were able to make suggestions which the commands welcomed and used effectively; but some of them also (and perhaps quite innocently) left a trail of misunderstanding and antagonism. Unfortunately some of the prejudices were not in low places. The failure lay partly in the fact that the men who went on these ventures traveled at too high a level, passed through the theater too rapidly, and oversold their equipment. Partly it lay in the accepted principle of the military that weapons under development that have not been approved after exhaustive tests on the proving grounds at home are not to be sold to commanding officers in the field. It would not do for an OSRD scientist to whet the appetite of harried field forces for implements that could not possibly be in their hands for many months, or that might not reach them at all because the whole available supply would be allocated to an area considered more critical by the highest councils of the over-all command.

Several factors contributed to the resentments that sometimes developed and that seemed to produce resistance to the use of civilian scientific aid in the Pacific theaters. More of the antagonism was due to normal human foibles than to logic. But human attitudes are not refashioned by a declaration of war; they may be only restrained by patriotic sentiments.

The officers of a field command must be welded into a team. They have been together a long time in difficult places and are responsible for what happens. It is not easy for them to understand a man who, perhaps younger than themselves, comes in a uniform but without true rank, enjoys their privileges but is not subject to their handicaps, who is not going to stay and sweat it out with them, who often gets "high echelon" conferences by going over their heads. Furthermore he might even go back to the mainland and quote them to make a point. The man who did this would be regarded as a menace, whatever the honesty of his intent and sincerity of purpose. In itself this would not be too serious if officers in responsible positions could avoid the natural impulse to generalize the behavior of one or two men into a conclusion as to how any and all civilians are likely to behave in a theater of war.

Unfortunately there were officers too, often in position to be very difficult, who made no serious attempt to understand why civilians were needed at the front and who appeared to be doing everything they could to prevent them from coming, or to keep them from being useful when they did arrive. The underlying motives behind such actions are hard to discover. Part of their attitude may be attributed to indoctrination in traditions of the Army and Navy, which tacitly seem to imply that an individual who is not literally and legally a part of the organization must be regarded with apprehension. Part of it certainly resulted from lack of knowledge about the OSRD organization and the ways in which scientists were helping out in the combat zones elsewhere.

Theater officers were inherently sensitive lest criticism of the performance of new devices under their control reflect on the skill or the discipline of the command. Their natural tendency was to try to fix things up in the theater rather than let the scientists in the laboratories become aware of the problem. If the fault were in reality in the theater, this would make little difference. But where it lay in the equipment itself it was serious. In the time schedules of war new gear may have been brought into action before all the "bugs" in its operation were found and before the real limitations that surround any piece of equipment were known. Although it had been tested adequately at home, it might have reached the zone of operations with inadequate instructions and been improperly installed and used on the first operational trials. Its failure would prejudice the officers against a perfectly sound device. On the other hand, the new weapon might perform so remarkably in its first use against the enemy that the officers would accept it as miraculous, expect it to do things for which it was not intended, and then be discouraged to the point of rejecting it when it did not live up to their hopes.

OSRD was, of course, anxious to make existing weapons more effective regardless of who had contrived them; but its primary responsibilities lay in research and development. Until firsthand information about the performance of a device in operation was available, modifications might be proposed that seemed sensible from the laboratory point of view but that were unrealistic in view of human limitations in combat. The expert who designed and tested a weapon could easily but erroneously conclude that anyone should be able to extract an equally satisfactory performance. The Divisions and the research laboratories of NDRC were aware of these fallacies from experience in the European area. They were eager to get their men into the theaters so that the directions of emphasis in their research effort could be determined more realistically. They felt, moreover, that if only the forces in the field could see or hear about the merits of a device they had produced, pressure from the theater would help to break some of the procurement jams at home. But it was always difficult to arrange entree for NDRC representatives into the Pacific. There was no civilian liaison office operating in the comparative freedom of a sovereign state. There was only the restrictive atmosphere of theaters of war under the absolute control of single military commanders and their staffs. Until OSRD could place its representatives on a more or less permanent basis at strategic positions throughout that area the military would not get the kind of help which the scientists surmised would be essential; and the scientists who did go out would not be able to operate with the freedom to assure a more intelligent, more efficient attack by the research laboratories on Pacific problems.

Consequently the primary purposes of Dr. Compton's journey to that area would be to spread a knowledge of the aid that might be obtained from OSRD, to find out quite precisely the directions in which that aid would be most needed, and to explore the possibilities for improving liaison with civilian scientific organizations of our allies.

One might properly ask why high authorities in Washington who appreciated the need for civilian assistance did not simply issue orders to the embattled officers at the front and send the scientists out. The answer lies in the long-accepted doctrine that in a theater of war the theater commander is virtually a czar. The War and Navy Departments at home refrain from intervening in the way he manages his area so long as he conforms to the broad directives they have issued. These general instructions give him considerable latitude. Officers, men, and civilians do not travel into or leave the theater save with his consent. Usually this takes the form of approval of a proposal originating among officers of his staff — or, rarely, in the agencies at home. If, as is so frequently the case, a particular need for scientific help is first felt well down in the chain of command, the proposed solution may be (and often is) prevented from ever reaching the attention of the general staff by the negative reaction of an unsympathetic officer occupying a higher position in the chain.

The reluctance of Pacific officers to ask for OSRD help was, therefore, not to be attributed primarily to prejudice or antagonism among the topmost generals and admirals of that area. They were reputed to be men of vision and liberal outlook who would probably welcome all the assistance they could get in technical matters once they understood the possibilities. But they were preoccupied with manifold problems of supply and strategy. They had to hold their lines against further Japanese expansion while they organized and trained the contingents that would open the gigantic attack. At that time many believed it would be necessary not only to recapture territory lost in the early months, but also to drive the enemy out of eastern Asia. Absorbed in such grave problems, they could surely not keep up with scientific progress in the home laboratories; and they might not even be aware of the numerous technical difficulties encountered by the troops. A brief personal conference with a man of Dr. Compton's stature could do much to familiarize them with the progress of the laboratories and with the effective aid rendered by OSRD field men in other theaters. They had no time to obtain this information from reading scores of technical reports. And, although top-command sympathy with the objective of placing scientists in the theaters could not dispel completely the opposition and the biases of men in lower echelons with whom the specialists would have to work, it could at least set up broad approvals that would encourage scientists to come out and prove themselves in day-to-day contact with the troops. Thus Dr. Compton's trip frankly had its missionary aspects. Both the OSRD and the Technical Services looked to him to smooth the way for increasing the flow of technical intelligence to and from the Pacific and for wider acceptance by our forces there of the field consulting services now offered them from home.

When the big transport settled down at Hickam Field on the island of Oahu, Dr. Compton was met by Brigadier General William O. Ryan, Commanding General of the Pacific Wing, and his executive officer, Lieutenant Colonel Ralph G. Lockwood, his hosts for the Hawaiian stopover. Then for four days he was engrossed in business conferences with the staff officers of the Central Pacific Area. He talked with Admiral Nimitz, Commander in Chief; Admiral Lockwood, Commander of Pacific Submarines; Admirals Sherman, McMorris, and Dunn; and with the key officers of the Navy headquarters staff. He also consulted with Lieutenant General Robert C. Richardson, Commanding General of Army forces in the area, and his staff. In the evenings he met these same leaders at social functions and continued his conversations with them informally. Here, as elsewhere in the Pacific, he was received warmly by numerous men in high official places who had been trained at M.I.T. and felt a personal responsibility for making his visit comfortable and successful.

Admiral Nimitz was friendly and became interested in the proposal for expanding the limited use of OSRD scientists in the theater on Navy problems. This was a hopeful sign of change in the attitude of resistance to civilians which the Navy had earlier maintained in the Pacific and, indeed, in some places at home. Later the Office of Field Service set up a group of specialists under Army auspices in the Central Pacific which provided considerable help to the Navy on an informal, unofficial basis. The more formal requests for aid usually went through Navy channels to be screened in Washington before they came to the attention of OSRD.

General Richardson was receptive to the suggestion that civilian consultants be attached to his headquarters staff. He had already talked with his officers about technical needs and had thought of requesting a group of "operations analysts" for the Army Ground Forces like those he had heard were doing splendid work for the Air Forces in other theaters. He asked that Dr. Compton stop off again on his return from Australia to consider the matter further. This was an added sign that there might be an entering wedge for extending civilian help in that part of the Pacific.

The take-off from Hawaii was delayed for several hours by mechanical trouble with the plane. Finally just after midnight Dr. Compton was again airborne, this time in a C-54 with a large cargo and eight fellow passengers. At Canton Island a tire damaged in landing postponed departure until the early hours of the next day. Dr. Compton was certainly learning that even the highest-priority passengers could not always keep a rigid schedule.

During the long hops he had a chance to look over the material in his briefcase from his scientist associates and from the Technical Services and to plan the optimum approach for collecting so much information in so short a time. He could also reminisce about the steps that had led to the establishment of this Office of Field Service which now claimed his major attention. He could review the reasons why scientists should be needed in the theaters at all, rather than in the laboratories. And, if needed in the field, why they could not simply become full-fledged officers in the military and naval arms so that the problem of helping the Services to work out effective means for handling *civilian* specialists and capitalizing their talents would never have arisen. Officers and civilians alike were constantly asking these questions, wondering especially why scientists should not become permanently attached to the Armed Forces, in uniform and with true rank, bound by all the military regulations — in short, why they should not be soldiers, sailors, and marines like their fellow men. Even at the war's end not every high-ranking officer in either Service agreed with the OFS answers; but more and more of the High Command had come to accept the OSRD point of view.

There were several justifications for transferring scientists from research to field application. The Army and Navy, ultimate users of the intricate new weapons, could easily recognize the need for highly skilled help in installing devices properly, keeping them in good operating condition, and instructing the GI in methods for securing the maximum benefit from them. More reluctantly they might admit that scientists could help to determine qualitatively and to evaluate quantitatively the Service requirements for new equipment. A man who knows what areas several models of sound detector will cover under average field conditions, who knows exactly how their performance will vary with changes in those conditions, how the instruments will withstand the rough treatment they get in combat, and who understands both the mechanical and the human factors that reduce their efficiency, is the person to select the model that will yield the best results in a particular situation. If he knows the operational plans, he can also determine how many of them will be needed. He may decide that none of the existing types will do and a new one should be designed and rushed into production on specifications he lays down. On the other hand, mindful that it takes a long time to bring about redesign back home, he may recognize that slight modification in the field of a model already in use will accomplish the purpose faster and equally well. Sometimes this man is an officer. But few officers have the necessary combination of technical knowledge and operational information. The scientist alone cannot reach sound conclusions either, unless he gains a familiarity with actual operating conditions and the intended uses of the device. He can only get such background satisfactorily through intimate contact with the conditions and with the personnel. The best judgments in such matters will obviously come from teamwork between the civilian scientist and the military man, teamwork that does not have to depend on long-range exchange of reports, that gets results because the members of the team work side by side in the field.

Tactical and strategic planning of military campaigns have traditionally and properly been the prerogatives and responsibilities of military men. Scientists are not trained for such activities. Yet a group of mature technical men with broad knowledge of the many devices to be utilized in an offensive could surely prove practical as *advisors* to the planning boards. The scientists would not make the ultimate decisions or issue the orders and supervise their execution; they would merely suggest the best weapons to use and the most effective methods of employing them. Skill in planning, based on thorough knowledge of equipment, might be fully as important in the outcome of an operation as improvement in the technique of using that equipment. The truth of this was recognized by the supreme command at home where Dr. Bush and some of his colleagues in OSRD were repeatedly called in on the master plans. It was equally true but not so readily acknowledged in the theaters, where tactical decisions often had to be taken hourly. To entrust information about past operations to civilian scientists was heresy in the minds of many officers — to let them participate in planning future ones seemed like downright treason. This point of view could not be changed by argument through the mails, or even by orders from Washington. Efforts to break it down in writing might only result in greater misunderstanding. It was a long process to win the confidence of these men to the extent that they would even invite the civilian consultant to attend staff sessions devoted to planning. Their apprehension would disappear gradually and only after the scientists had worked closely with them for many months.

The laboratory man sent to the field would have multiple responsibilities. He must see to it that new gear was properly adjusted and in excellent working condition before its first use in combat, and that it was handled correctly. He must strive to reserve it for the purposes for which it was intended and yet be alert to new uses to which it could be adapted quickly. He must do everything he could to increase the flow of information between the field forces and the laboratories, interpreting the practical facts to the technical establishments and the technical possibilities to the operating staffs.

There was still another reason for sending scientists to the combat areas. Officers are usually too encumbered with their duties of command and housekeeping to spend time analyzing past operations in order to learn ways of improving future ones. Moreover, such analysis may require experience with statistical methods, knowledge of the laws of probability, familiarity with the techniques for reaching reasonably valid conclusions from masses of incomplete data. These are things which many scientists acquire as a matter of course in their basic training. It would be a decided advantage to a theater commander to have a staff of such people, specialists in what is known as "operational analysis" or "operations research," available at his headquarters. They would have the requisite ability and could devote their full time to such studies.

Although the military men might concede that scientists would be useful in the field and invite them to come, they could not understand as easily why they should remain civilians. The simplest explanation lay in the indisputable fact that the supply of scientists was inadequate. Had technical men been drawn into the Services in large numbers, the research and development programs would have been utterly crippled. This contention carried greater appeal, of course, to those who had to steer research than to those responsible for command. One limitation on the number of experts available for field duty was the fact that not all scientists are endowed with the personal traits requisite to success in an activity where temperament, diplomacy, adaptability, and skill in self-expression may be as important as technical competence. This was appreciated more fully by military people than by research staffs. An able laboratory man who did not possess the characteristics which would justify calling him an effective "combat scientist" could make a more significant contribution to the war by staying in his laboratory.

The insistence of OSRD that its field men retain civilian status was based also on other considerations. These have to do with the nature of Army and Navy organization. For obvious reasons every member of a Service must be assigned a specific rank. Traditionally it has been an accepted principle that the rank borne by an officer is a measure of the power of his opinion. The fallacy of this doctrine is obvious when one compares individuals on the basis of their intelligence, experience, and training, and it leads to inequalities and injustices. Many a youthful GI, drafted from an important executive position in civil life, was decidedly more capable in many ways than the officers placed over him. The same thing happens in the world of affairs, of course, where the new employee may be inherently far more able than his immediate superiors. In both cases the greater ability may eventually be recognized in promotions. But this takes time. Applied to the functions of command or to the strictly military matters in which an officer of higher rank has had more training and carries greater responsibility than one of lower rank, the principle is reasonable. But applied to scientific matters in which the military do not have extensive training, it can be disastrous. Nevertheless it is a characteristic of the system.

Low rank almost inevitably reduces an officer's effectiveness at a high-level conference, while high rank precludes a free exchange of information between the officer and the GI except at the level of the foxhole. On the other hand, a civilian, free of rank, can converse with the commanding general one moment and with a corporal or private the next. In a conference his right to be heard and the weight given to his words are not dependent upon the clothes he wears or the title he holds. This has its less desirable aspects too, of course. Lacking the responsibility for command, the civilian may be and often is idealistic, impractical, and even "harebrained" in the opinion of officers with whom he deals.

In a period of expanding military and naval operations, commanding officers are continually short of able staff personnel. Officers assigned to them are commonly drawn into immediate administrative tasks. This means that an officer-scientist can never be sure that he will spend his time and energy entirely on the scientific work he feels is necessary. He may prove able in administrative duties because he is intelligent and skilled. If so, he may be held in them more or less permanently; and they may increase. His commander, admitting that this is wasteful of special talents, may be hesitant to change the situation because the man sent as a replacement might not be as useful in the administrative job.

Officers can not be moved easily from theater to theater, nor can they be spared readily for return to the mainland. A man assigned to one operating command becomes a vital part of a team. Substitutions take time and paper work and transportation, and are resisted, even if they only involve short visits. Continual shifting of officer personnel would wreck the morale of any theater in which it became the rule. Few scientists could be most effectively used throughout the war in a single theater. After solving the problems for which they were originally requested they could still be helpful enough on minor matters so that, if they were regular officers, the theater would not be willing to release them. But they would not be working at full efficiency. Meanwhile a critical problem might have developed in some other theater or at home that would require the attention of men with precisely their special technical skills. During the war it was believed that six months was the longest interval a specialist could remain away from the laboratories without getting thoroughly out of date. The course of scientific progress was so rapid that longer absence would cause a man to lose his qualification as an up-to-the-minute expert. Communications were not good enough for him to keep up by reading reports and letters from the development groups, or to supply the laboratories with the detailed information about field conditions that would be possible in a personal visit.

There was yet another reason for encouraging a constant movement of civilian scientists between the research organizations and the field, despite the resistance of those in the Army and Navy who failed to admit the need for civilian help. Theater personnel repeatedly proposed setting up their own research facilities to test and modify equipment, while the home laboratories were steadily forced to substitute local field tests under imagined and simulated rather than real conditions for tests that should have been made in the waters and over the ground where the equipment was to be used. To set up additional research laboratories in the theaters would have meant a further drain on the nation's already short supply of scientific brains. To predict the usefulness of new devices from their behavior under artificial conditions could only lead to disappointment with performance in the crucial testing ground of battle. Itinerant scientists on temporary missions could meet most of the needs that stimulated a desire for laboratories in the field. They could help to break down the Service restrictions against field testing of new gear, or they could bring back the detailed information that would make the tests at home more realistic. And, since officers are less mobile, as we have seen, it was preferable that these travelers be civilians.

In summary, the scientist sent to the field remained in civilian status so that he could deal with men of all ranks with equal freedom; so that he could avoid dilution of his work with routine administrative tasks; so that he could be moved quickly as the priority of needs for his talents required; so that he would retain a prime allegiance to the laboratory that had released him temporarily and would return as promptly as possible when it was felt that he was no longer able to work at full capacity on the field assignment.

Dr. Compton's short stops at Nandi in the Fiji Islands and at New Caledonia were without incident and permitted only sketchy sightseeing. He had left Canton Island at one in the morning; that night he dined in the hotel at Brisbane, Australia, site of the Allied General Headquarters (GHQ). For three weeks his schedule was a whirl of conferences, meetings, more conferences, visits to American and Australian military installations, civilian research and scientific liaison organizations, universities, industrial plants turning out new weapons like our own, and social functions at which he was the distinguished visitor and guest of honor.

General MacArthur was interested in the prospect of civilian scientific help in the Southwest Pacific Area (SWPA) but wanted assurance that the problems encountered by his men could be met most effectively that way. He welcomed Dr. Compton as a man eminently qualified to survey the needs and prepare proposals for specific action based on the opinions of a large section of his command. At GHQ Dr. Compton spent many hours with the military and naval leaders, men whose names have since been headlined in the story of our triumphs — Lieutenant General Richard K. Sutherland, Deputy Commander in Chief, Generals Casey (engineers), Marquat (antiaircraft), Kenney (Far East Air Force), Frink (Services of Supply), Admiral

Kinkaid — and with scores of their aides, staff officers in the GHQ organization, the Technical Services, the Services of Supply, and the Navy. He talked with numerous Australian civilian scientists and technologists and with many officer-scientists. Their conversations touched on virtually the whole gamut of research applied to war purposes.

He flew up to New Guinea with Major General Spencer B. Akin, Chief Signal Officer, who was later to play a key role in OSRD's relations with that theater, and talked at Port Moresby with General Whitehead, Chief of Staff of the Fifth Air Force; then over the Owen Stanley Mountains to Lae, Salamaua, and Finschhafen to see General Krueger, commander of the Sixth Army; and to Buna and Goodenough Island for sessions with the amphibious forces and with the Alamo Scouts who operated commando-fashion. He went to Melbourne and Sydney to discuss co-operation with the British scientists, especially in the fields of radar, radio, countermeasures, and communications.

In the chinks of his time he managed to swim at some of the famous Australian beaches, stopped at the zoo to see the duck-billed platypus, the kookaburra, koala, and other queer animals found only on that continent, and took in an occasional movie.

It was abundantly clear that the aid of science was needed in that theater and would be welcomed. A complete list of the items mentioned as pressing needs by the hundreds of men who talked with him would fill many pages. Some of the requests and the work done by OSRD personnel to meet them are described in later sections of this book. The great variety of problems on which the help of civilians might be sought can be recognized in an enumeration of only a few of the problems.

OSRD observers reported that SWPA seemed to be the "poor relation" in matters of equipment, munitions, supplies, and manpower. In some departments the forces were still managing on stores and materiel left over from the last war, items that had not been designed to withstand use in tropical jungles. The newer weapons in their hands that had been developed early in this war were already obsolete because much better ones had been produced and were in use in Europe. The combat units had too little, and they were doing the best they could with what they had. Repairing planes with "baling wire" and then going on bombing missions was almost as common an experience here as it was to Chennault's Fighting Tigers in Burma. Spare parts for equipment that broke down under severe conditions and long-continued use were not coming through fast enough. There was a widespread need for competent scientists and engineers to aid in conversions, or in constructing makeshift equipment with which to carry on current operations. There was also the threat of Japanese submarine action against the long supply lines to cut off even the little they did get. Defenses against this menace, based on the notably successful antisubmarine war in the Atlantic, would surely have to be strengthened.

Improved radar sets were needed for navigation, for aid in amphibious assault, for warning against the enemy's air raids, and for locating his shipping. Japanese barges, hugging the irregular coastline, were slipping through under cover of night to supply and reinforce the Nipponese positions. Techniques for detecting and disposing of them had to be developed without exposing our ships or aircraft to attack from shore-based guns or planes and without mining the waters we wished to use for our own ships later. Radar gear frequently performed peculiarly in the varied atmospheric conditions among the numberless islands. More information was wanted about how physical conditions affect the propagation of radar pulses. Reconnaissance squadrons wanted all the help they could get from devices to locate and jam the Japanese radar.

Some of the newer items already in use in all the other theaters — gun directors and fire-control equipment, new types of radio, radar, and other implements — had at long last reached this theater; but they arrived without adequate instructions and unaccompanied by technicians who knew how to set them up and use them. Some were damaged or thrown out of adjustment in repeated handling during the long journey. If not properly tuned, their behavior in the first operational use might be discouraging. Experts were needed to help get them into operation, to spread knowledge about their performance personally, and to assist in initial use of other new equipment that might soon be available.

Special devices to be designed for particular conditions were also in demand — belt conveyors for loading and unloading LST's and

LCT's, special containers to protect food and apparatus against deterioration, a machine for straightening the metal landing mats on temporary airstrips, highly specialized implements for close-in, undercover fighting and for demolishing underwater obstacles to landing operations.

Here, as in the China-Burma-India area, the troops were beset with malaria, fungus, and all sorts of strange maladies with which their medical officers had had little experience. The specter of permanent disability from one of these ailments haunted them continually and lowered their morale. Prospects that they could get away to duty in other areas were poor. A replacement schedule was already in effect, but it could only be applied in a limited fashion to this area because transportation facilities were so crowded. The medical men and sanitation officers were making a heroic stand against the forces of disease and decay, but they needed desperately consultation with the ablest specialists in psychiatry, dermatology, and epidemiology who might be procured on a temporary basis from the mainland.

It was evident that co-operation from American scientists would be welcomed by the Australian authorities. Their laboratories and manufacturers were developing and producing equipment much needed by our forces; but their research facilities and scientific manpower were even more limited than our own. The Australian Council for Scientific and Industrial Research (CSIR) urged that arrangements be made to send American experts on radio and radar to work with their technical men at the Radiophysics Laboratory in Sydney on an extensive study of radio-wave propagation. This would include investigations of the ionosphere to permit daily prediction of the most advantageous frequency channels for radio communications and also a study of the propagation of radio waves along the surface of the earth. This last was most important in short-range transmission through jungle and mountainous terrain. Certain types of radar equipment that had not been under intensive development in the United States or United Kingdom were being brought to pilot production for both Australian and American forces at this laboratory. It was proposed that we send a complement of specialists to the Radiophysics Laboratory along with a small stock of radar components already in production here which might be useful in the design of new gear adapted especially to the type of warfare peculiar to the Southwest Pacific.

It was not surprising that many of the requests from this theater related to specific pieces of apparatus and that few concerned long-range, broad problems. Dr. Compton had anticipated this at the time his Office of Field Service was being created. Much of the emphasis then was given to the new technique called "operations analysis" that had come into prominence as a means of making the special analytical abilities of scientifically-trained men directly applicable to military situations. The increasing interest in this specialty, as we shall see, was a prime factor that led to the establishment of the Office of Field Service. In some quarters it was even expected that this new unit in OSRD would be devoted chiefly to co-ordinating the further contributions American science might make to such analytical studies. But Dr. Compton and others had urged strongly that the description of proposed functions for OFS be broad enough to include many types of professional consulting, especially in regard to the complicated devices that were getting into the hands of the combat units.

The terms "operations research" and "operations analysis" came to be used more or less interchangeably. As is true of so many words of scientific flavor, people's concepts of their meaning varied considerably. In literal connotation they would apply to any careful, systematic, and critical study of military or naval operations. Such investigations would clearly have the purpose of evaluating those operations to determine the relative effectiveness of certain tactics or weapons. Ordinarily the operations studied would be those that had already occurred. The research worker would be trying to find out from experiences of the past what changes might be desirable in future operations of the same sort. The study could, of course, also proceed on a partly hypothetical basis in order to predict the probable success of different combinations of weapons and tactics in a forthcoming operation. Moreover, the operations studied could be either those of our own forces or those of the enemy. In modern warfare equipment is so much a part of any military move that the investigation might relate only to the performance of the equipment itself under operating conditions as compared with its expected performance based on laboratory and proving-ground tests or on theoretical considerations. Or it might be aimed at evaluating the performance of personnel in the operation of the equipment with a view to improved training and doctrine. On the other hand, it might consist of an analysis of the tactical disposition and employment of forces irrespective of equipment.

Operations analysis is aimed at answering such questions as: What patterns of flight for an air patrol will give the best protective coverage against submarines to convoys of various sizes, shapes, and speeds? What is the effectiveness of various bomber formations in terms of defense against fighters? Would a hundred 50-pound bombs create greater or less damage to a certain type of target than five 1000-pound bombs? With a particular combination of weapons and tactics, what effects does modification of either the equipment or the procedure have on the probability of success in either offense or defense?

It is easy enough to understand, therefore, that operations research calls for the sifting of vast quantities of information from operational reports in order to isolate and study the many individual factors that might affect either the behavior of equipment and personnel or the success of a tactic in a past or a contemplated operation. This information may be sketchy, incomplete, difficult to procure. Commonly it is not known in advance what details of a battle or a defense maneuver the officers should record. When the analysis begins this becomes clearer and revision of report requirements is recommended by the analyst.

Some aspects of this work are a normal part of the functions of military personnel; but in the midst of war too often the officers cannot spare the time for the painstaking, detached, scientific study that is required. It is best performed by groups of civilians who work in close contact with the operational people and who have no other duties to distract them.

As the techniques of such analysis are perfected, need for men trained in science and especially in mathematics and statistics becomes more acute. Scientists are not needed to reach the baldest conclusions; but a research man familiar with statistical variation and small sample analysis, a fellow accustomed to reasoning out a working conclusion from a mass of incomplete data, or to proceeding from a small number of cases to a general conclusion, can provide more accurate evaluations and predictions than a man without such experience. He can also point out missing data that should be secured in order to permit a valid conclusion. Moreover, the scientist is schooled in techniques for presenting his material in a quantitative way which can be more readily understood by the military man. This gives the officer a concrete and specific basis for action. The scientist's analysis may show, for example, that a certain change in flight formation has resulted in a 30 per cent increase in the probability of hits by enemy flak, whereas some other proposed change would increase the probability by 50 per cent.

The British were pioneers in developing groups of civilian operational analysts attached to their Armed Services. Under the leadership of Professor P. M. S. Blackett, eminent physicist and mathematician, such groups were established in the Royal Air Force and were known as Operational Research Sections. Their reports contributed greatly to the success of the Fighter Command in intercepting and dispersing German raids and of the Bomber Command and Coastal Command in devising better offensive formations for the bombers and improving tactics for seeking out and killing submarines that menaced Allied supply lanes to Britain.

Largely at the instigation of Dr. Bush, the American Army in 1942 had set up somewhat comparable groups. The Signal Corps created an Operational Research Division headed by Professor Everitt, a well-known communications engineer from Ohio State University. The primary activity of this group was to produce proper instruction manuals based on reports from radio communications systems about performance at field stations. In the Air Force likewise an Operations Analysis Division was established under the direction of Colonel W. Barton Leach, in peacetime a dynamic faculty member of Harvard Law School. This Division expanded rapidly and perhaps did more than any other agency to acquaint the Army with the usefulness of operations analysis. Operational Research Sections were first provided to the strategic and tactical air forces in Europe and the Mediterranean. Their work proved so valuable that there was a demand to create similar Sections for the Air Forces in all the other theaters. Eventually more than a hundred civilians were occupied in this program, most of them employed directly by the War Department for the duration. Many of them were furnished or trained by OSRD.

The Navy also had urged NDRC to start an Antisubmarine Warfare Operations Research Group (then known as ASWORG or Group M). This consisted of civilian specialists employed by Columbia University through an OSRD contract and loaned to the Navy. By the middle of 1943 the work of this group had contributed greatly to elimination of the Nazi submarine threat and the Navy was beginning to refer problems in other aspects of naval warfare to these OSRD analysts. Expansion of ASWORG was likewise a reality that would create pressure to release laboratory men.

If additional operational analysis groups were to be formed, the manpower would have to come from laboratories and war plants already hard hit by Selective Service and facing a multiplicity of requests for help beyond their primary jobs of research, development, or production.

As one group of operations analysts after another began to function in the Services, there was a tendency to refer to them all sorts of technical problems, sometimes far removed from the statistical and analytical work of operations research. The military soon discovered that these units contained specialists who could be helpful in many ways. In some commands they represented the only available consulting staff that had the time to worry over scientific and technological matters. Yet these were immediate and urgent and the civilians did their best to handle them. It was natural enough that an officer who had been channeling all his operational information on rockets to an operations analyst should turn to the same man when something went wrong with the launchers, fuzes, or firing mechanism. The analyst may have been an insurance actuary, a lawyer, or a mathematics professor before the war. His entire knowledge of rockets may have been acquired in a few months of reading operational reports, talking with laboratory men, and observing the behavior of rockets in action. He was on the spot. People looked to him for advice that he was ill prepared to give. Nevertheless he had a trained mind and he knew where to get the information. If the theater permitted, he could short-circuit some of the cumbersome channels and communicate directly with the technical people at home.

One result of this situation was a demand for including experts on various new weapons in the personnel of operations research groups. Another result was that soon the term "operations analyst" became almost synonymous in the mind of the military with "scientific specialist." Officers asked for a team of operations analysts when what they really wanted was a group of field engineers or a panel of scientific consultants who together might be able to tackle any problem that came up in the utilization of new gear. Some units of this type were set up at Army request and the military erroneously named them "Operational Research Sections."

Beginning in the early months of 1943 there was a growing sentiment in OSRD that the organization should extend its activities in supervision and advice on the use of equipment, and particularly that it should establish a subdivision devoted to integrating the demands for OSRD participation in operational analysis. Dr. Bush had felt, however, that operations research should be in the hands of the Services themselves and that they should provide for additional operations analysis units without pressure from outside sources. But it became evident that if this were done, OSRD would probably be called on to supply much of the manpower and would thereby lose too many of its people. Moreover, OSRD laboratories that had lost men to permanent employment by the War Department felt that means of assisting the Services should be worked out which would permit them to take a man back when his particular field mission had been completed.

Mr. Carroll L. Wilson, youthful executive assistant to the Director of OSRD, organized a comprehensive study of the varied needs of the Services for operations research and other types of field assistance, and evolved a plan for meeting them. This provided for the creation of a new subdivision which would supervise and correlate the activities of all persons connected with OSRD who were or might become engaged in operational research. It would also keep in close touch with the needs of the Army and Navy for field aid and would frequently look to other units of OSRD to supply suitable specialists. It would then hire or appoint them and loan them to the Services, arranging for a flow of pertinent technical information from such personnel back to the home laboratories.

This new unit would bring advantages both to the Services and to OSRD. It would not compete with but would supplement operations research already under way. Men of greater scientific attainment could be assigned to field duties because they would serve only on a temporary loan; and they would return to their research activities with a more practical outlook. The closer relations of the scientists with the operating groups in the Army and Navy would assist OSRD in planning the directions of emphasis for its research program. More realistic design and quicker modification to adapt equipment to field conditions would surely result.

In general, the setting up of such a subdivision would accomplish the desirable broad objective of creating a shift of personnel from laboratory research to field consultation. Ever since late in 1942 when the progress of the war gave some thin promise of victory for the Allied Nations and when devices and weapons of warfare developed by OSRD were reaching some war theaters in profusion, it had been apparent that a shift of emphasis in the utilization of scientific manpower would be appropriate. Experience of OSRD had shown that research and development activities could only come to fruition in quantity production and shipment overseas after many months or even years of research, development, design, and testing. Clearly, those weapons that would merely be in the initial stages of this lengthy process when hostilities ceased would be of little value to World War II. Furthermore, military dissatisfaction with performance of equipment OSRD had produced, although it resulted frequently from improper use, might react to delay the whole program of research and improvement. It was then a matter of greatest importance that OSRD transfer a substantial segment of its scientific brain power to improving the usefulness of weapons already at hand.

In summary, there were several factors that led Dr. Bush to set up the Office of Field Service late in 1943. In addition to the need for co-ordination in the whole program of operations research, it had become evident that a more orderly and comprehensive procedure was needed in the dispatch of OSRD people to field assignments of all sorts. The London Liaison Office was supplying such help as it could from its own personnel resources and on its own discretion; the BBRL and ABL-15 were making major contributions to the fighting on the

Continent in the fields of radar and radar countermeasures. The ASWORG was firmly entrenched in the Navy and was growing. The Air Forces had far-flung Operations Analysis Sections, manned partly with personnel detached from OSRD, and establishment of additional ones was in prospect. Representatives of OSRD were at various stations, even a few in the Pacific, under many different auspices. Intercommunication between them was poor. The pool of scientific manpower had been repeatedly tapped for field work but never replenished. Clearly some definitive action to bring about a uniform, effective way of working with the fighting forces and to guarantee the maximum utilization of the scientific personnel available was needed.

In the implementation of Mr. Wilson's plan, it was decided, therefore, to broaden the scope of the proposed new subdivision. Its basic directive was accordingly framed to include: supervision, direction, co-ordination, and integration of all activities of a field-service nature performed by OSRD or its contractors, including not only operations analysis but also field engineering on installation, maintenance, and modification of equipment; organization and operation of laboratories established in war theaters; field consultation and the work of special committees or missions for study of field problems; and exchange of information concerning scientific problems arising in connection with military operations. Along with these changes it seemed desirable also to substitute for the tentative name, "Operations Analysis Division," which had been used to describe the proposed organization, the more comprehensive label, "Office of Field Service."

On October 15, 1943, Dr. Bush announced the formation of this new major subdivision of OSRD. It was to operate in response to direct requests from Army, Navy, or other war agencies, and to make scientific personnel available only on loan for specified periods. Dr. Compton was selected as its Chief, Dr. Alan T. Waterman, Associate Professor of Physics on leave from Yale, as Deputy Chief, and Dr. Lincoln R. Thiesmeyer, geologist and member of ASWORG, as Head Technical Aide.

This, then, was the type of organization that stood ready to bring the weight of America's scientific resources to bear on campaigns in the Pacific. All that would be needed to set the wheels in motion for placing top-quality scientists in that area was an expression of genuine interest from the theater commanders. To canvass that interest Dr. Compton had undertaken his tour of the GHQ's.

If there were to be extensive OSRD-staffed projects in SWPA, it was obvious that there should be an office in the theater, preferably located at GHQ and operating with as much freedom as the theater commander would allow, to co-ordinate and supervise the work of the technical men sent into forward areas. Perhaps this could be an advance unit of the Office of Field Service. It should be headed by a top-grade scientist, aided by a staff familiar with both Army and Government procedures and able to relieve the scientists of the mechanical details of finances, credentials, and communications. This office would have to operate essentially as did the London Liaison Office, except that here the most important aspect of the job would be co-operation with the Armed Services rather than exchange of information with local research agencies.

The entire area in which our military operations were progressing from Brisbane northward was defined as a theater of war under MacArthur's jurisdiction. Compton was repeatedly advised that any OSRD activities in that area would have to be under the rigid military control of the theater commander. Liaison with the Australians might be desirable but would have to be carried on with specific theater approval and through theater channels. Communications between the scientists in the field and the home laboratories would have to follow the customary route from the operating technicians through the local Special Staff Section, the local command, the theater command, the Chief of Staff at home, the home Special Staff, and finally the War or Navy Department liaison officers to the OSRD units concerned. Requests involving any kind of procurement — of information, equipment, or personnel — would have to go through GHQ for endorsement before they could be honored on the mainland.

Near the end of January, 1944, Dr. Compton presented General MacArthur with a summary outlining many specific needs for the types of field service OSRD could furnish to meet problems revealed in the weeks of his discussions with theater personnel, and with a list of recommendations for setting up field projects to be staffed by OSRD, primarily through the Office of Field Service. MacArthur was enthusiastic. He said the report exceeded his best expectations, approved it, and assured Compton that he would carry out its suggestions. He then designated General Akin to act for him in all further discussion of details for an organization to handle the individual items.

The next morning Dr. Compton took off with Generals Sutherland and Chamberlain in the headquarters private plane (christened "Bataan") headed for the GHQ of the South Pacific Area (SPA) at Nouméa. This theater had become relatively inactive. There were few Japanese strongholds left and the South Pacific forces were operating entirely as task forces. It seemed likely that a reorganization would be made in the near future; but until then there would be problems to which OSRD might contribute solutions.

During his one-day visit in that theater, Compton lunched at Admiral Halsey's residence with Admiral Shafroth, Deputy Commander in Chief, and a group of officers including Commander Stassen and Brigadier General Ankenbrandt, and conferred with Lieutenant General Millard Harmon, with his brother, who headed the Thirteenth Air Force stationed there, and with General Barnett. These officers and their aides were also keenly interested in scientific and engineering help and had gone farther in analyzing their needs than had the officers of either the Central or the Southwest Pacific Areas. Colonel Leach's Operational Research Section attached to the Thirteenth Air Force had done such excellent work that the command was anxious to extend this type of activity to ground forces operations as well, and General Harmon asked that the Office of Field Service send out a group of specialists to study and advise on problems of jungle warfare.

At the return conference with General Richardson in Hawaii it was suggested that a survey similar to the one Compton had made for MacArthur be instituted. Richardson indicated a strong desire to take advantage of OSRD assistance but wanted a concrete plan of action. Feeling that it was important to return immediately to the United States and secure the necessary approval from Bush and from the military and naval authorities for implementing the ambitious program he had designed for the Southwest Pacific, Compton promised that he would request authorization to send out a top-notch scientist who could explore in detail the needs of this Central Pacific Area (CPA) and the best means for filling them.

* * *

Thirty-two days after he had left that field, Dr. Compton stepped from a plane at the Boston Airport. It was 2.30 in the morning. He was still in uniform. He was jubilant; his mission had been highly successful. Encountering by chance a member of his OFS staff while changing planes at New York, he had remarked: "I hope your efforts to get a bigger office force for OFS have been successful. I have a pocketful of requests from the Pacific. We'll need a lot of help and be very busy for the next few months to meet them all."

Compton had opened the way. At last the stage was set for OSRD to move into the Pacific and bring to the forces opposing Japan the same powerful scientific assistance it had been able to give to the men who were fighting the Nazis.

CHAPTER II

FROM VT-FUZE TO FUNGUS

SCOPE OF THE OFFICE OF FIELD SERVICE

A "POCKETFUL" of requests it was indeed. The Pacific commanders had appealed for aid on matters ranging from the marvelous new VT or proximity fuze, by which a bomb or shell is exploded a fixed distance from its target, to the difficulty of keeping optical lens surfaces free from the corrosive fungus that abounds in tropical areas.

For the next fifteen months the Office of Field Service wrestled with the problem of finding the right men to send out on the many varied assignments that resulted from these requests. Though most of the demands crystallized during Compton's visit were for experts to help combat the cunning of the Japanese and the perils of the tropics, some of them reflected the failure of scientific information to penetrate to the forward areas. There were hundreds of questions about the remarkable new developments of NDRC and its analogue, the Committee on Medical Research (CMR), OSRD subdivision responsible for progress in the field of medicine. There were also inquiries about work the Technical Services of the Army and Navy themselves had done that somehow had not yet been reported to the troops in the Pacific.

Compton's notebooks were crammed with entries — comments on performance of new weapons used in that theater, queries about the production status, availability, shipping dates, or operating characteristics of many kinds of material that had not yet gone westward, forecasts of the serious difficulties commanding officers expected as their lines stretched north and west. The field commanders wanted to see the new devices they had heard about, wanted them demonstrated in the field, wanted OFS to expedite the shipment of implements Washington had promised, wanted NDRC to remedy certain defects in radar or other gear.

Just to pass all these items along to the many people who would be most interested and able to take proper action took days of conference and dictation. To locate the scores of specialists who were needed was another matter. Some could be found in NDRC laboratories and sent out at once. It took weeks to find others whose specialties were not included in the OSRD program.

The types of scientific men that officers in the Southwest Pacific were eager to obtain as they laid elaborate plans to conquer climate, distance, terrain, equipment, and supply in chopping off the military tentacles of Japan were these: medical experts to study their second most important enemy, malaria, and to cure the fungus infections that sapped morale; electronics engineers to test a homing torpedo developed in the field; radio and radar research men to study propagation of radio waves and to design lightweight air-transportable radar gear; countermeasures experts to find ways of jamming enemy radar; engineers to assist in introducing an aerial bomb launched backwards to offset its forward path so that it drops on a target directly below the point of release; biologists whose skills could be used against tiny marine organisms that were destroying wooden craft and docks in tropical waters; chemists and chemical engineers to study the behavior of poison gases and smokes in thickly forested, humid areas; physicists to produce a fuze that would cause a bomb to explode about thirty feet above the ground; experts in time and motion analysis to unwind snarls in handling communications; men to analyze bottlenecks in transportation, failure of equipment, effectiveness of antiaircraft fire, and tactics of our air and surface craft in spotting and obliterating Japanese submarines.

The field units wanted some of the special devices Divisions 17 and 19 of NDRC had created for commandolike patrol operations; they wanted snooperscopes and sniperscopes, devices developed by Division 16 and using infrared light for communications and for sighting rifles; they also wanted samples of an antifogging liquid that would prevent the clouding of airplane windshields and bombing windows by moisture that condenses when the planes rise suddenly into cooler air; and they wanted large, portable oxygen generators developed by Division 11, NDRC.

The diversity of these requests from only one theater of the war gives but a preview of the multifarious activities in which the Office of Field Service became engaged as the war progressed. One can gain only an imperfect impression of the versatility of combat scientists and the comprehensive scope of OFS by glancing through the chapter titles of this book. Although the emphasis in our account up to this point has been on the Pacific, the work of OFS extended also into all the other theaters. There was still a major war across the Atlantic and, while scientific assistance from OSRD had already been provided in large measure, there were calls for additional aid from OFS to support the concerted assault on *Festung Europa.*

To classify OFS projects according to the subjects involved or the types of assistance required is difficult. Sharp distinctions can seldom be drawn, and overlap between the categories is inevitable. This is so, of course, because in the study of a scientific problem ramifications develop that lead into fields quite remote from the main or original subject. Moreover the OFS consultant commonly found himself called upon for advice on problems quite different from those specified in his assignment, because it was natural for officers to refer all questions of a technical nature to the recognized, available, technically trained visitor. A chemical engineer sent out to study flame throwers or incendiaries might be faced with appeals for counsel on food spoilage, deterioration of optical equipment, or evaluation of a new explosive. His project would then lie within several of the categories.

Although the Office of Field Service began in a limited fashion and fulfilled initially only a portion of its intended purposes, during the twenty-three months from its birth until the Japanese accepted unconditional surrender its activities had spread to many parts of the globe and included every type of assistance foreseen in the basic directive. It had dispatched nearly three hundred scientists and technical men on missions overseas, two thirds of them to the Pacific; had assigned two hundred to projects in the United States; had interviewed several thousand technical men; and had devoted considerable energy to answering questions, giving advice, and looking up personnel in response to a host of assorted requests from the Armed Forces. During the two years of its active recruiting OFS dispatched a scientist to a foreign mission on the average of every other day. On V–J Day seventy men were in various stages of preparation for departure. With the exception of a slight dip in the late summer of 1944, the growth curve of OFS approximates a straight line.

These men came from all the Divisions of NDRC and from the special committees and panels of OSRD as well as from war plants, hospitals, museums, and private research laboratories that were not connected with the comprehensive OSRD organization. Some went out as lone operators, others worked as members of field teams or survey missions. When OFS learned that most field problems concerned the instruments used in warfare, the great majority were drawn from OSRD or its contractors. More than 40 per cent devoted their major attention to problems involving OSRD equipment. This is one measure of the wide employment of such devices as radar, jamming instruments, rockets, guided missiles, VT-fuzes, bazookas, DUKW's, Weasels, and the implements and vehicles the laboratories of NDRC had devised.

It was not so much the general-utility scientist who was needed in the theaters. The Services already had many such men. It was rather the specialist, highly skilled, fully acquainted with the intricacies and limitations of his equipment, able to command the respect of technically trained officers, and facile in teaching the lowly GI how best to employ the bewildering gadgets placed in his inexperienced hands.

Several things contributed to the greater magnitude and broader scope of the OFS than had been envisioned. During the later part of the war a swelling flood of equipment contrived by OSRD was at last pouring into all theaters. In the days from Pearl Harbor until the landings in Italy, much of the research and development effort had to be directed toward the European campaign and the introduction of secret weapons had been on a relatively small scale. It had taken time to develop them, to secure Service acceptance, to get tooled up for mass production, and to prove their performance in combat. When both the quantity and the geographic distribution of the devices increased, difficulties with equipment became impressive realities to officers in the field, and the operations research teams needed specialists on materiel as well as statisticians. Groups like ASWORG and others that OFS established in the operating theaters worked quietly to win the confidence of officers and men. Once they had broken through the prejudices and demonstrated the value of civilian scientific help, the demands for more of it became a crescendo that mounted steadily until the days when suddenly atomic annihilation faced the cities of Japan.

So many people, both in OSRD and in the Services, had participated in planning for OFS that interest in the potential value of this new office was widespread. It was besieged at once with inquiries and with requests from many branches of the Armed Forces and from within OSRD. Yet, although this lengthy planning had wisely resulted in an exceedingly broad directive which would make OFS the channel and co-ordinating agency for all OSRD field activities, full attainment of that objective could not be accomplished at once, nor would this have been desirable.

In ETO, as we have seen, there were effective mechanisms for supplying technical consultation to the fighting forces through the Liaison Office, BBRL and ABL-15. They had such excellent working relations with the military that communications by teletype with their home laboratories were standard procedure. Shipments of both personnel and equipment were functioning smoothly in the hands of experienced administrative people at both ends. There was no real necessity that OFS attempt to exercise jurisdiction over a program so well organized and administered. Nevertheless, it was recognized that there might be many calls from ETO for OFS to undertake projects which could not be handled by these agencies. OFS would keep in touch with their field-service functions and might occasionally ask their help with new missions in that area.

Then, too, even after the creation of OFS had been widely announced to the military, it was evident that many requests for field aid would still come directly to the Divisions and their contractors as they had in the past, probably in increasing numbers as the channels through which these were sent functioned more efficiently with practice. After all, people in the theaters, in Washington, and in the Divisions had become familiar with the mechanics of getting such requests through. It would take some time to re-educate them to new procedures.

Under these conditions, it was clear that OFS could not suddenly absorb all existing field missions when its limited staff was already working to capacity keeping up with new calls for help. Not until the summer of 1945, when there was only one extensive theater to be served, was it possible to specify that OFS discharge the full function of co-ordinating all overseas activities of OSRD and its contractors in the Pacific.

During the months immediately preceding Dr. Compton's exploratory trip, the Office of Field Service had been exceedingly rushed. It had to establish the channels in the War and Navy Departments that would facilitate smooth operation, had to build its initial staff, and experiment with the procedures for securing and processing civilian personnel.

In order to furnish its field-service representatives with a name that would be only vaguely descriptive of their specific functions and would therefore provide both security and latitude in the performance of their duties, it was decided that all should be given the title "Field Service Consultant." Some would be specialists on equipment; some would conduct broad surveys on medical problems; some would be operations analysts; others might be intelligence investigators — yet all would carry a designation which identified them with the parent office without jeopardizing them in case of capture through revelation of their mission and disclosure that they represented a part of America's scientific potential.

In planning the designation of offices in each of the Armed Services which would serve as appropriate liaison with the Office of Field Service it was felt that this would have to be more than a perfunctory matter of setting up channels for funneling requests to OFS and for dispatching its consultants to the active commands. An interest on the part of the Service liaison office well beyond the mechanical routines of shuffling papers and processing people would be required. The liaison offices would have to be so placed within the Army and Navy organizations that they could keep the various technical branches of those Services alert to opportunities which lay in the use of OFS personnel. When a request from one military unit called for the services of a man already committed to a field or research project of critical interest to some other branch of the same Service, they would have to arbitrate the overlapping demands and establish the relative priority of the needs. They would have to be able to attach officers to field projects when this was desirable, to assist aggressively in handling the military processing of civilians, and to authorize short cuts when the urgency of a field need warranted irregular procedure.

These offices should also be so placed that they could quickly secure information available only from Service sources. They should be able to initiate and sponsor a project of broad interest to the Services, or a project that lacked sponsorship because its merits had not been recognized by other parts of the Services. Above all, the Service liaison office would have to maintain a consistently sympathetic attitude toward the introduction and better use of items developed by OSRD. On the one hand, it would have to guard OFS personnel against breaches of military courtesy, sidestepping of military regulations, or setting up of activities that would impede military operations, and on the other, it would have to do everything possible to facilitate their work.

These requirements made it obvious that a Service liaison office should represent a high echelon that had cognizance of all subsidiary branches, bureaus, or departments. It would have to make requests upon them that carried the force of orders from the General Staff.

The Navy was the first of the Services to take notice of and attempt to utilize the Office of Field Service. As soon as the plan for creating this new subdivision had been approved by the OSRD Advisory Council, Rear Admiral Julius A. Furer, who was the Navy's Co-ordinator of Research and Development, informed the Secretary of the Navy about this move. Accordingly, on September 10 the late Secretary Knox addressed a communication to all Navy bureaus and offices, announcing the formation of OFS. He encouraged the Navy Department to take advantage of this opportunity for securing technical help, and emphasized that the scientists thus made available would be under Navy regulations regarding security and under Navy supervision in the performance of their duties. At the same time he designated the Office of the Co-ordinator of Research and Development (CRD) as the single channel through which arrangements with the Office of Field Service were to be made, and OFS enjoyed the cordial co-operation of this office throughout the war.

Not until some weeks later was the Army sufficiently acquainted with OFS to begin asking for its products; yet in the end, it was the Army that became the larger consumer. Out of a total of eighty-seven separate OFS projects fifty-five were Army-sponsored and ten were under joint auspices of both Army and Navy.

The Office of the Co-ordinator (which late in the war became a subdivision of the Office of Research and Inventions under Vice-Admiral Harold G. Bowen) remained the official channel of the Navy for OFS throughout. Since it had already functioned for many months as Navy liaison with NDRC, stood in a position of general cognizance and authority in the Navy, and had personnel familiar with the routines of processing civilians and handling communications, it was ready to assume this role likewise for OFS.

In December 1943 Lieutenant Thomas F. Creamer, USNR, was detailed to OFS to serve as a liaison officer on Navy matters and as a special assistant to Dr. Compton. Lieutenant Creamer had acquired familiarity with several NDRC Divisions during a previous detail at M.I.T. and his intelligence, energy, and enthusiasm proved decidedly useful in many aspects of the OFS program.

In the War Department there had been a Liaison Office for NDRC which was accustomed to handling matters of production and equipment. It was not properly placed, however, for handling personnel. Dr. Bush took up with the War Department the matter of setting up an Army liaison channel for OFS and the first decision was to designate the Operations Division (OPD). This was influenced by the presumption that OFS projects would lie close to operations. In the course of negotiations with OPD for the first OFS field project for the Army — a mission of consultants on jungle warfare requested by General Harmon in the South Pacific Area — OPD began to realize what a time-consuming rigmarole of detail would be involved in servicing OFS personnel. OPD was already under sufficient pressure handling all operational matters in the continually expanding theaters. Consequently, during these negotiations the War Department suddenly shifted the responsibility for liaison with OFS to the New Developments Division (NDD) which then remained the major Army channel for field-service activities throughout the war.

The New Developments Division was likewise not accustomed to handling personnel matters; but because it was in a position of authority in regard to all new developments it had the power to make necessary arrangements. It was a Special Staff Section composed of officers of the General Staff Corps. Its Director at that time was Major General Stephen G. Henry, a decidedly able officer of wide acquaintance in the Army, whose eagerness to introduce and make the best possible use of new weapons and devices was matched by his enthusiasm for taking maximum advantage of the skills of scientists either in or out of uniform. General Henry was ardent in his support of OSRD and keenly interested in the concept of transferring scientific talent through OFS from research to field use. His personal backing was never withheld and did a great deal to smooth the way for OFS in the difficult first days of its dealings with the Army.

In August 1944 General Henry's assignment was changed to that of Assistant Chief of Staff, G-1. The following quotations from a letter he wrote to Dr. Compton at that time reflect his attitude toward field service and his enthusiasm for the teamwork that had been developed between OFS and NDD: ". . . Civilian and military partnerships are not natural alliances. What you and your staff have done — the selecting, processing and assigning of the country's foremost scientists for this important work — has been pioneering of the hardest kind.

"Only history will tell the whole story of how much good is being done by the Office of Field Service. I'm satisfied, however, that through the tireless efforts of you and your staff thousands of American families will be able to welcome home many a young man who otherwise might have been lost to them or permanently incapacitated through the lack of adequate equipment, or improper care. . . .

"My new job, I regret to say, is pretty much divorced from all this that we have been doing together, but I like to think that maybe there will be times when I can continue to help you in some small way in connection with your many duties. I'm yours to command, believe me."

His successor as head of NDD, Brigadier General William A. Borden, was also vitally interested in the possibilities for assisting the field forces by sending scientific talent to the front and was thoroughly co-operative. With his unwavering encouragement the civilian and military partnership became even firmer during the remaining months of the war.

Colonel Leach's operations analysis groups in the Air Forces were proving popular in the Army. The New Developments Division did not want to interfere with a program that had a head start and was going well; but it did wish to serve as a medium for stimulating similar activities in the Ground Forces. The net result of this and of other factors was that from the outset NDD declined to handle processing of OFS men for Air Force assignments. Consequently OFS had no single channel with the Air Force. Requests originating in different units came through various offices.[1]

This created difficulties that finally led to arrangements to set up a single office in the Air Force that would function in parallel with NDD for processing OFS men and handling OFS communications on AAF matters. In the summer of 1945 when plans for channeling all OSRD field groups through OFS were being formulated, the office of Brigadier General J. F. Phillips, an Assistant Chief of Air Staff, Materiel and Services, was designated for this. Colonel W. G. Brown, who had been Air Force Liaison Officer with NDRC, was assigned to supervise the processing. This office began to function late in July, 1945. NDD assisted Colonel Brown in regularizing and simplifying procedure so that by the end of the war the two Army channels were operating similarly and were dividing between them the task of dispatching three or four score OFS men to MacArthur's theater.

The Armed Forces found in OFS a new mechanism for procuring civilian scientific manpower. Here was a speedier way of getting better men than they could through the customary wearing technique of seeking all the approvals necessary when one wants to set up a new Table of Organization (TO), or expand an existing one. Yet OFS was not designed to function merely as a personnel-procurement agency. It was not created to assist the military in sidestepping complexities of their own machinery.

Sometimes the Services also looked upon OFS as a means of getting less highly qualified technical personnel than scientists. It was often apparent that what they really wanted were technicians. OFS did not have the authority, however, to employ either technicians for routine assignments or administrative and clerical personnel lacking scientific training. Consequently, every Service request had to be scrutinized carefully. Many did not stand up under this examination. Some had originated through ignorance of officers about the true purpose of the Office of Field Service; others were doubtless suggested without much thought simply because that seemed an easy way to solve a manpower problem.

In any case, when OFS did have to refuse such proposals, it always

---

[1] Operations Analysis Division; Air Communications Office; Operations, Commitments, and Requirements; Assistant Chief of Air Staff, Training; Assistant Chief of Air Staff, Intelligence; etc.

attempted to help. Its senior staff members could suggest other possible sources to which the Service could turn, could consult on administrative or technical aspects of the proposed project, initiate an exchange of scientific information, or put the interested officers in touch with the types of people they sought. In this way OFS was able to render a great deal of help to the Services that does not appear in the formal record of projects it accepted. Altogether such activities required considerable time and energy, sometimes as much as was needed for setting up a major mission. Nevertheless, this was essential to cementing good relations with the military.

A basic principle of OFS was that it would operate only in response to direct requests from the Armed Forces or from another Government agency and that the scientific personnel made available to the military would be merely loaned rather than released. The initial period was not to exceed six months. If extension of the loan was desired by all the parties, this could be arranged — repeatedly for the duration if necessary. Requests that could only be satisfied by assignment of technical men on a more permanent basis would be referred to the Scientific Personnel Office of OSRD, which had been helping the Services to locate competent specialists for employment by the War and Navy Departments.

A "project" of OFS was essentially a job for which it procured and assigned personnel.[2] The request might be for a single man or a group of men to survey for a few weeks scientific aspects of a military problem in order to advise the directions in which further help might be needed. Such missions were generally looked upon with disfavor by theater commands because, unless followed rather promptly by definitive action

[2] OFS might have regarded each of the requests Compton brought back as a separate project. But, as the work of meeting them proceeded, the definition of a "project" became less precise. Two major branch offices of OFS were eventually set up, one in Oahu and the other in Australia. These logically became foci of OFS in the theaters. The establishment of such an office could be considered as a single project and the requests it handled as subdivisions of that project. This was the case with the OFS group at Hawaii, which retained its base of operations at Oahu to the end of the war and functioned as a closely knit, coherent unit. The OFS office in the Southwest Pacific, on the other hand, moved from Brisbane, Australia, to Hollandia, New Guinea, then on to Leyte, and finally to Manila. Men sent through that office were detailed to duty which often took them thousands of miles from the OFS headquarters for many months. They were widely dispersed through the theater and had to operate almost independently. It was more convenient, therefore, to regard the branch office at GHQ, SWPA, as one project and each of the requests for personnel to be co-ordinated through it as a separate additional project in the OFS records. Requests for equipment or for information were never treated as projects, but as subdivisions or outgrowths of project activities.

in the dispatch of additional men who would stay to work on the problem, the officers could see no tangible results other than that a scientist or group of scientists from OSRD had enjoyed an interesting junket, had run around to high-level conferences, taken advantage of the privileges accorded to senior officers, and probably carried back a highly distorted picture of real conditions at the level of the foxhole.

Although many of the requests truly originated without fore-knowledge of OSRD representatives, it must be admitted that more than one that appeared on the face of it in the formalities to have come from a Service branch was actually instigated by OSRD people who suggested the underlying idea to an appropriate officer.

Ordinarily requests for OFS assistance began with informal negotia-tions. Very few came in as documents out of the blue. Eventually the requesting office sent a letter to the Chief of OFS via the appropriate military channel. In effect this was most commonly merely a paper confirmation. Frequently all arrangements had been completed and the personnel sent out by the time it was received. In this sense, OFS operated to a great extent "on the cuff." Its fundamental phi-losophy was that to get the requisite manpower on the job at the earliest possible moment was the important thing. Paper work could follow after the fact. Had OFS not adopted this attitude, very few of its men could have been on the scene in time to be effective. Neverthe-less, the very fact that this new and unproved unit showed a tendency toward such unconventional operation created many a raised eyebrow among those so steeped in Government formalities that they would refuse to act until the proper document was in their hands, even though a delay might affect thousands of American lives or give the enemy an edge.

Commonly in negotiations with the Services about a proposed project and then with the personnel recruited as prospects for the job, the first task was a precise definition of the field problems. In many cases officers were merely aware of the existence of a difficulty. They could not or did not have the time to analyze it and select its com-ponents in order to specify the most fruitful directions of attack. The military man who saw the need and initiated the request may not have known enough about science to tell exactly what particular kind of specialist would be needed. The free and clarifying discussion between a requester in a theater and a supplier at home that could lead to effective selection of personnel was impossible through overloaded channels of communication. OFS officials had to evaluate and define the needs as best they could with the meager information sent from the theater and then try to find the right specialists for what they concluded the problems would be. Occasionally this resulted in sending the wrong man or, as was more often the case, the problems could not be sufficiently defined in advance. Then the field consultant found that his first responsibility on arrival in the theater was to seek out the officers, help them to delimit their needs, and plan his effort toward solution.

There were, of course, many requests that specified the kind of man needed in some detail, or even named an appropriate candidate known to the officers in the field as a suitable specialist; but more commonly the needs were spelled out only in a general way and OFS was to exercise its judgment in selection. Its recommendations were generally accepted without question.

Once OFS had groups of its specialists with administrative facilities in the theaters, they became the channels through which the communications from the military were ordinarily transmitted. The requests were therefore screened by scientists on the spot. If there were ambiguities, these OFS men could pursue the matter further, clarify and define the problems, and then, by letter, teletype, or telephone, interpret them to their scientific colleagues in the procurement offices in Washington.

In the fluid situation of war, circumstances that created a particular problem and led to an urgent request had often altered completely by the time the OFS consultant arrived on the spot. The change may have come so quickly that there was insufficient time to process a cancellation of the request through military channels. So the scientist arrived in the theater for an assignment that had lost its priority or had become totally unnecessary. In such cases, however, the officers usually found some other way of utilizing the man's special abilities.

Occasionally, through no fault of the military immediately concerned in the field, of the central office of OFS, or of the individual, a specialist on certain equipment that should have been shipped at about the time he left the country found himself at an operating base well in advance of it. In fact, in one case the ship carrying the gear broke down in mid-ocean and the equipment never arrived until the war was over. Patience under such trying circumstances, adaptability, and willingness to turn one's energies to other problems were characteristics that distinguished the "combat scientist" from the ivory-tower research man.

Every man going out was anxious to fortify himself with reference works — technical reports, copies of correspondence and other documents pertaining to the equipment or the special field he was to represent. He would undoubtedly be able to solve many of the problems from his experience and from information in his head; but he felt safer with at least a modest collection of technical data.

Groups of OFS consultants at more or less stationary field headquarters developed libraries for the whole command they were serving. ASWORG collected what was probably the most comprehensive file of reports on antisubmarine warfare in existence, and its library on operations research was doubtless the best in the country. OFS groups in the Pacific also developed collections which were exceedingly useful during the war. They contained not only material procured from the United States through the OFS central office but also technical reports from Service branches on the mainland and operational reports originating in the theaters. On many occasions an officer was able to find in them reports that should long since have reached him through channels in his own branch of the Service.

In 1943 OFS expected that such information would be needed in the rapidly expanding spheres of OFS interests. Mrs. Madeleine T. Schneider, physicist who had served for some time as Technical Aide in the office of Dr. Compton at M.I.T. and was familiar with the work of several NDRC Divisions, joined the OFS staff as a part-time member to gather this material.

As the quantity of scientific information to be exchanged increased, OFS developed a special unit to handle acquisition and forwarding of the data. Administrative personnel without scientific training would have been useless in such a function. To follow the content of technical correspondence and reports and act intelligently in referring items called for a senior scientist. Dr. Gladys A. Anslow, Professor of Physics and Dean of the Graduate School, was made available by Smith College in the summer of 1944 as a part-time consultant to supervise and co-ordinate the flow of technical information through OFS. To assist Miss Anslow in implementing this program, Miss Virginia Sides, fresh from undergraduate training in chemistry, became a Junior Technical Aide. With the addition of Mrs. Schneider, this group constituted the Information and Communications Section of OFS, which provided liaison between the Field Service Consultants and the groups at home.

In the later history of OFS a schedule of regular teletype conferences between the major Pacific field units and the home office was instituted. This was consistent with the quickening tempo of the war and the improved position of OFS in the theaters. Requests for information, personnel, or equipment were then largely contained in the teletype records and the official correspondence became a perfunctory matter of formalizing for military endorsement needs of the theater that had already been made known to OFS.

In the thought that OFS would become the focus for all operational research activities involving OSRD personnel, one of its first functions was to transfer the Navy's Antisubmarine Operations Research Group (ASWORG) from the jurisdiction of NDRC Division 6 and Columbia University by placing the entire personnel of the group on the pay roll of OFS. In order to provide continuity in the technical supervision of ASWORG, Dr. John T. Tate, physicist from the University of Minnesota and Chief of Division 6, and Dr. Philip M. Morse, physicist from M.I.T. and Director of ASWORG, were named Assistant Chiefs of OFS, responsible in their dual capacities for the scientific direction of this Navy project.

This was the largest single project of OFS both in terms of the number of men involved and in the geographic distribution of their assignments. More than seventy specialists were employed in its work, about half of them added after the transfer to OFS. Its members were located in North Africa and London, in Trinidad, Brazil, and Newfoundland, in Hawaii and the Philippines, at Boston, Quonset, Langley Field, Miami, and Fort Lauderdale. The success of ASWORG in helping the Navy to solve antisubmarine problems established the organization and its methods so firmly that the Navy finally extended the scope of its responsibilities to activities of our own submarines in the Pacific, to naval air operations, and then finally to all types of naval operations.

Dr. Morse came to occupy in this country a position comparable with that of Blackett. He was the Navy's foremost expert in this new technique and was consulted by both Services on the potentialities of his methods for solving their most distressing operational problems.

Whereas Morse's team had concentrated in the early days on such relatively simple matters as the operation of a single aircraft on convoy patrol or submarine search, it was later dealing with the complicated operations of whole task forces. To meet these broader needs ASWORG was reorganized and renamed. It became the Operations Research Group (ORG) and was made responsible to the Readiness Division in the Office of the Commander in Chief (COMINCH). Its services proved so valuable that at the end of the war it was taken over from OSRD with somewhat reduced manpower to become a permanent part of the Navy organization.

When Compton returned with his broad program for aid to the Pacific, the Office of Field Service and NDD swung into high gear at once to implement it. Within a month Dr. George R. Harrison, physicist, Dean of Science at M.I.T., had been appointed an Assistant Chief of OFS and was on his way to Brisbane as the first head of an OFS branch office at MacArthur's GHQ. In general this office would represent the whole of OSRD to the widely scattered Service personnel in that vast region. MacArthur decided to place it under supervision of General Akin since much of its concern would be with radar, radio, countermeasures, and communications, the fields for which General Akin had been given responsibility. Accordingly, it was set up as the Research Section (R/S) in the Signal Office.

In the months that followed, over a hundred OFS consultants went out through the Research Section to assignments indicated in the requests Compton collected and to others that developed when the island-hopping began. As these men were deployed to the farthest reaches of the theater, R/S became the funnel for a continual stream of information that poured back to the laboratories and the Pentagon, information about Japanese radar, rockets, nonmetallic land mines, booby traps, suicide planes, and many other topics.

For about a year until we were once again entrenched in Manila the operations of this Research Section were beset with difficulties. GHQ moved repeatedly and the office personnel were constantly changing. The top commanders were often two thousand miles away for weeks at a time, across water dotted with Japanese-held islands over which scientists were not permitted to fly. Consultation with them was infrequent. Communications were poor and co-ordination or supervision of the projects by the R/S was virtually impossible.

Disadvantages in the way the Section had been set up within the military framework led to changes in its auspices, which meant repeated shifting of the channels through which it had to carry on its business. Strictness of the theater in enforcing them caused exasperating delays in sending a communication to the mainland. Under these conditions it was obvious that scientific aid could not be brought to the troops in SWPA as effectively as it had been to those in Europe, until there was a greater concentration of the forces in one area and until the military had agreed to greater flexibility in arrangements. This discouraged the laboratories from releasing their most able men and intensified for the home office of OFS the problem of recruiting.

The individual field men in SWPA had to go out into the jungles, depend on local resources in ill-supplied regions, send their messages through devious and unreliable channels, and fight their way back to headquarters with the most meager transportation. They could rarely discuss their problems with each other or get immediate action on the travel and fiscal details that might plague them, as could the men in a coherent and stable group like ORG. The substantial accomplishments of the combat scientists who went to that area despite these handicaps are a tribute to their courage, imagination, and patience.

Everyone agreed that the needs of the fighting forces in SWPA for scientific help were manifold and immediate and OFS persisted in its efforts to meet them. For a year it experimented with organization and learned to work with the military in the trying conditions imposed by geography and by failure of lower echelons to comprehend and permit the freedom in which scientists must operate. This brought rich returns in the summer of 1945 when the theater approved a plan for establishing at Manila a major unit of OSRD, set at topmost levels and granted the same sort of liberty that had made it possible to throw the full weight of American science behind the attack on Hitler. The activities of the Research Section, fraught with discouragement and delay, had paved the way for what would have become the largest single field effort of OSRD had the curtain not been drawn on the war so suddenly.

As he had promised General Richardson, Dr. Compton secured an outstanding senior scientist to survey the needs of the forces in the Central Pacific Area (CPA).[3] Dr. Paul E. Klopsteg, physicist and Director of Research at Northwestern Technological Institute, President of the Central Scientific Company, and Chief of Division 17, was made an Assistant Chief of OFS and left for Oahu in March 1944. For a month he consulted with officers of the headquarters staff and the technical services, and returned with an extensive list of needs like the one Compton had compiled and a suggested plan for organizing a group of civilian specialists to meet them. This called for a "balanced team" of experts from various fields of science who would tackle these needs first and who then might be able collectively to handle almost any technical problem faced by the Army in that theater. It was to work at GHQ as a special subsection of G-3 and report directly to the Army Chief of Staff.

Dr. Lauriston C. Marshall, physicist from the faculty at the University of California and formerly Director of BBRL, was chosen to head this balanced team and departed for the theater in May, accompanied by Professor John E. Burchard, formerly Chief of Division 2 and later Deputy Chief of OFS. Burchard remained in Hawaii only a few weeks to assist in establishing the group, and returned to Washington to become the major consultant in OFS on the policies and expansion of this project.

A short time later, on the basis of his contacts with the officers and a priority listing of problems for that theater, Marshall recommended that the balanced team have a permanent staff of twenty-three and include experts in radar, communications, and countermeasures; flame throwers, incendiaries, rockets, smoke munitions, and chemical warfare; special vehicles for amphibious operations; analysis of weapons and structures; cargo handling, ship design, and sanitation.

The Commanding General approved this expansion to a permanent

[3] Later, when the South Pacific Area (SPA) became inactive and was combined with CPA, this was called the Pacific Ocean Area (POA), still under over-all command of Nimitz. Later when MacArthur took supreme command of all Army forces in the Pacific it was known as the Middle Pacific theater (MIDPAC).

staff more than twice the size of the group originally requested, and authorized a Table of Organization at that strength. By October of 1944 OFS was sending additional personnel on short missions to the theater but did not add them to the TO as regular team members. Some were detailed forward to work with the Navy or the Air Forces and were merely channeled through the group at Oahu. Eventually it became an OFS policy to attach all OFS men destined for the Central Pacific to Marshall's team for administrative purposes and co-ordination. Throughout 1944 and the early months of 1945 the total personnel of the group increased steadily. By the end of the war nearly fifty men, including those assigned for short special missions, had been attached to this OFS project.

Soon after its formal establishment this balanced team was designated by the Army as the Operational Research Section (ORS). The name would, of course, only be appropriate in a broad definition of "operational research." It was, however, one which would convey to the military men in the theater and at home an implication that this was a group of civilian specialists who could be given access to operational information and who were conceivably part of the whole theater organization. This connotation of the title, Operational Research Section, to Army personnel developed, as we have seen, because the work of operations analysts from Colonel Leach's office was beginning to be recognized in all areas. Colonel Leach had visited the Central Pacific early in 1944 and had succeeded in firing the imagination of General Richardson's staff officers with the potential value of operations analysis. As a result the Air Forces had asked for an Operational Research Section in CPA.

Before Marshall left for the theater, conferences were held between OFS, NDD, and Colonel Leach to avoid duplication and possible discord between two civilian groups having the same group name but working in the same theater under different Army auspices. It was agreed that the OFS team would not attempt a job that could be defined primarily as operational analysis for the Air Forces. Leach's men might turn, however, to the specialists of Marshall's group for help on matters involving equipment. Thereafter the liaison between these organizations was close and the relations were cordial.

The single most important and certainly the most colorful OFS project in the European theater was the ALSOS Mission. This was a joint Army-Navy-OSRD activity [4] in which a group of the nation's outstanding physicists, chemists, metallurgists, engineers, and other scientists were sent into territory recently won, close on the heels of or even along with our advancing armies. Its primary object was to secure an immediate over-all picture of German scientific research in the war. America and Britain wanted especially to find out with the greatest possible speed what progress the Nazis had made in the critical field of atomic energy.

From the days when American troops were driving up through Italy until MacArthur sailed into Tokyo Bay, OSRD sent some sixty scientists into enemy-occupied and finally into enemy territory. Most of them were attached to ALSOS and their activities constituted an impressive example of the co-operation of civilian scientists with the Armed Forces in the achievement of a common objective.

The work of these investigators involved the stupendous task of assembling accurate information regarding the personnel, laboratories, institutions, and industrial firms engaged in scientific war research for the enemy. They had to apprehend promptly and question scientists, engineers, laboratory workers, and technical men. They had to capture documents, equipment, and facilities, examine hundreds of files, translate and evaluate a mass of correspondence and records, and send prompt résumés of their discoveries to authorities in America.

Besides the critical field of nuclear energy, reports of all this snooping dealt with Nazi activities in such pertinent fields as aeronautics, biological warfare, guided missiles, infrared devices, incendiaries, jet propulsion, metallurgy, military medicine, proximity fuzes, and submarine acoustics. While the interest of the High Command was concentrated most heavily on possible German efforts to create atomic weapons, they also wanted the secrets of anything that we could turn against Japan or that we might expect the sons of Nippon to unleash against us.

ALSOS was only one of many intelligence teams that operated on the Continent. Accounts of their combined success in ferreting out the answers to these vital questions have appeared in many places in the

[4] After some months the Navy established its own comprehensive intelligence mission in Europe; thereafter ALSOS was an Army-OSRD project.

public press, of course without reference to the part that ALSOS played in uncovering the information. Several salient facts are evident in all of these reports. Contrary to our early fears, German science was not organized for research on military problems as effectively as was Allied science. Yet the inventive genius of the Nazis had created an amazing array of new devices that might have altered the whole outcome had they also had our capacity for production. We won; but the margin of victory was alarmingly small. It could have been even smaller had they trusted their Axis partners with their topmost technological tricks.

Naturally, the manner in which the military and scientific intelligence men of ALSOS had to operate to achieve results must remain a military secret. Their adventures would fill volumes that could rival the best detective fiction.

The brief account of the *major* OFS projects — the ORG, R/S, ORS, and ALSOS — packed into these pages but elaborated in later chapters of this book,[5] is by no means the whole story of OFS. What other projects lacked in size, duration, or manpower they made up in colorfulness, dramatic excitement, or long-range significance. Many exploits of the Field Service Consultants from OSRD are a fair match for the sensational experiences of their brothers in the Services. One had his scalp laid open when a swerving Army truck tossed him out of a jeep; but two days later, propped up in bed looking like a swami, he was extracting vital information from Nazi prisoners. A team of OFS communications experts persuaded the Army to "steal" the Eiffel Tower upon our entry into Paris, and soon had it operating as the radio mast for Allied broadcasts. The same group stayed up all night helping to untangle kinks in the master telephone switchboard that had been distorted by the spiteful and distracted Germans.

None of the OFS men were shot down, though many were shot at. One was caught between enemy cross fire. Another left his tent only a few moments before a Jap fighter zoomed out of the clouds to strafe it. None was subject to military discipline, but a few were chased by the Military Police. Some were hospitalized, and several spent anxious months getting rid of tropical skin disorders.

[5] See "Conning Tower to Quarter-deck" for the story of ORG; "Island-Hopping" for the story of R/S; "Brain Trust in Hawaii" for ORS; and "Scientific Sleuthing" for ALSOS.

The civilian scientists in uniform had their duller moments too. They sloshed through mud, waited dismally for official papers, shivered with malaria. Many an expert, fatigued from a day of jouncing over roads torn up by heavy equipment and shells, sat on a hard campstool that night to pound out a scientific report on his portable typewriter. One group spent weeks rearranging their personal affairs, getting their uniforms, insurance, and credentials, and purchasing equipment, only to have their mission canceled as they sat on the West Coast waiting for the final hop over the Pacific.

This chapter is too crowded already to leave room for relating how an OFS man became Mayor of a German town for several days, how another spent weeks behind the Japs in a Burmese jungle, or how a third diverted a river in New Guinea to get gravel for an airstrip. The personal adventures and technical accomplishments of these men and their fellow scientists in the many diverse projects of OFS are related in other sections of this volume. This one has furnished only hints of what it meant to be a combat scientist.

CHAPTER III

MANPOWER HEADACHE

THE SEARCH FOR PERSONNEL

UNTIL the Nazi juggernaut rolling across Europe in the spring of 1940 had made this country look to its defenses, never before in history had the scientists of the United States been called upon in such numbers and for such varied applications of their special skills to military problems. Research and development organizations and war plants had taken scientists by the hundreds from the universities, colleges, and research institutions. Selective Service rules, enforced by many conscientious people who lacked the imagination to see that a scientist working in a laboratory on a new explosive may increase the power of hundreds of men on the battlefield, had decimated student enrollments in science so that there was little hope for replenishing the supply of technical men. Many able research men, convinced that war was imminent, had enlisted voluntarily.

Where, then, would OFS get the experts it needed? Theoretically many of them should come from the research laboratories of OSRD in order to bring about the desired shift of scientific brainpower. But that would not be easy. The mere creation of a unit by OSRD to coordinate field activities did not establish a demand upon an NDRC laboratory to release to this new and untried group men who were so essential to the critical studies under way. After all, these also were sponsored by high military authority. Admirals and Generals were interested in them and would be disturbed if they fell behind schedule. The OFS would have to grow slowly, feel its way in relations with the military, develop expeditious ways of appointing people and sending them out, establish itself as an efficient agency, and demonstrate its right to priority in the allocation of personnel.

Industrial employers outside OSRD had the same reactions. They too were running night and day on war contracts and were under pressure from the brass hats. Their technical men could not be released except for matters of the greatest urgency.

The NDRC laboratories had answered many requests from the Services for specialists on equipment even before OFS appeared as a potential "raider" of their manpower. The demand was especially acute in the field of radar. Commonly the Army and Navy applied pressure to take the men over on Service pay rolls, preferably in uniform. By 1943 the Radiation Laboratory at M.I.T. had already lost about a hundred in this way. It attempted to counteract these incursions by setting up training programs for commissioned officers who could be assigned to projects at the Laboratory on development of radar gear. They would then be ready to go out with the new equipment as semi-experts. A Manpower Committee headed by Dr. Waterman, Compton's alter ego on many matters in NDRC, also set up a training program at the Laboratory for civilian newcomers to OSRD. Men of good scientific or engineering background, with no previous special knowledge of radar, secured in a few months an over-all understanding of the equipment and were then sent out also to help the military. They came from biophysics, geophysics, physical chemistry, industrial engineering, geology, and other scientific disciplines whose manpower had not been as heavily taxed by the demands of military operations as had physics, mathematics, and electrical engineering. Since these men could be used in operational analysis and administrative or consulting positions, some of the pressure on the Radiation Laboratory to release its research physicists was relieved. But now the stress was being applied again, not directly from the Services this time, but from within OSRD through OFS.

At first it did not appear that the Divisions of NDRC would be a fruitful source for OFS recruiting. Was there hope of drawing more men from the educational institutions? The small colleges could make little further contribution. They had no sizable groups of young instructors and graduate students to feed into the war program; nor did they have research staffs only partially engaged in teaching that could be transferred to war work. The few scientists remaining in their small departments were needed to instruct in AST, V-12, and pre-flight programs and would not be available until these had been curtailed. The larger institutions had lost the bulk of their student enrollments; but hordes of Army and Navy trainees crowded the classrooms and dormitories. The Services had added more and more technical material to the basic indoctrination for these men, and the universities and technical schools had to double their teaching staffs in mathematics, physics, meteorology, and other special subjects. When there were not enough instructors to go around, professors in economics and fine arts and history were pressed into service. They attended special courses early in the morning to review the physics they had in college years ago. Later in the day they were teaching it to GI's. Surely OFS could not expect to take many more scientists from the educational programs of the country; but perhaps a few could be found.

The alumni placement bureaus of M.I.T., Yale, and Princeton produced important leads. Dean J. W. M. Bunker of M.I.T., appointed as a special consultant to aid in OFS recruiting, searched the staffs of many institutions for the names of scientists who might eventually be available for OFS work. Dr. B. A. Thresher, Director of Admissions at M.I.T., soon joined OFS also as a special consultant, and for fifteen months assisted the staff in securing men for special projects. In the spring of 1944 Dr. David M. Delo, Professor of Geology at Knox College, stopped teaching meteorology to potential Air Force crews and became a Technical Aide in OFS. Eventually he took over the main responsibility for the procurement and processing of field-service men.

The search for personnel, although pursued widely throughout the United States at first, was limited later mainly to the major centers of OSRD research. The men who carried on the procurement work found that their own personal contacts were always important factors. If one had a thorough acquaintance with scientists at Harvard, Chicago, or Columbia, it was natural to turn to those institutions first in seeking candidates. Moreover, as the calls were increasing for men who knew NDRC equipment, acquaintance with the OSRD Divisions became even more significant to successful recruiting. The Scientific Personnel Office of OSRD, which had extensive records of NDRC contractors' employees, was also a helpful source of information.

If the OFS had been a relatively small operation, as was originally expected, involving the services of perhaps fifty to one hundred specialists for duties overseas and a similar number to increase operations analysis groups at home, recruiting would not have been such a headache. But in less than a year OFS had exceeded these early estimates, and by the close of the war its roster included 464 names.

Because of the emphasis given to new devices and weapons, it had appeared that this would be a war of gadgets and technological skills, a physicists' and engineers' war. Consequently OFS anticipated that men trained in these subjects and mathematicians for operations research would be in greatest demand. Calls for men from almost every other scientific field soon developed, however, and OFS found itself negotiating even with marine biologists and ornithologists. It was not their knowledge of oceanic life or of birds, but their familiarity with the terrain and the weather, the people and the vegetation of tropical islands that might be vital to men in stinking jungle foxholes.

Ordinarily the OFS man used his special training directly in his field assignment. But scientists frequently demonstrated their versatility and adaptability. Many used their collateral training rather than the specialties in which they had made their prewar record. Biologists studied the behavior of submarines, convoys, and patrolling aircraft. Geologists became administrative officers, studied land-mine countermeasures, and helped Army officers develop a manual on jungle warfare.

The field-service scientist generally had to know more about his special subject than any officer whom he might encounter in the theater; but breadth of training was quite as likely to win him respect and co-operation as was its intensity. And still more important was a practical outlook. One commander expressed this succinctly in a telephone negotiation, "The Navy needs a solid, practical, down-to-earth scientist for this job, not an 'Oh-the-wonder-of-it-all' type."

Although nearly half of the Field Service Consultants had graduate degrees in science, 32 per cent had only undergraduate college training. Yet these men had years of practical experience as significant as and often more pertinent than advanced education. Many of them had received intensive indoctrination through their work with OSRD, which was equivalent to graduate study in its intellectual challenge.

Military commanders could not wait. OFS had to move swiftly in selecting and hiring its men. Names of candidates were secured, references consulted, employers approached, and the men brought to Washington for personal interviews. In this initial screening an original list of candidates was often reduced as much as 60 per cent. Considering the reluctance of employers to release key men and the severe specifications that an individual must meet for field service, it is not surprising that only about half of those who came to Washington for negotiations were eventually attached to OFS; nor that the qualifications of over a thousand men had to be evaluated to secure the two hundred scientists employed directly, who constituted less than half of the field men loaned to the military.

Under Civil Service requirements there is a standard procedure in making new appointments. First the employer must submit to the hierarchy of Civil Service a description of the job to be performed. This is then classified to determine the relative merit of the position in rank (grade) and salary within the whole system of Government employment. If such a position on his organization chart is approved, an "opening" at a specified grade is permitted. The employer then seeks eligible people for this position, either in the lists maintained by the Civil Service Commission or through his own recruiting. When a candidate is found, his qualifications are submitted to decide whether or not he is the man for that opening. All this routine and paper work must precede any final employment arrangements with him.

Long before OFS was formally established it became obvious that such machinery would be much too slow to keep up with the rapid pace of war and that it would be simply impossible to write out in advance satisfactory descriptions of the complicated and variable duties of men who would be sent to the field as experts. How could one tell, for example, what a chemical engineer sent to Okinawa as a specialist on rockets might be asked to do? Moreover, what chance would there be of prying top-notch technical men loose from important war work to occupy positions limited by grade and salary classifications of Civil Service? Congress saw the difficulties and authorized OSRD to employ professional people by means of contracts without regard to these regulations. Such a contract was an agreement between the individual and the Government under which his services would become available at a rate not to exceed $25 per day plus transportation and the traveling expenses allowable to employees in federal service. This contract could be negotiated in a few hours — a Civil Service appointment might take weeks.

Consequently it was fully expected that most OFS men would be procured in this way, would be personal-services contract employees. Actually only about half of them were. The disadvantages involved . in repeated switching from one employer to another for only short intervals created opposition even to this simple procedure.

These contracts had desirable elasticity in that they could be written either for a man's full time or any part of it. This made it possible to secure men who could not be released completely from other war activity. The contract provided that the individual would be paid only when actually employed (WAE). Thus a man from a war plant could spend a few days a month working on special training devices for the Navy in Washington, two or three weeks as an OFS consultant to the Air Forces in Florida, and the balance of the month supervising production of gadgets in Detroit.

The contracts had provisions about compensation and working hours; but OFS consultants paid little attention to them. They were not on the job to expand their incomes or to follow rigid time schedules. They were there to render much-needed services, regardless of hours, working conditions, or compensation. Many of them in theaters regularly put in a seven-day week, often working until midnight. None completed a tour of duty owing the Government any time. A good many accepted such contracts at substantial personal loss. Some came from average incomes of $25,000 to $50,000 a year in private professional practice. In all income categories not a single man hesitated to take a field assignment because of financial considerations.

Many men were merely detailed to OFS by their employers. This was infinitely simpler than the individual contracts. As the pressure increased and OSRD contractors became the primary sources of field men, more and more consultants were borrowed in this way. This was possible when the field work was appropriate to the contract under which they had been working. Had the war continued an additional six months, probably 80 or 90 per cent of the field-service people would have been merely processed through OFS as an intermediate co-ordinating agency. As it was, more than a fourth of the consultants were provided on detail.

In some instances the employer preferred to retain a man on his own pay roll, to pay his full salary and loan him to the Government at no cost other than a provision to cover his traveling expenses. Such appointees did not serve as dollar-a-year men, but without compensation (WOC).

Although these several mechanisms gave OFS considerable leeway in employment negotiations, it was early discovered that yet another must be added. In some instances an employer was unwilling either to release a man to the Government pay roll or to loan him without compensation or on detail. The employer would agree, however, to make him available provided he could remain legally on the same pay roll, and OSRD would reimburse the company for his salary, transportation, and incidental expenses. This was particularly desirable if the man would have to sacrifice his pension or seniority status by transferring to Government employment. It was also preferable if either the employer or the employee suspected that a more permanent separation might be encouraged by this temporary one. Moreover, on occasion OFS might want not only to procure the services of special technical personnel from a particular industrial corporation but also to request that it provide test or other equipment required by the individual or group on field assignment.

Accordingly, in April 1944 Dr. Bush gave OFS authority to negotiate and recommend for his approval contracts between OSRD and industrial firms or educational institutions to take care of such contingencies. These were known internally as "company contracts." Nearly fifty people were attached to OFS by means of this sort.[1]

Altogether then there were seven[2] different ways in which OFS might secure personnel. Each had its special brand of paper work and complications. Rehearsal of them would be wearying. OFS officials will never forget that sometimes they had to call as many as six differ-

---

[1] As the volume of such business grew and it seemed that it might become extensive, a man experienced in contractual procedures was needed as an advisor to the Chief of OFS on these negotiations. Mr. Alf K. Berle was procured on a WAE basis. He took over general supervision of these company-contract matters and also provided counsel in connection with procuring and shipping special equipment to field projects.

[2] a – personal-services contract, full time
 b – personal-services contract, WAE
 c – appointment without compensation, WOC, from non-Government employer
 d – detail of Government employee from within OSRD or other agency
 e – detail of non-Government employee from contractor of NDRC, CMR, or other agency
 f – company contract with OFS
 g – Civil Service, primarily for securing central-office staff

ent people by long distance just to get permission to talk with a particular candidate.

More than three fourths of the men who went out for OFS had held some previous position in the far-flung OSRD organization. There were many requests, however, that called for men whose specialties were not included in the OSRD program — for a medical mycologist to study fungus diseases in New Guinea; a shipping expert to solve the problem of overcrowded port facilities at Honolulu; industrial engineers to help the Army simplify its paper work; and scientists who could ferret out the secrets of the enemy's research because they spoke his tongue.

Virtually every man with whom OFS negotiated had to be willing to undertake foreign travel. Even many of those who were attached to apparently stable activities in the United States could never be certain when a call might come from a theater for their immediate departure. Those who remained in this country moved around freely to Army or Navy installations, research laboratories, and war plants, collecting data for operations research, acquiring information on NDRC activities, or assisting in training programs for military personnel. Thus the Office of Field Service was truly a field agency.

Few OFS assignments were completed in less than the standard six months that had been set as a maximum initial appointment.[3] Members of a stable group like ORG remained on duty for an average of eighteen months. Men who went out on other field projects found that after almost a month of preparation and processing through military channels, it took them several weeks more in the theater to learn their way around and become well enough acquainted with the local situation to begin effective work. This made the period of a man's overseas assignment shorter than the military had counted on originally. None of the men were held overseas at the insistence of the command, however. Either a man's services were extended with his consent and that of the employer who loaned him, or he was replaced and an overlap with his successor was arranged. But theater headquarters felt that the usefulness of scientific consultants was

[3] The average length of affiliation with OFS of field-service men on the Government pay roll was 11 months; for men on detail from non-Government employment it was only 4 months. A few "missionaries" completed their work in a month or less.

greatly impaired by constant shifting of personnel. For this reason OFS frequently made verbal arrangements with a man beforehand to stay beyond the six months if he was needed and everything seemed satisfactory. OFS tried to bring its men back periodically for refresher visits. The chief obstacle to this plan was not reluctance of the Services, but shortage of transportation. Each member of a field team could not expect a regular trip home every six months; but the key individuals did return at least that often.

Considering that OFS scientists went to every theater of war, usually reached their destinations by plane, traveled about in all sorts of military conveyances, frequently went right up to or over the front lines and were close enough to daily operations to hear the noises of battle and see the wounded and captured, the casualty list was extraordinarily low. Not a man was killed and only three or four suffered injuries, from which they have entirely recovered. None are maimed or blind, but some fully expected to be. One was on a naval vessel attacked by a Japanese suicide pilot who missed by inches; several were in planes that crashed; one was thrown out of a jeep that collided with a truck; and a few were tossed out of bed by the buzz-bombs.

Field Service was also an activity characterized by youth. Though the youngest OFS consultant was 19 and the oldest 64, the average age of the field men was 36. Since the group from 25 to 40 made up nearly three fourths of the total, OFS was continually battling with Selective Service to retain its men. Many of them would be sent out in uniform and to combat zones, to work and sleep with the troops, subject to many of the hazards of military operations, to perform special technical duties that others could not handle. The Armed Forces had specifically asked for their services. It would take years to train replacements for them in the nation's scientific and engineering program. But the Draft regulations were not designed to acknowledge that a young technical man might be of greater service to his country in the laboratory or on a special scientific mission than would a hundred men with rifles. And there were no provisions that would make the task of appealing the cases of scientists any less involved, any less demanding of the precious time of still other scientists at home who could best present those cases. The same pile of official papers had to be filed, the same elaborate justifications written, as were required for the unskilled factory worker or clerk.

The fact that many of these men were Government employees increased the difficulties. The Government was particularly anxious to disprove the charge that it was harboring draft dodgers. The cases of its employees had, therefore, to be scrutinized also by special committees, and this meant more paper work, telephoning, and delay. Even though OFS actually lost very few men to the Draft, it did begrudge the energy that had to be dissipated in fighting through cases that were so obviously worthy at a time when every moment and every ounce of energy of its overworked and undermanned staff were so sorely needed on other work.

In general a very young man could not be sent to an active theater, partly because he was not sufficiently experienced either in the technical fields or in human affairs to operate successfully among large numbers of men of his own age. The GI often found it hard to understand why an outwardly comparable youth could be in the theater in civilian status, chinning with the high-ranking officers, receiving several times the salary, and enjoying freedom from the restraints placed upon the enlisted man. The soldier may have felt that he was just as intelligent, just as capable; yet he had been drafted away from activities considered less essential. In civilian operations analysis groups at home youngsters did, however, prove exceedingly valuable.

There were, of course, exceptions at both ends of the age scale. There was Brian O'Brien, Jr., 19-year-old expert on infrared devices, who deferred his acceptance of a Navy commission to spend months as an OFS man in the uniform of a civilian Navy Technician on a carrier in the Pacific. And there was the 62-year-old medical man, Dr. Joseph G. Hopkins, who flew to New Guinea and stayed with the active units throughout the Philippines campaign.

There were headaches too in building a central staff to operate the Office of Field Service since, unhappily, most of its members had to be employed under the arbitrary rules and cumbersome mechanics of Civil Service. The inflexibility of this system even in peacetime is under criticism from many sources. It was certainly not adaptable to the wartime needs of a rapidly moving organization. Hundreds of hours that officials of OFS could have spent on matters related more directly to winning the war had to be devoted to the paper routines of Civil Service.

This can not be rationalized by admitting that war itself is wasteful, or contending that otherwise the staff would have been filled by patronage. OFS had come into existence when most of the competent secretarial, stenographic, and clerical people were already thoroughly tied up in war activities. To transfer them was difficult. Not until early 1945 did it have a sufficient complement of effective secretaries and enough clerical people to handle the myriad routines. More than half of them did not come from lists of eligible candidates provided by Civil Service. OFS located them and then had to persuade the powers that be to employ the recruits at the proper levels.

Although the total roster for the Washington office lists 45 people who held Civil Service appointments, about half of them were only attached for a few months and several for as little as two weeks. The corps who handled the welter of administrative detail generally averaged only about 14 and was periodically as low as 10. Social pressure to engage in more glamorous work of agencies closer to the war zones, to enlist in the Services or in such activities as the Red Cross, was strong, and OFS lost a number of able people from its initial central staff in this way. The turnover was high and OFS had a continual struggle to develop a well-trained central group and establish efficient procedures.

Fortunately there was no such struggle to fill the top positions. Compton, Waterman, Burchard, Harrison, Klopsteg, Tate, and Morse were all loaned to the Government without compensation. If OFS had had to depend on Civil Service to supply men of this stature, it could never have moved into operation swiftly or carried the swelling volume of responsibilities.

The continuous lack of office staff militated against all attempts to follow the rigid compartmentation of employees' functions that characterizes a normal Civil Service operation. It was impossible to prescribe job specifications in advance for office personnel with any certainty that the people who would occupy those jobs could be restricted to the duties outlined in the paper descriptions. No doubt that can be done in a large and rather stationary organization where each day's business can be placed easily into categories and parceled out among the many workers. But in a small and quickly changing unit that can not forecast the duties of its staff from one day to the next, it is stultifying and futile even to attempt it.

OFS had to find people who were adaptable, ready to double or triple in brass. They had to be willing at times to spend their energies on mundane details normally handled by personnel of much lower Civil Service grade and salary classifications, and yet capable on occasion of accepting responsibilities far beyond those expected of secretarial and clerical personnel. The initiative, imagination, and poise of an office girl was fully as important as her mechanical proficiency.

For the major administrative positions OFS had to have men of thorough training in science, not because scientists are necessarily better administrators — in fact, the reverse is usually the case — but because they could understand the technical implications of the military problems, could help the Services in defining their needs, and could then interpret these to a technically trained candidate for field work in his own language. They were more effective in recruiting, and the field man felt more at ease in the knowledge that his interests were in the hands of fellow scientists.

The administrative staff also had to be young in its outlook and vigorous, had to consist of men who would think fast and act quickly, men who were not bound by tradition, and who would not give in to the perpetual frustration of red tape. To find them was difficult enough; to hold them from Selective Service was even worse because for many months deferment of men under 38 who were engaged primarily in administrative duties was not permitted. The fact that these duties could not be carried out as effectively by a person with less than graduate training in science did not seem to count.

The readiness of the staff and of other units in OSRD to operate on an exceedingly irregular schedule and to work untold hours overtime with no thought of extra compensation was also a major ingredient in the success of OFS. The military personnel with whom they dealt in Washington were operating on 24-hour-a-day, 7-day-week schedules. Understandably they could not be strict respecters of traditional business hours. Neither could commanding officers and enlisted men at the fighting fronts. They went through one sleepless campaign after another to the verge of exhaustion. Surely, then,

CENTRAL STAFF OF THE OFFICE OF FIELD SERVICE

(Includes only those who served at least three months)

Chiefs
Karl T. Compton
Alan T. Waterman

Deputy Chiefs
Alan T. Waterman
John E. Burchard

Head Technical Aide
Lincoln R. Thiesmeyer

Assistant Chiefs
John E. Burchard
George R. Harrison
Paul E. Klopsteg
Philip M. Morse
John T. Tate

Special Assistant
Lt. Thomas F. Creamer USNR

Technical Aides
David M. Delo
Madeleine T. Schneider
Virginia V. Sides

Special Consultants
Gladys A. Anslow
Alf K. Berle
J. W. M. Bunker
Harvey Fletcher
W. S. Hunter
B. A. Thresher

Secretarial Staff
Mary Azbell
Helen Bashkin
Anne Cummings
Alice E. Dawborn
Doris Dozier
Cornelia Golding
Georgia V. Hart
Miriam Madden
Elizabeth Marshall
Mildred A. Mooney
Charlotte B. Phillips
Elaine Thomas
Helena E. Vahey
Madelon Vose

Administrative Assistants
Ruth T. Mithun
Geraldine G. Morse

Stenographic and Clerical Staff
Sylvia Hedden
Della F. Holbrook
Leola Kangas
Pearl P. Paris
Catherine L. Shea
Lady Ruth Smith
Anna S. Turfley
Vera L. Watts

civilians on the home front could not think in terms of a 48-hour week. Radiograms from GHQ that called for immediate attention came in many times late in the day or on a Saturday afternoon. Someone stayed to take all possible steps at once, even if this meant canceling personal engagements or continuing on the job through Sunday. The meaning of such performance, prompted by a high concept of patriotic duty and repeated many times by members of the central staff, is impossible to assess in terms of the lives of American boys that may thereby have been saved.

OFS learned that the men who were to prove successful as Field Service Consultants also had to have an unusual combination of personal qualities. Personality and temperament were commonly as important considerations as the special technical competence of the individual. In addition to his intellectual ability, the field man had to be skilled in human relations, able to get along amicably with men of all ranks and degrees of education, patient in the face of inexplicable and often inexcusable delays, willing to accommodate himself to the methodology of the Army or Navy, and unwilling to interpret channeling of his work as a personal reflection. He had to be something of a diplomat and sufficiently modest to allow others to take credit for the achievements which may, in reality, have resulted chiefly from his efforts. He had to be ready to work side by side as a colleague with his former students, or with men who may have been his opponents in professional controversies, with men from many different scientific disciplines, ready to forget technical differences in the common goal of furnishing the best information possible to the using Services. He had to be prepared to apply the logical techniques of his general scientific training to problems outside the field of his own specialty. He could not be either arrogant or self-conscious and timid. He had to forget the highly technical jargon of the scientific laboratory and express his ideas or describe his equipment in terms understandable to the nontechnical officer or to the GI. He had to be physically sound to withstand exposure to extremes of climate or tropical diseases, able to take in his stride the irregular schedule of living and the physical hardships of ill-supplied forward areas. Naturally he had to be prepared for the hazards of combat and the possible tortures of capture.

These were the traits that characterized what OFS came to call the "combat scientist." Obviously, a great many scientists would not meet those specifications, nor did they need to in order to be successful in their normal pursuits. Not all of the projects of OFS called for men with such exceptional traits. Not all OFS men could be characterized as combat scientists, but a good many were, far more than one would gather from reading the dry fodder of their technical reports. The situations that had to be met with diplomacy, the physical difficulties under which the men operated, and the variety of ways in which they provided helpful counsel on matters beyond the scope of their special assignments are seldom detailed in the written record.

The supply of scientific men as a whole was meager enough — the supply of combat scientists was distressingly scanty.

CHAPTER IV

HIGH-PRESSURE EDUCATION

BASIC TRAINING FOR THE FIELD MAN

THE ARMY and Navy have always had to lay out programs of basic training to turn masses of civilians with infinitely diverse backgrounds and abilities into efficient military units in which every individual has at least a standard exposure to certain fundamentals of organization, procedure, paraphernalia, and behavior. In order to expand suddenly to the numerical strength demanded for total and global war, this indoctrination has to be accelerated and its content pruned to absolute minimum essentials. Yet even these occupy so much time that schedules for garrisoning all the new stations and replacing troops at the fighting fronts can not be met without compression and intensification of training. Education under high pressure and on a vast scale necessarily becomes characteristic of a wartime society, and is applied to the transformation not only of raw recruits into disciplined fighters but also of unskilled workers into reasonably competent technicians, and of potential leaders into efficient officers.

As a civilian agency of the Government which would send its representatives out to operate within the frameworks of military organizations and on foreign soil, OSRD had a similar responsibility to equip all of them with at least a standard modicum of knowledge about the civil and military regulations that must control their actions. Ideally, it would have set up a formal basic-training schedule for all prospective field men. This would have occupied several weeks and been comparable with the fundamental indoctrination that all their uniformed associates received. But the fevered haste of war research and the scarcity of scientific personnel would not allow diversion of technical talent from the laboratories, war plants, and medical centers any sooner than was absolutely necessary. And the urgency of theater needs dictated that the time devoted to preparations for departure overseas be the very minimum required to immunize the experts and give them suitable credentials.

The military could be sure that the vast majority of those placed in basic training would have practically no acquaintance with the sub-ject content of the course. The men who were to comprise the roster of the Office of Field Service, on the contrary, had varying degrees of familiarity with the things that would constitute basic instruction for field men — provisions of the Espionage Act; procedures for han-dling secret material; organization and functions of OSRD; Govern-ment regulations covering travel and financial matters; major aspects of military organization and etiquette. Many had never before held Government appointments. Some had no connection with and little knowledge of OSRD prior to their OFS assignment. On the other hand, some had served in the last war and others had previously been out as consultants to the Armed Forces in this one. They knew their way around in military channels and red tape. Some had been with OSRD for many months; some had even helped to organize it origi-nally. To subject them all to a standard basic training would have been inefficient and wasteful.

The first responsibility of the Office of Field Service when it had hired or appointed an individual was to ascertain that he had sufficient orientation in OSRD itself to be sent out as one of its representatives. If he had come from an NDRC or CMR laboratory or the administra-tive offices of an OSRD unit, or had been connected with one of the special panels and committees, there was little need to acquaint him further with the nature and purposes of OSRD. If there was time, he could become familiar, however, with the work of some other unit about which he might very well be questioned during his mission but with which he had not come in contact because of security re-strictions. Thereby he could also become an emissary from an OSRD research program other than the one in which he had been working. Furthermore, a knowledge of something beyond his own specialty would certainly increase his prestige among the officers and GI's with whom he was to work in the field.

The time available between the first OFS contact with an individual and his departure from the country varied so greatly from case to case that a systematic program of orientation could not be devised. Under the guidance of the OFS central staff each man had to acquire as much information as the schedule and his preoccupation with the many details of preparing for assignment would permit. To fill the chinks between appointments while he moved from office to office in Washington for processing, the individual could look over material OFS had gathered for "inoculating" newcomers to OSRD. He might read the basic directive of OFS, publicity releases about OSRD, selected reports from NDRC Divisions and technical branches of the Services, and Army and Navy field manuals designed for civilian appointees. OFS might arrange for him to see certain training films or visit appropriate OSRD laboratories and military installations. If he happened to be in the office when an OFS traveler returned from a field project, he could learn much in a short time by talking with this man. He could also pick up a good deal by reading correspondence from OFS representatives on location, or by conversing with a staff member who could spare a few moments from the mad rush of administrative matters. Many a successful field man secured virtually all his basic indoctrination across the lunch or dinner table from OFS senior staff members.

In the early days this unorganized, informal indoctrination proved decidedly helpful; but as the tempo of the war increased and the urgency for dispatch of field-service men was heightened, less and less attention could be given to such preparation, desirable as it might have been. The reluctance of employers to release their men and the complicated red tape of getting them ready for field work made the average time approximately a month from receipt of a Service request until the man left the country. During that time the individual was so busy preparing himself for the mission and arranging his personal affairs that a formalized, continuous indoctrination schedule was impossible. Fortunately, the number of Field Service Consultants who came to their assignments from a long background in OSRD increased, so that systematic orientation in OSRD at least became less important; but some of them were still quite innocent of military protocol and etiquette. More thorough knowledge in these subjects might have prevented minor embarrassments.

In order to familarize its personnel with the work of OSRD, the OFS was clearly dependent upon the co-operation of NDRC. Apart from their readiness to support the OSRD program as a whole, the Divisions were eager to help. The time they spent with an OFS man destined for a field mission might bring them rich dividends. He might give people in the theater their first knowledge (or a greater understanding) of equipment that these Divisions had produced.

Moreover, some of the Divisions were desperate for additional technical personnel. Occasionally OFS frankly admitted that a man sent to them for indoctrination was not yet earmarked for a specific assignment. If an OFS project did not require his services within a short time, it might be possible to transfer him to NDRC. In this way OFS located several high-caliber people and turned them over to the Divisions.

It was evident that Field Service Consultants of OFS would have to cross the rather rigid security lines NDRC had established between its Divisions, more freely than any other OSRD people. In doing so, however, they would have to be constantly on guard lest they give information received in one Division to persons in another who were not authorized to have it. The field-service man needed the information to improve his own effectiveness as a consultant in the operational areas. And he could not be a good salesman for OSRD unless he knew rather precisely what was going on in its various research and development branches.

Early in its experience OFS found that the number and nature of requests made by the Services could not be predicted. Sometimes the call was for experts on NDRC equipment, who could only be procured from the laboratories where this equipment had been developed. Other calls, for operations analysts, could be filled by the assignment of people with no previous OSRD connection. The Army or Navy frequently deliberated for some weeks before crystallizing a request to OFS; but once it had been made, they usually insisted that it be filled "the day before yesterday." Obviously the lengthy rigamarole of security clearance, employment, immunization, and other processing would not permit this. To meet the situation OFS established a pool of scientists and engineers who began their immunizations, received basic indoctrination, and were partially processed for field service. They were then available on call.

Frequency of the requests determined the length and intensity of training these men received. While awaiting military assignments they strengthened their technological backgrounds, extended their scientific

horizons, and broadened their contacts with OSRD. The purpose of
this was not primarily to train men as specialists on OSRD devices.
But by reading reports or examining equipment and watching its operation an indoctrinee could at least acquire a useful conversational
knowledge of some aspect of OSRD research and development to supplement his general technical competence. Employing men and placing them in training was admittedly an expedient to occupy them use-
fully until an assignment developed. If OFS had not arranged some
such stand-by activities, men that became available at a particular
time would have been lost to other employment. Such a pool had
the further advantage of avoiding an unnecessary drain on the manpower of the NDRC laboratories which might otherwise have been
asked to furnish personnel for assignments that did not require the
highly specialized abilities of the research man.

Early in 1943 Selective Service had reduced the programs of our
educational institutions; and some of industry's war contract work
was being cut. Scientists and engineers from these activities were
seeking other outlets for their skills. Although at the time there was
no immediate and certain prospect of a field assignment for each
man, OFS considered it advisable to hire some of them. Occasionally
negotiations with the Services led OFS to expect that a formal request
for a certain type of individual would materialize shortly. In anticipa-
tion of this a man of the right qualifications was sought, perhaps even
employed by OFS. Such a step was not considered an improper gamble. Scientific people were so scarce that, if the military request was
not forthcoming, some other unit of OSRD could readily use anyone who possessed the ability and personal qualities for a field assignment.

The Radiation Laboratory, already experienced in providing an
over-all survey of radar equipment for men who were not attempting
to become specialists, was in particularly good position to aid with
informal orientation of OFS personnel on short notice. Several men
were assigned there for varying periods and acquired a fair knowledge of radar that was useful in their field assignments.

When the pressure from Selective Service became acute in the
spring of 1944 to draft even graduate students in the sciences, OFS
was able to recruit thirteen exceptionally able young men from the

Institute of Gas Technology in Chicago. They had been high-honor graduates in chemistry or chemical engineering and were pursuing graduate work on special fellowships. Although they had no knowledge of the work of OSRD, it was felt that their abilities could be turned to good advantage either in OSRD itself or in other war research.

In the early months of its operation OFS was able to dispatch several men from its reserve to urgent theater requests much more quickly than would otherwise have been possible. By the summer of 1944, however, it became evident that the theaters were demanding more and more specialists on NDRC equipment, rather than men of general training. Accordingly OFS abandoned its attempt to maintain a pool of men who had but meager contact with OSRD, and concentrated on obtaining experts from the Divisions.

The central staff of OFS was ill-equipped to provide indoctrination in military protocol and etiquette. It had to depend on its Service liaison offices for this instruction. Ordinarily the branch of the Navy that had asked for a consultant undertook to prepare him for the assignment. The Army apparently attached less importance to a basic training for civilian specialists. It was left largely to the common sense of the individual to pick up what he could in his contacts with the military while he was still being processed and later as he worked in the field. In the early days, the New Developments Division under General Henry attempted to give each Field Service Consultant who went out under its auspices a somewhat formalized indoctrination. Officers in NDD explained Army organization, gave the men Army training manuals to read, and arranged visits to near-by military bases where they could observe equipment and talk with officers about the special problems they would encounter in forward areas. However, as NDD grew in importance in the Army organization and accepted heavier commitments, its officers were under too much pressure to give indoctrination of OFS consultants much attention. Both General Henry and later General Borden were conscious of this and regretted that it should be so. Nevertheless they were unable to secure additional personnel to plan and administer such training programs. Moreover, the time in which a man had to be fully prepared for departure was generally so short and his schedule so full of other matters that he rarely got more than a perfunctory hurried conference with an Army officer or two, whose minds were often preoccupied with other matters that seemed more important. They may also have been completely inexperienced in techniques for giving impressive indoctrination. Fortunately, when this stage was reached, most of the OFS men either had acquired a "know-how" in dealings with the military from earlier experience in OSRD, or they were being sent to report in the theater through one of the OFS branch offices where they would find colleagues schooled in military matters to guide them.

In the Navy's ORG the situation was quite different. Here the training of a new man did not have to be sandwiched into an otherwise full schedule. It constituted a part of his initial work in the group, where continuity of indoctrination was possible. On his first day of duty he was asked to read pertinent Navy regulations and an instruction manual carefully prepared by members of the unit. This outlined the place, purpose, and functions of the ORG in naval organization, and the procedures which he would find advantageous in working with officers. It cautioned him about handling classified information, indicated the kind of records he was expected to keep, outlined the pitfalls he should avoid in dealings with the military, and laid down the philosophy that was to guide his attitudes as a civilian counselor to the Navy. Revised periodically, this was a sort of Bible and the man was asked to reread it frequently.

For some weeks the new ORG man familiarized himself with the kinds of work done by the group, with the various fundamental techniques of operations analysis they had developed, and with the results achieved by other similar units in the British forces and the Army. During this course of selected and supervised reading he was always in touch with men who could elaborate and explain from their own experience. He became conscious at once that he was part of a cohesive unit. He sensed group loyalty and group responsibility. He was surrounded by civilians like himself who had been through the mill and were available as advisors and instructors. Through the example of associates he learned something about diplomacy in handling the frequently delicate situations that arise when civilians, only imperfectly understood and therefore regarded with suspicion, are functioning within the Navy and have access to its most classified operational information. He would never be sent out as a representative of ORG to work with officers at an advance base or aboard a line vessel until he had demonstrated not only his ability in the technical aspects of operations research but also his skill in human relations.

Even though a man came to ORG from "operational research" elsewhere, it was never assumed that he knew the methods and could start right out with full responsibility to tackle a problem alone. He was first assigned to work with a man of senior caliber and experience. He learned by doing, and he had to demonstrate aptitudes and an analytical quality of mind that would soon justify placing him on his own. The length of this preliminary indoctrination was varied to suit the capacities of the individual. Few men were really doing effective operations research until they had been group members for at least a month. This meant that needs of the Navy had to be anticipated and allowance made for this basic training in the recruiting schedule as ORG expanded.

A feature of the ORG program that served many purposes and added to the over-all training of its men was the monthly meeting at which group members presented "papers" on methodology and results. These were attended by the full complement of ORG men in Washington and by ORG men at Atlantic bases whose duties permitted. Naval officers immediately concerned in the problems discussed and members of the British Admiralty Delegation were invited as guests. The meetings served to intensify the solidarity of ORG as a working team. They provided an opportunity for members preoccupied with analyses in one aspect of naval warfare to keep posted on the problems faced and methods used by their colleagues in another. Like the formal meetings of any scientific organization, they afforded discussion of methods and fundamental principles of analysis. This constituted education not only for new members of the group but also for the guests in uniform.

The papers were rehearsed and monitored with meticulous care. Charts and drawings executed with professional skill by one of the group members proved invaluable as aids to the speakers. Although the material was presented in a semipopular fashion, omitting some of the more abstruse mathematical considerations and concentrating on the conclusions and results that would guide Navy doctrine, Professor

Blackett remarked after attending one of these sessions that the quality of the presentations compared very well with those of the Royal Society in England.

In these meetings the operations analyst learned the importance of expressing himself vividly and confidently, learned to handle the searching questions of experienced officers, and to defend publicly among his scientific peers the methods that had led him to a particular conclusion. All of this created, of course, an *esprit de corps* that was unmatched in the other major projects of OFS whose personnel were transient and had to operate in an atmosphere of field urgency rather than in a setting of detached, objective investigation where the scientist feels more at home.

The well-planned and lengthy indoctrination of ORG men was a far cry from the high-pressure, shot-in-the-arm type of education so many wartime "experts" received. Only because ORG was a stable organization that retained its personnel essentially for the duration was it possible to develop such a systematic, coherent, and continuous schooling for new men. Moreover, Dr. Morse refused to compromise with demonstration of ability. Regardless of pressure from the Navy, he would never send out a man who had not proved himself first in the minds of his fellows and of officers in the central training ground in Washington.

In February 1944 Dr. Compton received a letter from Mr. Bennett Archambault, head of the OSRD London Office, suggesting that it might be desirable for OFS to take over supervision and staffing of American participation in the analytical work of two units operating under jurisdiction of the British Research and Experiment Department, Ministry of Home Security. In London and at Princes Risborough, a small town outside London, these groups worked with problems in physics and structural engineering for better air-raid protection, assessed bomb damage, and helped to select the best weapons for our air offensive. A number of OSRD people had already taken part in this activity. The Princes Risborough group had become the equivalent of an independently operated Air Ministry Operations Research Section for weapon and target analysis and structural and economic intelligence. Its facilities had been made available to the American

Strategic Air Forces. Officials believed that this activity should be broadened and continued until the end of the war in Europe. They felt that the lessons learned could be used against the Japanese. Although the work was primarily under British auspices, increased American aid was sought; and it appeared that OFS would be the logical co-ordinating agency.

At about that time the United States Navy was becoming increasingly interested in the work at Princes Risborough as a possible training ground for personnel for its Air Technical Analysis Division (ATAD), which undertook basic studies to be used in planning air offensives against Japan. Commander Francis Bitter, physicist from the M.I.T. faculty who had been chief of the Navy's very successful operations analysis group on mine warfare, was anxious to institute such a program. He was now in charge of an ATAD group which had begun a comprehensive study of the probable vulnerability of Japanese targets to various weapons and the economic effects that might be expected from tactical and strategic assaults on Nippon that were planned by the Navy. OFS had already helped to supply analysts for Bitter's staff; but he wanted to extend the scope of this work and was pressing OFS for additional personnel.

Requests were also coming to OFS in increasing numbers from both the Tactical and Strategic Air Forces in Europe through the Operations Analysis Division (OAD) of the Air Force under Colonel Leach. They wanted men familiar with applications of the theory of probability, with terminal external ballistics, with the characteristics of various high-explosive bombs and incendiaries, and with techniques for measuring bomb damage.

At Princeton University, Division 2 (Structural Defense and Offense) had established an experimental station staffed with experts in these subjects. With the active co-operation of the Applied Mathematics Panel (AMP) of OSRD, Division 11, the Navy Bomb Disposal School, and the Air Forces, the Princeton University Station (PUS) had given several groups of architects and engineers recruited for Colonel Leach short courses in these special fields. Subsequently these men became key members of Air Force Operational Research Sections from Brittany to Burma. Some of the officers from the ATAD group had also taken these short courses at Princeton. With expansion of the war in the Pacific in prospect, additional Operational Research Sections were contemplated. Colonel Leach and Commander Bitter approached Division 2 and OFS to supply the personnel needed for extension of both the OAD and the ATAD work, preferably after a course of training similar to that previously furnished by the Princeton Station.

To co-ordinate these interests it therefore appeared logical that OFS should sponsor a special program of indoctrination, somewhat broader than the one given earlier by PUS. It would have to be more intensive because the type of man whom OFS was empowered to employ would have a more advanced and highly specialized background. The program would involve similar participation by AMP, Division 11, and branches of the Services.

Representatives of OFS, AMP, the Divisions concerned, Princeton Station, OAD, and ATAD held a round-table conference to consider the whole problem of finding and training the people who would be needed by the group in England, by the Air Force, and by the Navy. Dr. H. P. Robertson, mathematical physicist of the London OSRD office, and Mr. Marc Peter, Jr., architect and head of the American group at Princes Risborough (PR), who had just returned from the United Kingdom, described the work at PR and emphasized that it would be the best place for trainees to learn to interpret aerial photographs from preraid and postraid reconnaissance. The PR group would be delighted to furnish this training, and the men sent there after suitable study at the Princeton Station would in effect become additional temporary hands to relieve the need for more personnel at PR. It was not felt desirable, however, that OFS take over supervision of the entire Princes Risborough program.

All the agencies present agreed to co-operate in another semiformal but brief course of indoctrination to develop bomb damage "experts." Plans were drawn for the Princeton Station to take the lead in such a program again. OFS was to recruit and supply the men. They would be given a six-to-eight-weeks course which would include a review of mechanics, introduction to the theory of probability, terminal ballistics, and photointerpretation at Princeton. This would be supplemented by the reading of operational reports available in the Princeton Library, work with the Statistical Analysis Section of AMP in New York, study of reports of Division 11 in Cambridge and in Washington, visits to experimental testing grounds at Norwood, Massachusetts, and at Edgewood Arsenal, Maryland, and study at the Navy Bomb Disposal School in Washington of the characteristics of the many types of bombs and fuzes in use by our forces and by the enemy.

If time permitted and the indoctrinees had not yet been committed to other assignments, it was hoped that they could also visit the Army Air Forces Training School at Orlando, Florida. Here they would be in close daily contact with Air Force personnel who would soon be going overseas to operations. They would attend classes with them, would sit in on briefing and participate in practice missions, and in general would soak up some of the atmosphere which they might later encounter in an Operational Research Section of the Air Forces. Then they would be sent to Princes Risborough to help the staff there while they learned more about photointerpretation and acquired a better firsthand knowledge of the techniques for selecting the right combination of bombs, fuzes, flight formations, and incendiaries to create the greatest damage to a specified target.

These plans materialized in a course that began at the Princeton Station on April 15, 1944. The group of trainees was smaller than had been expected, because the whole plan had crystallized rather suddenly and there was insufficient time to recruit a larger class. The contingent sent to Princeton by OFS consisted of Professor Albert G. H. Dietz, civil engineer from M.I.T., Messrs. Morris Atkin, Arthur L. Otto, and Frank Claessens, civil engineers, Mr. Earl K. Bowen, mathematician from the faculty at Northeastern University, and Mr. Abbott Byfield, Technical Aide in Division 11 and chemical engineer. All of them were mature junior men of considerable training and experience. They pursued the program vigorously and would have welcomed the opportunity to complete the curriculum originally outlined. Unfortunately, however, long before they had finished even the first part of it at Princeton, requests for men of their background with even a scant indoctrination were so pressing that OFS had to call several of them to other assignments. The rest continued through the session at the Bomb Disposal School and then they too were drawn into OFS projects.

As was expected, the need for men of such training was not fully satisfied by the small group that undertook the first semiformal indoctrination. Accordingly, in the summer Princeton Station and the other participating agencies were again persuaded to offer a course of the same sort. Seven more men were sent through the paces. This group included Richard D. Burson, Maurice Barron, Egidio Picardi, J. Virgil Proctor, and Ellsworth Rose, civil engineers, Dr. Donald P. LeGalley, physicist, and Dr. Maxwell Reade, mathematician. This time negotiations for field assignments did not proceed swiftly enough to prevent completion of the course. These men had the benefit of the Orlando training as well as a more intensive and longer contact with AMP and with Division 11. Since several of them were rather mature, the course could proceed on a more informal basis and the senior men assisted with some of the instructional work. This was a decided relief to the Princeton Station because use of a few of its most able men in the teaching staff for the previous courses had created serious dislocation of their experimental research.

In the summer of 1944 it appeared that a considerable extension of operations analysis would be requested by various other branches of the Army that had expressed a growing interest in this technique. Expecting that it might be asked to set up one group after another, OFS made preliminary plans to develop a more high-powered, semiformal indoctrination course in which a contingent of senior men of exceptional caliber would be trained to head operations analysis teams. Under the tutelage of an outstandingly competent and broadly experienced man they would spend some weeks becoming thoroughly familiar with the methodology and results of operational research carried on by the British and by the various American Sections, and would then be peculiarly fitted for leadership in operations analysis. This plan was never implemented, however, because it proved impossible to procure men of the right caliber for a program that would first require weeks of *training*. They were too critically needed in fields in which they were already highly competent. Moreover, the gradual change of emphasis from attention to the need for operational analysis to the more immediate need for specialists on equipment was becoming apparent in the field.

Civilians in Uniform

Quick lunch for OFS men and their military aides close behind the front lines in Europe

Drive Yourself

The combat scientist had to be mobile, too

CHAPTER V

RED TAPE AND BRASS BUTTONS

PUTTING THE SCIENTIST INTO UNIFORM

THE SCIENTIST is accustomed to great freedom of action in the laboratory. The regulations he observes are the laws of nature and the dictates of his conscience. He regards the clothes he wears as unimportant, and the papers that concern him are the notes on his own work and the reports of his fellow investigators. It is natural for him to rebel against restrictions, paper work, red tape. He is generally ignorant of and impatient with the regulations that limit individuals in large organizations, particularly in Government and the Military Services. But in order to do his part in the all-out war program he had to (and did more or less) adjust himself to them.

It would be tiresome to enumerate the intricacies of federal machinery that attended the transformation of this independent worker into a regimented specialist in uniform. Certainly the rules will all be different in a future war. Yet one who has not experienced them can scarcely appreciate the bewilderment and annoyance of the combat scientist who had to struggle through the formalities before he could devote his full attention to the technical problems of his field assignment — which he could not help thinking were of greater import than a proper set of papers with the right signatures in some Washington filing cabinet. Nor can one visualize without seeing at least a part of the picture of bureaucracy the moments of near delirium and exhaustion that came to those who fought against time in wrestling with the red tape necessary to a change from drab laboratory apron to shiny brass buttons.

The success of the Fifth Column in Europe made Americans cautious. Even though an individual held a position of importance and was respected in his community, it was not simply assumed that he could be trusted with the war's secrets. The fact that he once worked for the Army on the layout of air bases would not necessarily prove that details of our latest battleships would be safe in his hands. It could not be assumed that just because a man could qualify as a scientist he could also be considered a loyal citizen. It was necessary to operate on the principle that everyone was under suspicion until his integrity and loyalty had been confirmed. And the proof lay in careful investigation. Its thoroughness was governed not only by the importance of the confidential information the man might be asked to guard, a matter largely of opinion, but also by the procedures and efficiency of the investigating agency.

To start the process the candidate for OFS work filled out forms in septuplicate. These were not concise and simple ones of the sort one would expect in such urgent business, but complicated, legal-size sheets. For detail and complexity they were matched only by the formidable blanks the harassed taxpayer faced in the days before a pay-as-you-go plan brought simpler versions. Then there would be weeks of waiting while investigators checked his record.

This procedure was known as security clearance. It usually took a week to ten days, but as the pile-up of cases swamped the investigators, a month was considered normal. When the report finally came back that the man was "cleared for work of a confidential nature," his right to information bearing a "restricted," "confidential," or "secret" label was established. "Top secret" matters were entrusted only to persons who had undergone a much more exhaustive investigation.

Since OSRD was so closely involved with all branches of the Armed Forces, was in touch with the planning of future military operations, and was designing both our own secret weapons and the defenses we would use against those of the enemy, all OSRD personnel had to be cleared thoroughly.

Getting cleared and wading through a mass of papers to establish his employment or appointment by the Government were just introductions to the red tape that bedeviled every candidate for a post with OFS. There was still the involved series of steps that came to be known as "processing." This was mental hazard enough to a man who would remain to work with the military in this country. A specialist going overseas found it even more perplexing because it meant that he would have to get military as well as civilian credentials, would have to buy a uniform, and have permission from his Draft Board and from the State Department to leave the country. Some OFS men were more or less familiar with these tedious proceedings. But to most of them the processing was a bewildering maze of details, a seemingly endless round of official documents, and a disheartening array of regulations. Processing consisted of two major sequences. One involved the steps any civilian would take to go abroad in peacetime — become immunized, obtain a passport, arrange financial matters, and secure the right papers. The other included special steps necessary because of the war — security clearance; permission to leave this country and enter combat zones; extra-hazard insurance; an appropriate uniform, correct for the theater and the season; official military credentials and travel orders; permission to take a camera if necessary and to carry official papers; and so on. Altogether the processing unit of the OFS office listed nearly a hundred separate matters that must be considered by every Field Service Consultant before he dashed for the plane that would take him overseas.

The relationship between some of the processing steps is so close that a delay in the handling of one can start a whole chain of cumulative delays. A holdup on security prevents employment and issuance of military papers. This in turn prohibits the time-consuming purchase of a properly fitted uniform. A Government employee cannot secure tickets for travel reservations until he has the necessary official "transportation requests" that are used in lieu of cash and that waive the customary tax on transportation. He cannot receive these without the requisite travel authorization, which cannot be made out until the formal employment papers have been executed. Under wartime travel restrictions it was more important than ever that the consecutive items in such a sequence be handled systematically and efficiently. Under the Government system of compartmentation the various aspects of processing had to be handled by different offices in different agencies. In many matters, therefore, OFS could only initiate an action and then follow it up persistently because of its relationship to some succeeding action in the total procedure.

Usually there were six to ten OFS men in all stages of preparation simultaneously, and in early August 1945 there were seventy. To shepherd impatient or bewildered novices through the details, keep action going in the right order, straighten out snarls, and meet implied or actual deadlines set by the military was altogether a frantic operation. The staff of OFS was certainly no place for psychoneurotics.

Always there was pressure for speed. When the Army or Navy decided that an individual was wanted, he was usually wanted post-haste. But even with high priority from the military and great pressure within OSRD, it was rarely possible to prepare a new recruit for assignment overseas and get him on the plane within less than a week. The normal interval before departure was at least a month. This was a source of distress all around, but little could be done to shorten the process. Exceptions always interfere with systematic handling of standard cases. When these are piling up beyond the capacity of people to keep abreast of the day's business, it takes considerable pressure from high authority to interrupt the normal routine.

For all theaters immunization for smallpox, typhoid, typhus, and tetanus was required. For tropical areas yellow fever was ordinarily prescribed, and for certain Far Eastern theaters cholera and bubonic plague. Since the complete series would normally require forty-two days, many a man who came to Washington for just the preliminary interview about an OFS job found himself at the Pentagon Dispensary with his sleeves rolled up, getting four or five shots at once so there would be no delay in processing him if he accepted the assignment.

Most of the steps in the military aspects of processing had to be taken by officers. A civilian administrator could not, for example, authorize the wearing of a uniform, set up a travel priority for a flight by military aircraft, or issue official travel orders to a combat zone. OFS had to depend, therefore, on its liaison officers in the Army and Navy either to produce the necessary papers themselves or see that this was done correctly and in time.

In NDD Colonel Kent Lane assumed the major responsibility for handling all OFS matters, including supervision of the military process-ing details. As the volume of business with OFS increased, Lieutenant Colonel Joy Dow, Lieutenant Colonel Hammond H. Henderson, Major Thomas O. Davis, and other officers joined him in this work. Under Colonel Lane the procedures for handling personnel and the channels for communications were standardized and the basic patterns of OFS relations with the Army were established. Colonel Lane was essentially "a civilian in uniform" who detested paper work and red tape and whose fundamental attitude was usually that of the expediter.

Under General Henry the New Developments Division had, like OFS, begun in a small and modest way, never exercising the full authority of its basic directive, never staffed sufficiently to do so, building its reputation within the Army. When General Borden assumed command, the directive had been extended so that NDD was given authority to supervise and co-ordinate all scientific and technical missions of civilian and military personnel to theaters of operations on matters of research and development. Theoretically it could become the agency to handle the military processing for all such missions of the whole Army. Had there been adequate staff to handle it, this might have proved the most efficient way of forwarding all OFS business with the Army.

As NDD had grown, however, it had taken on increased responsibilities and the officers were able to devote only part of their time to OFS projects. An increase in staff to cover processing of OFS men going out through NDD had been requested but was slow to materialize. Mrs. Jeffress, secretary to Colonel Lane, became proficient in these matters and virtually carried the load alone.

Recognizing that it could not handle all the work itself, NDD then determined that when a project had been initiated by some technical Service branch, the military processing would be carried out by that branch, with NDD merely co-ordinating or supervising. This could work well only if all such branches were equally familiar with the procedures — which was, of course, far from the case. Not uncommonly officers in the branch of Army or Navy that wanted an OFS consultant were unacquainted with the regulations for handling civilians, and OFS had to explain them to these officers. Those who knew the score from handling previous cases had been transferred on short notice. Such transfers are inevitable in wartime. Moreover, the many individual subdivisions of suddenly dilated organizations could not possibly be comparably familiar with the proper mechanics. Naturally this caused untold delay — especially when the same office had to be educated several times. On the other hand, the very existence of a stable OFS staff, up-to-date on the systems, proved advantageous to the utilization of scientists by the military arms.

* * *

If the work of the scientist from OFS would not require him to leave the United States, or if he was to operate entirely in England, he could wear his regular civilian clothes. In a combat theater, however, he would have to be in uniform. The change from mufti to brass buttons created a wholly separate set of hurdles.

If his mission would take six months or more, he would have to acquire a substantial wardrobe. Fortunately, it did not all have to be purchased before he left. The military had Post Exchange (PX) stores in the theaters and he would have access to them. The weight limit on baggage for air travel was fifty-five pounds. This must include wearing apparel, documents, special equipment, and personal items. If he simply had to have an exceptional quantity of documents or special apparatus for his work, the allowance could be raised. But any excess over twenty pounds had to be authorized by the theater and an exchange of radios would mean further loss of time. Even the fastidious soul could not expect transport planes crowded with vital personnel and materials to carry all the shirts and officer's pinks he might wish for dress occasions.

The civilian specialist wore an officer's uniform, but there were no insignia of rank on his shoulders. Whether or not he wore a necktie, an officer's visored cap, or the peaked garrison cap, whether he had metal "US" pins in his lapels and a theater patch on his shoulder depended on the regulations established by the local theater commander. Usually the nearer to the front lines the scientist went the less formality he encountered.

Entitled to wear the officer's blouse (coat jacket) with brass buttons, many a man packed this away as soon as he arrived in the theater and never put it on again until he started for home. When a top-level officer could attend a conference or a social function in trousers and a tropical worsted shirt, an OFS consultant on his staff would have felt conspicuous in a jacket.

To guard against imposters the military had rules that would prevent an unauthorized person from acquiring a Service uniform. It was not possible to walk into any store and buy one without still another piece of paper, official permission from Army or Navy to purchase the regulation outfit and accessories. Only when a formal theater request naming the individual was in the hands of the military liaison office

in Washington could such authority be given. If this was not received
until a few days before he was to leave, a frantic scramble to get the
proper uniform might have resulted. The nearest store might not have
his size in stock at that moment. It might have only winter uniforms
when he would need sun-tans. Tailors might be too busy to alter the
garments to suit his unique dimensions. Many a Field Service man in
the final stages of preparation in Washington had to rush to Baltimore or New York for a blouse or an outsize shirt, or even had to
leave, hoping there would be time in San Francisco to pick up something not available in the eastern stores.

The scientist who went out for the Navy was appointed as a "U.S.
Navy Technician." He wore the regulation blues, grays, or khakis.
Over the left breast pocket of his blouse there was an embroidered
eagle clutching mechanic's tools. These same insignia were worn by
other civilian appointees of the Navy regardless of their training or
intended functions. Consequently the bluejacket could not distinguish
between a Coca-Cola-machine maintenance technician and a top-
ranking physicist or engineer from OSRD. Early in its history OFS
attempted to persuade the Navy that the work of scientists in war
theaters might be facilitated if they could somehow be distinguished
from other civilians at the front and suggested that a special emblem
be devised for OFS specialists. The ORG men were permitted to wear
special collar pins that identified them with the Operations Research
Group in Washington.

When OFS began to send men out on Army missions in 1943 the
War Department usually appointed a civilian specialist as "Expert
Consultant to the Secretary of War," or as "Technical Observer." At
first most of the scientists were placed in the latter category. Here likewise no distinction was made between the highly competent engineer
who would operate at staff level and the technician sent out by a manufacturer to service field equipment. Some civilian maintenance men
were also frequently appointed as "Technical Representatives." Yet
their uniforms, insignia, and credentials were otherwise identical with
those of the Technical Observers. This added to the confusion of
theater personnel in attempting to identify the civilian visitors who

were using their jeeps and planes, eating their food, and complicating their housekeeping.

The New Developments Division, impressed with the disadvantages of this situation to the expert personnel it sent to the theaters, secured a revision of Army regulations so that two new types of appointment were authorized — "Scientific Consultant" and "Operations Analyst." This occurred in the fall of 1944 and thereafter most OFS personnel bore one of these designations. The nature of the work an individual performed governed his title. Equipment specialists were called Scientific Consultants; men assigned to the Operations Analysis Division of the Air Forces or to projects in which they really did operations research were appointed Operations Analysts. Although appropriate for many OFS travelers, the term Scientific Consultant was clearly not a wise one for a specialist engaged in intelligence activities. In that case the less descriptive appointment "Expert Consultant" was used.

Shoulder patches with the words "Scientific Consultant" or "Operations Analyst" embroidered across them were designed and eventually issued by the Adjutant General's Office (AGO). They replaced the large triangular white patches worn by Technical Observers. Distribution of these new patches was delayed by military red tape, however, and throughout the winter and early spring of 1945, therefore, OFS men went out bearing the new titles but still wearing the Technical Observer's shoulder patches, or none at all.

The scientist in Army uniform carried two cards issued by the AGO. To obtain these he had to file a whole series of documents with the Army — evidence of his security clearance, proof that he was not jumping the Draft, certificates of his health and immunizations, and a statement from his local police headquarters that he was not evading prosecution for a misdemeanor or a crime. Then he was photographed and fingerprinted and the AGO cards were held until his official military travel orders had been prepared.

One AGO card specified that he was a noncombatant and a civilian, entitled to sleeping quarters and meals of the type received by officers. The other assigned him an "assimilated rank." According to regulations this was based automatically on the salary he received. The standard schedule of true military ranks and corresponding salaries was the guide in selecting the assimilated rank for each case. Nevertheless, even though some of the OFS men commanded high salaries and held positions of great responsibility in civilian life, the War Department was reluctant to follow this schedule literally and issue appointments carrying assimilated ranks higher than Colonel. Late in the war when greater confidence was felt in OSRD civilians, a few higher appointments were authorized. Since the majority of men OFS sent out were scientists of some maturity whose income in private life was well above the average, the normal relationship between chronological age and income that obtains in a military organization did not apply to them in the assignment of assimilated ranks. There were entirely too many OFS Colonels and not enough Captains and Majors. This sometimes proved more of a handicap than an advantage to people whose presence in the theaters was not always accepted with enthusiasm.

The assimilated rank was only intended to protect the civilian in case he was captured. It was hoped that when the enemy examined his AGO credentials they would treat him as they would an officer of the same true rank under terms of the Geneva Convention. In practice, however, this synthetic status was frequently used in connection with billeting or other arrangements. The individual had to fit into Army routines, and a Sergeant in charge of billets or an MP on guard was accustomed to dealing with everyone in terms of rank. Although the OFS man was always advised before he left Washington that he should certainly not flash an AGO card to impress military personnel, he was frequently required to show it.

An OFS consultant loaned to the Navy was given a Certificate of Identification that carried his photograph and fingerprints and authorized him to take passage on naval vessels and visit naval establishments. This corresponded to the AGO card and was issued by the office of the Chief of Naval Operations (CNO). If he was going overseas, the Navy Technician also received from CNO a Letter of Credentials that outlined his status and the purpose of his assignment. To obtain these documents he filed almost the same set of papers required by the AGO.

The Navy had no system of assimilated ranks. Navy Technicians were accorded the privileges granted a commissioned officer. This had its drawbacks, since the billeting officer was never sure whether the OFS man should be quartered with the men of junior rank or with the scrambled eggs. On the other hand, it avoided the embarrassment that might have arisen had he been given a simulated senior grade and assigned to work under a junior officer.

A Navy Technician was required to salute the flag, the quarter-deck, and the officer of the deck on boarding and leaving ship; otherwise he would merely return such salutes as he might receive from enlisted men who recognized his status as essentially that of an officer. As a matter of courtesy Navy Technicians often saluted officers of senior grade. The total number of such special civilian appointees was relatively small and many enlisted personnel were unfamiliar with the regulations and etiquette that would apply to them. One rather youthful OFS scientist who had visualized himself returning salutes on every hand reported with amusement that the only ones he received in four months with the Navy came from two drunken *soldiers* in a bar in Chicago.

Army regulations specified that men with assimilated rank were not entitled to be saluted. In practice, however, in order to avoid embarrassment to the many GI's who were unfamiliar with such rules and who had been drilled to respect the uniform of an officer, the Field Service Consultant of OFS usually returned any salutes given in error.

The most important document carried by the OFS traveler in uniform was his military travel orders. These were "cut" (prepared in duplicate) in Washington by the AGO or CNO. They specified the approximate date on which he would leave, assigned him to a particular overseas shipment, designated the means of travel he would use and stated its priority, outlined the mission he would perform, and told him where to report on arrival overseas. Ten copies were usually issued in Washington because each important office on his itinerary would require one. Such orders were not usually needed for travel within the United States. They were sometimes issued simply because officers at bases would understand better how to receive and treat the visitor if he bore credentials of a sort familiar to them.

Traveling without orders was either hazardous or impossible. They were the first and frequently the only documents the officers wanted to see when a man reported for duty. Without them he was at the mercy of friends in the Service to arrange his functioning in the area and any subsequent travel. With them, and with patience, he could go almost anywhere. On one occasion OFS permitted a party to leave without official travel orders. This was done only after strong protest to the sponsoring office which had insisted they were unnecessary, that the Letter of Credentials would be sufficient. If the OFS men had not been senior scientists with many acquaintances among high-ranking officers in the theater who issued temporary duty orders, the result would have been utterly disastrous. As it was, embarrassment and delays nearly wrecked the mission. Thereafter OFS refused to loan a man to the Services unless proper orders were guaranteed.

Much depended on the exact wording of the travel orders. If they stated that "travel by commercial and/or military aircraft is *directed* as necessary for the accomplishment of an emergency war mission," the commercial air lines automatically gave the man a priority to the port of embarkation (POE). This would be immediately invalidated, however, if he made the mistake of stopping off to bid farewell to relatives, or for personal business not provided for in the orders.

The priority for the overseas part of the trip was established by the theater commander.[1] But there were circumstances at this end beyond his control. More than once OFS and NDD turned handsprings to get a man ready for departure by a certain deadline on a specified priority, only to learn later that he spent five days waiting at Hamilton Field, California, for a backlog of transport pilots or other military personnel to clear through ahead of him.

It is well to pause here for a moment in our narrative to pay tribute to the energy, imagination, and utterly selfless attention to the job of the small group who constituted the central OFS staff. They will receive no medals, theater ribbons, or commendations from Admirals and Generals, yet without their willingness to ignore working hours, job descriptions, and the impatience of harried travelers, the whole program would have foundered. They had to enjoy only vicariously the thrills of flying the Pacific in a bomber, hobnobbing with the brass

---

[1] Very few OFS men traveled on Priority 1 or 2. The majority had Priority 3, and for return travel from the theaters Priority 4 was common.

hats, riding the surf at Honolulu, or walking triumphantly through Nazi cities. Theirs was the battle of the paper work, red tape, and regulations in the crowded melee of the home front. Its agonies were the inevitable muddles in transportation arrangements, fiscal details, and communications that developed in a system which requires that many offices, staffed with people of varying competence and familiarity with procedure, handle the components of a matter.

The din of this battle was the jumbled sound of multiple long-distance calls, hurried interviews, pounding typewriters, feverish dictation, agitated searching for documents in circulation, all conducted simultaneously in open offices without soundproofing or partitions. Their campaign slogan was "Hurry" and their objective was to get the OFS men to their field posts with utmost dispatch and to free them wherever possible from the distractions of routine administrative detail so their attention could remain on technical problems.

They made mistakes, as people do who work under pressure with procedures new to them and when there are no guiding precedents. Occasionally in mental lapses induced by fatigue or confusion they were less efficient than they would have liked to be. But, except for their effort, many a field-service scientist might still be trying to get on a return steamer from Okinawa or to clear his accounts with the Government.[2]

The OFS traveler needed more guidance and help with his expense accounts than in any other aspect of his Government affiliation. Nothing aggravated him more than to be forced to take time and thought from his pressing technical work to do the detailed bookkeeping required by official regulations and to fill out the complicated vouchers. Again and again he had to justify in writing and with precisely the right phraseology the things he had done to get on with his mission swiftly — explain why he had taken that short trip by plane instead of going the cheaper route by rail, why he had rushed across the city in a taxi to keep an appointment with the Admiral when buses, trolleys,

[2] Despite heroic work of the central staff, some men *are* still struggling to get their fiscal records straight — because they were too careless or cryptic in making them out the first time, because they ran around doing things that are taken for granted in industrial expense accounts but are sins akin to treason under the Government, or because their papers, now out of OSRD hands, have been mislaid, misfiled, or buried in some Washington office.

and subways were available, sign a special statement that he had to have a bedroom rather than an upper in order to protect the vital secrets he was carrying — all of this so that the clerks who audited his vouchers but knew nothing about the nature or the urgency of his work would see that he had acted in accordance with the letter of the regulations and would authorize the Treasury to repay in full the amounts he had spent.

Such expenses would be taken for granted in the business or academic world from which he had come. There it was his own discretion that decided whether minor costs in a particular action were less important than the end results. In private business the degree of confidence placed in a man to protect the best interests of his employer financially are commensurate with the degree of responsibility of his position. Expense vouchers are simple. And even though they can be padded by unscrupulous individuals, the liberal policies of industry toward the travel accounts of its representatives would long ago have been abandoned if serious losses had resulted.

Over the years in peacetime the number of penny-pinching special rules and the infinitely detailed procedures that have grown up around expenditure of public funds for travel would simply floor the average citizen who recalls astronomic appropriations that were apparently spent in other matters with no such time-consuming and costly accounting. Those rules and methods were designed for peacetime operations and, even though some modifications were made to adapt them to the wartime needs of OSRD, they still were too inflexible, too mechanical, too complex to permit maximum efficiency. When time was so vital, many an OFS man paid for things out of his own pocket and went on with his work rather than spend valuable hours writing up accounts in the elaborate form required by the Government. All too often he had to be rushed off to a war zone without a chance to digest the plethora of regulations that were so foreign to his previous experience.

The girls of OFS, many of them likewise newcomers brought into Government service during the war, tried to learn the regulations and did their best to help the field men keep their records straight. And when they were too perplexed to answer a question on some item or to rectify an error, they could turn to Mrs. Mae R. Magee, head of the

Travel Unit in the OSRD Fiscal Office, whose long experience in the Government and patient sympathy with the scientists who were so naïve in fiscal affairs remedied many headaches.

In the early days Mrs. Ruth T. Mithun, an Administrative Assistant from December 1943 until the autumn of 1944, took a major responsibility for processing under the general supervision of Dr. Delo, and saw many field men through the agonizing routines with graciousness and good humor. She was replaced by Miss Geraldine G. Morse, who brought to this nerve-wracking position a maturity, poise, and ability in maintaining the morale of her harassed associates that proved invaluable when the volume of detail and the pressure increased.

When OFS was created, the Overseas Service Division of the OSRD Liaison Office in Washington already had experience in preparing OSRD personnel for foreign missions. It had firm contacts with the State Department, with the Joint Chiefs of Staff, and with the various Service and civilian transportation and medical agencies that might be involved in handling the details. It was therefore logical that this office should serve as the medium for channeling and expediting arrangements for passports and immunization of all OFS travelers also. The relationship between OFS and this Division was so close that it functioned almost as a part of the OFS staff. Under the capable direction of Miss Barbara Caldon and later of Mrs. Frances F. Giggal, it contributed greatly to the success of the whole processing operation.

The complexity of securing a passport under normal peacetime conditions is well known. During the war it was immeasurably worse. Not only did the individual have to supply the customary documents — birth certificates, affidavits, letters from employers, photographs — he also had to furnish evidence that he was invited to leave the country on an urgent mission and was not simply evading his Draft Board. It was difficult enough to get all these papers in a hurry from their different sources. Making sure that they would be assembled by the Passport Division to guarantee release of the passport in time was even harder. More than once a Field Service Consultant picked up this necessary item as he rushed by the OSRD Liaison Office at DuPont Circle in a taxicab headed for the airport to meet the flight set in his orders. When the situation was as close as this, Mrs. Giggal and her associates were left almost prostrate from the nervous excitement of straightening out crossed wires in the State Department and getting visas from exceedingly busy Embassies. But the rider had caught the final brass ring on the merry-go-round of his frenzied processing.

Before he left the POE, the scientist and his fellow passengers got a thorough briefing on what to do if the plane deposited them in the middle of the Pacific or Atlantic. None ever did, but the possibility was stressed realistically, along with the specter of explosion in mid-air from carelessness in smoking. He was told to wear warm clothing for high altitudes, bring reading matter to relieve the tedium of monotonous stretches of open water, put essential toilet articles and a change of underwear in his small knapsack (musette bag). He might not have access to his heavier luggage for several days because forced landings due to weather or mechanical trouble could throw the trip off schedule.

When his credentials had been checked he remained on call for the take-off. Now he had time to review his processing list once more. Had he taken care of insurance, made his will, set up a power of attorney, gotten traveler's checks, left an APO address with his family and friends? Were his affairs back at the laboratory or plant in order? He had put on metal "dog tags" that showed his name, immunizations, and blood type in case of accident. But had he written thank-you notes for the farewell parties, secured a bottle of Scotch for the commanding officer, sent candy to the OFS girls who helped steer him through the forest of regulations — and packed rayons for their counterparts overseas? There were extra cigarettes in his luggage and addresses of friends to look up, but where was that worrisome little pamphlet about Government travel regulations?

Sometimes he could check over these items for several days because the weather closed in or a batch of serious-looking officers holding higher priorities came through, apparently bound for mysterious operations. Then here he was — after rushing madly to get everything set in time — just sitting. Well, that was what those good friends at OFS had warned him to expect — the old military system of "hurry up and wait." They told him he would get a lot of that in the next few months. If he could take it in his stride, he would get things done and return home with the everlasting gratitude of the command. But if he snorted around and felt that all this reflected on his importance, that his scientific colleagues and the officers in Washington had deluded him about the urgency and importance of his trip, he would make himself most unhappy and would throw up the worst possible obstacle to successful accomplishment. If he tried to get around difficulties by flashing his assimilated rank, he might find himself hopelessly enmeshed in red tape. The military have a quiet and effective way of putting such a boor in his place.

Finally the zero hour came. In a strange uniform and laden with documents, identification cards, messages for friends in the theater, instructions, and misgivings, he climbed aboard the big transport. Perhaps he was still suffering from immunizations. He was certainly dizzy from the whirligig of processing. Now he must remember to keep his pockets buttoned and his hands out of them, assume a military (but not too military) attitude, and return salutes as though he really were an officer.

As the roaring engines drove the loaded plane down the broad airstrip he thought of his destination — the strange places he had just been reading about in yesterday's paper. He could almost hear the racket and confusion of conflict. Perhaps he would have a chance for a crack at the Jerries or the Japs himself; maybe he would be captured and tortured — or hit by a stray bullet or a piece of flak — and then. . . .

Suddenly he was airborne and the great adventure was on.

CHAPTER VI

CHECKS AND CHANNELS

KEEPING OUT OF TROUBLE

T HE COLLEGE PROFESSOR in a small institution where he is the whole department in his field can go directly to the president of the school about an administrative matter. Without permission or approval of anyone he can correspond with a colleague in a sister college, university, or industrial laboratory about some technical item, may even take without delay certain actions growing out of this correspondence, because no endorsements must first be obtained. In peacetime, if he wishes to pass along information on his scientific work to a fellow scientist in Russia or Rangoon, he does so without submitting his letter for review by the State Department. He can even criticize in writing the work of his associates or the policies of his employer and there is no censor to delete his phrases or prevent the statement from reaching the addressee.

In a larger institution where he is only one of many members in a science department he would not think of going to the president about some matter that concerns his department without talking it over first with the department chairman. This represents delay, but at least the chairman is a colleague in his field who speaks the same language. The professor can still communicate freely with the outside world on most technical matters, however; but in many things he must get approvals before he can act. The larger the organization in which he works, the more he begins to resemble a mere cog in the machinery, the more circumscribed are his communications, and the less chance there is that the people who must review and approve them will really understand their content. Yet, on purely technical matters he is still rather free — that is, unless he works for an industrial laboratory that keeps the technical information guarded as a trade secret.

In an enormous organization like an Army or Navy and in a war the channelizing of all communications becomes an absolute requirement and affects every individual working in the gargantuan structure.

Channels must be followed in order to maintain discipline, protect military secrets, minimize duplication, and guard the reputations of those in positions of leadership. The speed at which a matter can be handled through the proper channel is determined by many factors, some of them purely mechanical and some entirely human. The number of hands it must go through; the intelligence, efficiency, and sympathy of those who must forward it along; their familiarity with the procedures; the quantity of such items they must handle and their preoccupation with other duties; the complexity of the matter and the manner in which it is presented; the distances it must travel from one desk to the next or from a field unit through GHQ to the home offices; its urgency relative to other items — these are but a few of the elements that make operation within channels a nightmare even to those who create and must defend them. The continual shifting of military personnel because of combat casualties or replacement schedules is an added complication; and the constant need for censorship is a perpetual deterrent to the swift dispatch of information.

Any such channel has all the defects of an artificial and arbitrary device created by human beings. Like any formality, it may be cumbersome, illogical, and subject to revision or simplification. But often it would take longer to go through the involved mechanics of securing a change in the channel than it would to learn to follow it. Moreover, like any regulation, it is open to exceptions. Yet violation of the proper channel can lead to serious trouble and should only be attempted when the circumstances are unusual.

Most of the scientists who worked with the military during the war had never before experienced the discipline of having to follow such prescribed procedures. But, like everyone else, they simply had to adapt themselves to the system and learn to work within it; yet they could not help resenting that so often their comments, recommendations, requests for materials, and even their reports on purely technical matters had to pass through the hands of people who could not even understand them before they reached the attention of someone who could. Sometimes the individuals in intermediate positions along a channel were most co-operative, admitted their ignorance, and rubber-stamped an item to move it along quickly. But even then there had been what seemed to the scientist who initiated it a wholly unnecessary delay. And he might have been the only one who could fully appreciate the imperative nature of the matter. Just to stop his work and explain that urgency to the military handlers would take precious time — time that might mean the lives of others in the maelstrom that is war.

It became almost axiomatic that every group of scientists had to have at least one man who would serve as an expediter, would learn the channels, follow through the action personally, even carry the papers himself from one officer to the next in order to eliminate the time wasted in sending it through an interoffice mailing system and to assure that it would receive prompt attention at each stage. He had to be a technical man who could understand its immediacy and interpret this to nontechnical officers. He had to be willing to forego his own desire to do scientific work in the war in order to make the work of scores of his fellow scientists more effective. His was a job that called for tact, persistence, and alertness. If he was pleasant and diplomatic, he soon won the confidence of the commanding officers and persuaded them to authorize simpler channels or to place a high priority on any of the matters he presented for action.

In an area where there were many travelers from OSRD, a whole office force of scientists and administrative personnel was necessary to promote good relations with the theater commanders, to negotiate with officers, and educate civilian newcomers to the proper channels. In the European areas the OSRD Liaison Office served this purpose. It was in position to confer on behalf of OFS directly with the GHQ's, to transmit communications on technical or administrative matters through State Department channels, to aid OFS travelers by introducing them or even by procuring military credentials and access to the combat areas. More than one officer became familiar through friendly conversation with the scientists of OSRD's London staff with the possible assistance he could procure from OFS. More than one OFS man was sent to London in civilian clothes and accredited there for attachment in uniform to a field project on the Continent. Military processing was somehow faster and easier up closer to the front. At the London office he received guidance for his mission or help with his fiscal affairs and the office was then posted on his whereabouts in order to help quickly. This also familiarized him with a nonmilitary channel for sending reports and requests back to OFS that commonly proved faster and more direct than the military channels which he would normally have to use. Always with the approval of the military, he might take advantage of this; but he usually sent his dispatches concurrently through the Army or Navy channels also, just to be sure all interested parties would get to see them.

One advantage of the OFS system for sending personnel on missions was that they went as representatives of a high echelon office such as NDD to report to GHQ and to be attached at staff level to the command. Although they were often detailed to work directly with the officers and enlisted men of a lower echelon, they had immediate access across some of the channels to an authoritative body in the Service and through it to a high level in Washington. This meant that they would be unlikely to get trapped in low-priority work, that their communications could get through more promptly and would carry appropriate weight, and that they could move about more freely in the theater. It also meant greater responsibility on them to observe discretion in reporting incidents or situations which reflected on the command or that were considered the theater's own business to be taken care of without advice or prodding from home. They also had to be careful not to express their own opinions or the views of individual officers as though these were the opinions of the Commander in Chief.

When one speaks of "attachment to the command" it must be understood that this means attachment in the technical sense. The scientist was responsible during his stay only to the commanding officer and was entirely dependent on his co-operation to provide billeting, transportation, communications facilities, and permission to leave the theater. He was expected to conduct his correspondence as would an officer, censoring his own personal mail but honor bound to keep it personal. He also enjoyed the privilege of freedom from postage. His official communications went through the appropriate office of the theater staff after review by the officer to whom he was directly responsible, thence through the theater AGO to the Service liaison office at home (e.g., NDD). This office forwarded them to OFS which in turn distributed any necessary information or requests to NDRC, CMR, or other agencies.

At first all communications of OFS men in the Pacific theaters except strictly personal letters had to follow these steps and pass through the hands of NDD and OFS for appropriate distribution. Although these agencies at home attempted to handle the material quickly, there were such delays in getting the papers cleared through the chains of command in the theater and dispatched that the total lapse of time between the first drafting of an item and its receipt by the addressee was entirely incompatible with the immediacy of the matters discussed. This applied even to communications that both the civilians and the military had agreed were urgent enough to be sent by radio. Even a radiogram had to be drafted and approved along the line before it could be coded for transmission.

After some months the theater commands recognized that this nullified one of the most important functions of an OFS consulting staff in the field, which was to promote a *rapid* flow of technical information. Accordingly, the Field Service Consultants were finally permitted to transmit, without the usual staff consideration, purely "technical" letters directly to any civilian agency in the theater or on the mainland, but only on condition that they contained the statement, "This letter does not necessarily reflect the views of the Commanding General," and that copies were sent concurrently for information to the theater AGO, to OFS, and to NDD.

In SWPA Harrison made an abortive effort to set up an independent channel through State Department facilities like the one in England, through which purely administrative matters such as travel vouchers, salary checks, and correspondence relating strictly to employment could be forwarded. He believed mistakenly that this had been approved by the Army. It seemed logical because it would save the time of both the scientists and the officers if such items did not have to be reviewed first by the military. They were internal fiscal business of OSRD that he thought would not concern the Army. Through the co-operation of the American Consul at Brisbane he had planned to send such material through the diplomatic pouches. But this brought a sharp rebuke from the command when the Army discovered it; and thereafter everything had to go via the more sluggish military channels.

In the fall of 1944 the Operational Research Section at Oahu was finally allowed to use the transpacific radiotelephone for communications with the home office of OFS. The conversations were, of course, monitored by censors both in the theater and on the mainland and a representative of G-3 usually sat in on them in the theater. Commonly the subject matter was submitted to the military, at least in sketchy form, in advance of the call. For reasons of security the messages had to be phrased carefully. But one scientist conversing with another can convey a great deal of information in rather innocent words that the enemy could not understand, especially if there has also been an exchange of correspondence to which the speakers can refer in such terms as: "We agree with your item eight and have a man ready to leave shortly." Requests that had to have military endorsement would still have to go through the usual channels, but advance notice of them could be telephoned to OFS so that action could begin at once, perhaps even be completed by the time the formal confirmation came through. The liberality of the Army in permitting this kind of operation saved untold days of grief for everyone concerned and speeded up immeasurably the help they themselves had requested.

A few months later when the weekly teletype conferences with Washington were arranged, they were attended in the theater by representatives of Marshall's team and of G-3, and in the Pentagon by senior staff officials of OFS and at least one officer from NDD. These conferences likewise accelerated the whole pace of OFS activities both in the theater and at home and brought such desirable results in POA that soon it was possible to establish similar periodic teletype exchanges with R/S in the Southwest Pacific. The Army had learned in both theaters that OFS men could be trusted with such freedom and that to give it to them paid handsome dividends in speedier, more effective scientific aid.

None of the Field Service Consultants was ever court-martialed or given other punitive discipline. If they did slip in minor matters — and no doubt many did — the whole thing was ironed out in the theater without formal action. In a few instances of carelessness about security the home office of OFS was asked to warn the violators — or did so on its own account before official notice brought more stringent measures.

The Office of Field Service had its share of prima donnas whose behavior irritated their military associates and embarrassed their civilian sponsors. It had some dreamy-eyed and absent-minded wizards who were sent because they were the only men who had the special talents needed. But most OFS representatives behaved themselves in the theater and were accorded the privileges that relieve the tedium of working under adverse conditions — membership in the officers' club and liquor locker and social invitations. They became fast friends of the military men, bent elbows with them, and were able to promote their projects by night as well as by day in the informality of the BOQ.

The gradual lifting of restrictions on official mail and other communications and the impressive list of individual, personal commendations for technical achievements that is still growing in the files are evidence enough that the men of OFS met the challenge of observing channels and kept out of trouble.

CHAPTER VII

CONNING TOWER TO QUARTER-DECK

SCIENCE BACKS UP THE FLEET

ONE DAY in 1944 a force of American destroyers was escorting a flotilla of landing vessels in treacherous waters. Suddenly and without warning an explosion rent one of the LST's. A Japanese submarine had somehow maneuvered into position and its torpedo had found the target squarely. Fortunately the LST did not sink at once and for some time the escorting ships were occupied in rescuing the men aboard her and screening these operations. The commander of the destroyer division sent the rest of his force on with the flotilla and his own ship stayed to search for the enemy marauder.

By that time the submarine had surely sought escape; but in what direction — at what speed? How should he begin the search? The commander was armed with tables especially designed for such a situation. These had been prepared by the Navy's Operational Research Group of civilian OFS scientists in Washington. If they were followed with precision, the sound-detection gear of a destroyer could pick up the enemy submarine hours after it had attacked, regardless of the direction and speed of its attempted escape.

The "search plan" was complicated; but the commander had confidence in it. All night his destroyer followed the geometrical gyrations recommended in the tables. Eleven hours later the sound officer reported the enemy submarine dead ahead. A deep rumbling explosion under water and a strong smell of diesel oil soon guaranteed that the war patrol of the Jap sub had been summarily terminated. This incident is typical of the way in which the patient, thorough work of analytical wizards in the ORG enabled the Navy to destroy many German and Japanese submarines.

In April 1942 only a few months after we had declared war on Germany, the Nazi submarines had already taken a terrific toll of Allied shipping in the Atlantic. We could not hope to set up and supply springboards for the assault on Europe if this menace was not elimi-

Eternal Vigilance
U. S. Navy Liberator on antisubmarine patrol

Last-Minute Check

An airman tests his flexible gun before flying into the fight

nated. Rear Admiral W. D. Baker of the Antisubmarine Warfare Unit in the Office of the Commander in Chief (COMINCH), U.S. Fleet, had been deeply impressed with the success of British Operational Research Sections in assisting air and surface craft to locate and dispose of undersea raiders in the waters around Britain. He asked the Co-ordinator of Research and Development to take immediate steps for establishing a similar activity in the U.S. Navy. This request was passed to OSRD and in May a group of seven civilian specialists under Dr. Morse became the nucleus of ASWORG with headquarters in Boston. A short time later the main part of the group moved to Washington, which thereafter became the focal point of ORG operations.

Until the middle of 1943 the Army Air Forces shared the tasks of action against subsurface craft. This responsibility was largely concentrated in the First Bomber Command, later the Antisubmarine Command, with headquarters in New York. Members of ASWORG worked there and also at the operational test unit at Langley Field, Virginia, where new equipment was tried out and squadrons were trained for the special tasks of air patrol. Later the Navy assumed the entire responsibility for the antisubmarine effort, and all of its operational activities in this field, including ASWORG, were collected in a new administrative subdivision of COMINCH known as the Tenth Fleet.

The urgency and the complicated nature of the U-boat problem demanded the full energy of ASWORG's scientists on antisubmarine activities until the fall of 1943, when the Office of Field Service began to transfer the members of this group to its pay roll. By then ASWORG had increased to a technical staff of thirty-five men, which was more than doubled before the end of the war.

Naturally it is impossible to describe here the work of each one of these specialists. No other OFS project dealt with such varied subject matter or involved a more continuous interchange in the assignment of its men between home bases and the field. It was a fundamental principle of the Group that a large section of its manpower should remain as a central corps working with the general staff in Washington, carrying on the more theoretical tasks of statistical analysis, interpreting tactics, and devising new ones, and assisting the Navy in writing its tactical doctrine. Members assigned for temporary field duty worked with the users of new weapons, applied ideas for new tactics in practice, and recognized new problems that were transmitted to the central body for further study. Free interchange of information and personnel between the field units and the home office was essential. Constant rotation of assignments permitted field men to renew their acquaintance with laboratory developments and provided an opportunity for training other members of the group for field work through practical experience.

Some ORG representatives spent their full time at test stations evaluating new devices as they came from the laboratories, comparing their performance, learning their limitations, and devising countermeasures that might be used against them if the enemy came up with similar gear. Others flew with air patrols hunting submarines. One crossed the Atlantic with the first destroyer-escort group to accompany a convoy to England. Another went to the coast of Japan as a member of the crew on a war patrol of one of our own submarines. One took a combat trip with a baby flattop to North Africa. Another was on a carrier under attack by the kamikaze in the Pacific. Yet few were hurt and none was killed.

The story of the way an ORG man stationed at Casablanca helped the Navy to keep Nazi U-boats from going through the gateway to the Mediterranean illustrates the methods these Field Service Consultants used in a systematic effort to anticipate the enemy's moves and then outfox him. In the winter of 1943–44 the German subs had created havoc in the Mediterranean. They were getting through by running submerged at Gibraltar. We were having our troubles at Anzio and it was vital that this menace be eliminated. John R. Pellam, youthful physicist who is now back at M.I.T. completing graduate study interrupted by the war, was the ORG man on hand in North Africa. Working in close co-operation with a representative from a British Operational Research Section, Pellam thought he could prepare a trap. He knew from his contacts with the research and development program at home that planes equipped with special gear that had not yet been tried out in an actual operation might be just the thing. But he wanted to know more about the probable behavior of the enemy submarine as it approached in the darkness and then slipped through under water.

Pellam studied the peculiar currents which might make it possible for a vessel to coast in at certain times with its engines cut so that sound-detection apparatus on the patrolling surface vessels could not pick it up. Then he arranged to go through the Straits in a British submarine to observe how and where it would drift and to deduce the tactics it might take to avoid discovery. Finally he suggested the trap.

British destroyers took up stations at the places he designated and planes followed search patterns he worked out. After several days they spotted an approaching enemy submarine on their radar. Then the tactics Pellam had recommended were carried out and the combined air and surface forces caught their prey. Within a few weeks they caught another and then still another. From then on the Mediterranean was effectively sealed to Nazi underwater craft.

In 1943 we knew that German blockade runners were successfully crossing the South Atlantic, bringing tin, rubber, and other strategic materials from Japan. The problem of stopping them was brought to an ORG man stationed with the Fourth Fleet of our Navy at Recife, Brazil. To the uninitiated it looked as though it would take almost a whole air force plus a whole navy to cover the vast ocean area with patrols to catch them. But the ORG man in Brazil, Dr. Jacinto Steinhardt, trained biochemist who had been abroad on special studies for the Rockefeller Foundation, believed that such problems could be reduced to relatively simple analysis.

Steinhardt knew that the distance from his station in Brazil eastward to Ascension Island is about 1400 miles, roughly the railroad distance from New York to Minneapolis. An airplane flying between these two points and equipped with radar searching apparatus in operation continuously can sweep a path on each side of it for a known distance. On a return trip flown some distance either north or south of the original course a similar path can be swept. It was possible, therefore, to work out a flight pattern for patrolling aircraft such that any ship heading northeastward would sooner or later fall within range and be seen on the radar screen, regardless of the direction of its course or the speed of its travel. Airplanes are so very much faster than ships that a group of them can search considerable areas of the ocean in the few hours while a blockade runner moves into range.

Soon Steinhardt had evolved such a scheme for searching the South

Atlantic with radar-equipped planes. Our squadrons in Brazil were given a search plan in accordance with his recommendations. On the first operational trial the Fourth Fleet got a submarine not known to be in that area. Later, using this same method, the *Weserland,* the *Bergenland,* and the *Rio Grande* were all sunk in a period of forty-eight hours. The Navy and the Air Force were utterly amazed to discover that effective patrol could be maintained across the South Atlantic with only a handful of planes instead of a whole air force. Again the availability of a scientifically trained man with a good fund of common sense who could devote himself to careful analysis of the problem at hand had paid off.

In the antisubmarine war the technique of searching limitless areas of open water proved to be a science in itself. The development of adequate search plans or techniques for screening our own forces defensively was a problem that involved many variable factors — the speed and behavior of the submarines; the speed and tactics of the individual aircraft or surface vessel, or groups of either or both; the effectiveness of visual lookouts; the performance of new "eyes" provided by radar and underwater-sound-detecting apparatus; climatic conditions; visibility at sea; human limitations in the handling of equipment and interpretation of reports; the geometric arrangement of the craft on patrol and of the prey they were hunting. There could be nothing haphazard in attempts to work out the courses and tactics which would give the best chances for sighting an enemy or avoiding him.

These factors were reduced to concrete values, either real or assumed. Then through elaborate calculations simple rules and tables were devised. But this whole operation involved the sifting of vast quantities of information. It had to be gathered from many sources. Consequently throughout its history ORG worked very closely with Navy Intelligence, with the British Admiralty, and with all other agencies engaged in operations analysis who might have discovered new techniques for reducing the complicated data to simple formulas. ORG men worked in the Operational Research Sections of the British forces, and their young scientists came to Washington for temporary tours of duty with ORG.

In the late months of 1943 Dr. Kenneth V. Thimann, biologist from the faculty of Harvard University, was working with the ORS people in London. In a careful study of losses sustained by convoys they observed that the number of ships sunk in each attack seemed to be independent of the size of the convoy. They reasoned that if the convoys were increased in size, there would be fewer sailings and thus fewer total losses. Trials of this theory proved the deduction sound. Gradually the sizes of our convoys increased until more than a hundred ships at a time were crossing the stormy North Atlantic from New York to Halifax to the United Kingdom in the late spring of 1944.

As the war progressed and German submarine skippers learned that we were catching them with radar, they began using devices that would pick up the signals sent out by our search gear. It was not difficult for them to do so because the radar pulse must strike its target with sufficient energy for the reflected portion to return to the detector at the source. This gave the German equipment strong signals and the submarines promptly submerged when they intercepted them. It produced a dilemma for the American forces. Should we continue to use the radar, give away our presence, and thereby cut down the number of sightings? Or should we stop using radar and depend only on visual means or on underwater sound from surface craft, both of which cover much smaller ranges, and thereby also whittle the possible number of sightings per patrol?

The analysts of ORG tackled this problem by obtaining from operational reports the total number of contacts that had been made between our planes and enemy submarines and comparing this with the mathematical probability of such contacts, assuming that the detection gear worked perfectly. The result was a recommendation that the type of radar then in use should be turned on only when it was most needed, that is, when the visibility was low, or at night. In the meantime our laboratories developed new radar search equipment operating on different wave lengths. When this was installed the Germans were unable to detect it. They were baffled for almost a year. Eventually they developed search receivers that would pick up this new radar signal; but by then they had lost a great many submarines.

Some months later a similar problem was faced in the Pacific. Submarine skippers, convinced that Japanese aircraft must have radar search receivers capable of detecting our submarine radar, were turning off their equipment. An ORG group compared the number of contacts our submarines were making with Jap planes in a given time in the same area both with and without our radar. Allowing for the difference between the range of radar and that of visual methods for sighting, the results showed an approximately identical number. This was interpreted as sufficient evidence that the Japanese were not gaining an advantage from such equipment if indeed they had it. Influenced by experience with the Germans, our skippers had overestimated their Pacific opponents; but ORG demonstrated that we would gain by continuing to use our radar.

Late in the war the introduction of "*Schnörchel*," fantastic breathing mechanism which made it possible for German submarines to run for many hours without surfacing to recharge their batteries and take on fresh air, intensified the problem of search for both surface vessels and aircraft. It is one thing to spot a surfaced submarine on the radar screen. It is quite another to pick up a *Schnörchel,* an object not much bigger than a periscope, particularly if the sea is the least bit rough. The probabilities for sightings of *Schnörchel* were decidedly low. Accordingly ORG men devised wholly new sets of search plans to provide convoy coverage and to control shore-based air patrols that would continue to keep the enemy marauders well away from Atlantic shores.

When intelligence reports indicated that the Nazis were developing a special submarine that could travel at exceptionally high speeds even when submerged, modifications of the ORG search plans and of tactical doctrine to deal with this threat were made and were ready for operational use.

When the U-boat campaign had been effectively curtailed it seemed desirable to apply experience gained in the Atlantic to the Pacific war. The problem was, of course, not so much one of seeking out and destroying enemy submarines, but rather of helping our own submarines to cut the Japanese supply lines. In November 1943 two members of ASWORG were sent to Pearl Harbor at the request of the Commander Submarines Pacific. Appreciation of their work soon led to the establishment of a five-man subgroup of ORG, eventually called the Submarine Operations Research Group (SORG), which had its analogue in the Washington office and continued to function until after V-J Day. Then in March 1944 a representative was sent to headquarters of the Seventh Fleet in the Southwest Pacific in response to the request Compton had brought back from Admiral Kinkaid.

In the summer of 1943 the Navy set up an experimental unit at Quonset, Rhode Island, devoted to antisubmarine developments, and ORG members were assigned there to learn firsthand about tactics and equipment, to assist in devising tests and in analyzing results. Later a surface vessel section of this unit was set up at Fort Lauderdale, Florida, and ORG members were on duty at that station until the end of the war.

In the fall of 1943 it was clear that information gained from air attacks against submarines might be applicable to other aspects of naval air warfare. Commander Bitter requested the assistance of ASWORG in expanding the statistical and analytical section of the operations research group he had established in the Air Technical Analysis Division. Dr. A. A. Brown and Mr. Howard Hennington, mathematicians who had concentrated on air attacks, were assigned to this duty. With the active aid of OFS in recruiting and through additional loans from ORG they developed in ATAD a separate subsection of twelve men. At first it was unofficially integrated with ORG but was eventually combined officially as a subgroup known as the Air Operations Research Group (AirORG).

By the fall of 1944 most of Morse's analytical aces were working on problems other than antisubmarine. It was considered inappropriate to have the group as a whole assigned to the Tenth Fleet. Accordingly, it was renamed the Operations Research Group and reassigned to the Readiness Division of COMINCH. Two more new subdivisions were then created, one known as PhibORG to concentrate on problems of amphibious operations and naval gunfire support, and one (AAORG) to deal with antiaircraft fire from our own task forces and from enemy ground installations. ASWORG, considerably reduced in numbers, then became merely a subgroup. In the summer of 1945 AAORG was reconstituted as SpecORG. It continued analysis of antiaircraft actions, studied the proper placement of air patrols around a task force, and concentrated on problems of improving the air defense of surface vessels.

The remainder of the ORG personnel constituted an Operations Research Center (ORC) to which theoretical and analytical problems covering more than one field of naval warfare were commonly assigned.

It operated under general supervision of Dr. George E. Kimball, physical chemist from the Columbia faculty who was one of the early members of ORG and succeeded Dr. William B. Shockley, physicist from Bell Laboratories, as its Deputy Director.

The Center took care of administrative details for the entire ORG and maintained an Intelligence Section for distributing technical reports and exchanging scientific information. Its purpose was to create a reference library and to keep both the men in Washington and those in the field abreast of latest developments in civilian and military research organizations and of the techniques that were proving useful in operations analysis wherever it might be practiced within the Allied forces.

This Section was capably administered by Mr. Abraham C. Olshen, insurance examiner from the State of Oregon. His alertness and facility in negotiations with the many agencies concerned brought an increasing flow of material to ORG. This aggregated 1600 reports a month by the end of the war. About 500 of these were given only limited circulation and were returned to their sources within twenty-four hours. Those retained by ORG were carefully abstracted and cross-referenced so that they constituted a true research collection rather than just a file, and by the summer of 1945 this included some 15,000 items. Repeatedly the Navy sent its officers to Olshen's records for information.

The ORC also maintained a machine section equipped with I B M machinery and expert operators who could reduce to codes and punch on cards the multitude of details contained in operational reports. The technical data on each incident were thereby recorded in simplified form. For an American air attack on a submarine the card records would carry such information as the time of day, condition of the sea, visibility, direction of approach, course, and speed of both the submarine and the attacking airplane, type of gear used in detection, type of bomb or depth charge released and its fuze setting, and evasive maneuvers. By running the cards through the machine it would then be possible, for example, to select for analysis or tabulation in only a few minutes all the incidents that involved a daylight attack under conditions of good visibility and with an approach from astern. The I B M group produced nearly half a million such cards during the war and issued nearly 5000 tabulations and summaries. It also reduced to such tabular form information on casualties to our merchant shipping, attacks made by our forces on enemy surface and subsurface vessels, air-to-air combat operations, casualties to our fleet, and the daily disposition of our ships all over the world. The value of such systematic records became so apparent that ORG was asked to maintain similar equipment at Pearl Harbor so that analysis would not have to wait until the records had been sent to Washington for sorting and tabulation.

The I B M records constituted much of the source material to which the masterminds of ORG would turn in the battle that was not only one of equipment but also one of wits. It is easy to understand, therefore, that the very existence of an ORG had to remain a secret. This "combat team without guns" was under rigid security restrictions because it had access to some of the most highly classified records of the Navy.

The Operations Research Center also had a Chief Petty Officer and a complement of WAVES assigned by the Navy, and civilian office girls supplied by OSRD, whose function was to relieve the technical men of many routines and to shield them from the distressing impact of Government procedural formalities. For many months Miss Emily B. Mitchell and Mrs. Dorothy Rawlins, who headed the civilian group, guided the men through channels, across channels, and around channels and saved them untold hours of tedious detail. J. Allan Hauter, suave insurance man who functioned as a technical aide and executive assistant to Morse and Kimball, was commonly the man behind the scenes in negotiations with the Navy and with other Departments of the Government. His persistence in unraveling complicated situations added greatly to the mobility of the Group.

Through its close contacts with sources of intelligence ORG became aware in 1943 that the Germans were planning to use a torpedo equipped with acoustic gear which would listen to a ship's screws and then direct the lethal charge to "home" on the hapless vessel, much as a bloodhound follows a scent. This was a matter of deep concern to both the British and the American Navies. Their experts had each designed a provisional countermeasure. When, late in the fall of 1943, the Nazi acoustic torpedo became a reality and was first used against British ships, ORG was not content with the proposed countermeasures. Dr. Edward A. Uehling, brilliant physicist from the University of

Washington, who later became the Director of Research of the Group and, concurrently, Director Readiness Research of the Readiness Division of COMINCH, insisted that accurate measurements be taken of ship noises and of noises made by the countermeasures. Immediately ORG men were dispatched to help in making them. In the meantime Dr. Uehling and a small group associated with him on this critical project in Washington made an analysis of the probable behavior of such a torpedo based on what it should be ideally. They then helped the Navy to design a more effective countermeasure. It was adopted at once by both the British and the American forces and eventually eliminated losses from this devilish Nazi weapon. Not much more than a month elapsed from the first casualty attributable to this device before the specialists of ORG had analyzed it and found the effective countermeasure. The Germans were simply dumfounded at the speed of the Americans in diagnosing their secret weapon.

Dr. Morse and his associates frequently wondered whether the Nazis had a similar operations research group. A careful study of enemy activities seemed to show, however, that they made many mistakes that would have been avoided if any such analytical organization had been backing their offensive and defensive tactics. The Americans had pretty well concluded that there was no Nazi counterpart. This was later confirmed by Konteradmiral Godt who took over as Commander of Submarines from Admiral Doenitz.

One of the toughest assignments given to the small advance guard of ORG that went to the Pacific was to discover what weapon Japan was using to sink our submarines. Many of our undersea craft simply disappeared and were never heard from. Dr. Robert F. Rinehart, able mathematician from the faculty of the Case School of Applied Science, who had won his "N" in devising plans for air search in the Caribbean, proceeded in his customary unassuming manner to collect what information he could that might form a firm basis for reasonable deductions. He studied all the reports of our submarines that had narrow escapes in brushes with the enemy. He climbed into a submarine and went out on a war patrol himself, and was able finally to deduce one of the major causes for our losses. Security prevents its disclosure; but it was something to which the Navy had not given serious thought. Rinehart then recommended certain changes in equipment and tactics which were ordered by the Commander of Pacific Submarines. According to their skippers, at least three American subsurface vessels were later saved as a result of these recommendations. Rinehart's success in handling what had appeared an almost insoluble problem won such confidence of the Pacific command that thereafter expansion of ORG outposts in the Pacific was more rapid.

Early in 1945 Dr. Arthur F. Kip, youthful physicist who had been ORG's successful representative in London for many months, went out to study task force operations in the Pacific. As the carrier he was on lay off Okinawa it was attacked by a suicide pilot who very nearly accomplished his mission. By that time the Japanese suicide bombers, or kamikaze, had become the Navy's major problem and members of ORG worked feverishly to help develop adequate defenses against them.

The task of assessing the reports that came in to Washington on incidents involving these suicide bombers was a mean one. Understandably in the excitement of such vicious assaults the accuracy of officers' notations was considerably affected and their reports were conflicting. Three observers would each swear to a different number of attackers. The accounts were full of inconsistencies and omissions. ORG turned the job of sifting them over to chess champion Reuben Fine, who managed to make enough sense out of the confused data to recommend evasive tactics that should be used when the angle of an attack was high and other tactics when it was low. This was only a step toward solution. The kamikaze problem was admittedly a more difficult one than had been the Nazi submarine. There is, however, little question that had the war lasted longer, the powers of induction, deduction, and calculation of the OFS analysts would have provided even more impressive aid toward its solution.

Knowledge ORG gained from studies in the Battle of the Atlantic was found applicable in many ways to the Pacific struggle. ORG studied the desirability of creating co-ordinated groups of our submarines organized like German wolf packs. How large should they be? Where should they take up their battle stations and when? What tactics should they follow? What would be the optimum number of submarines for such groups? In what geometric pattern should they be arranged and at what distances apart? One item to consider was the frequency of contacts that our submarines had made with Japanese ships when operating independently, compared with the probable frequency of such contacts if they were to hunt in groups. Another was the ability of our ships to keep in touch with one another under differing conditions. The effectiveness of the antisubmarine measures used by the Japanese also had to be taken into account. The ORG men developed a theory as to the amount of improvement of group operations compared with individual operations under differing conditions. When this was translated into actual operations, a careful study of the results showed that they agreed closely with the theory.

The ORG specialists compared the effectiveness of strikes from American carriers on Japanese shipping and shore installations with strikes that were made against practice targets, and the results were used in planning such operations. They studied the accuracy of naval gunfire in amphibious landings — an exceedingly ticklish and critical problem because the close-support bombardment from ships off shore must lay down a screen just ahead of our advancing forces, but not close enough to create casualties or make them seek cover. They studied techniques of using ship's radar to locate Japanese mortars that were creating such destruction in amphibious landings. They worked out procedures for our submarines to follow in running through minefields. These proved so effective that when more than a dozen were operating in the Japan Sea not one was lost to mines in the dangerous straits. They analyzed flak to determine the effectiveness of enemy antiaircraft fire and found weak spots in the Japanese antiaircraft defenses. Working partly on theory and partly on empirical information, they designed the safest courses for our planes to use in approaching defended ground positions. Vice-Admiral Marc A. Mitscher reports that these courses saved many of his carrier planes.

ORG analysts studied the optimum complement of aircraft for fast carriers, assessed various bombsights used by the air arm, studied night-fighter operations, worked out improved tactics both on offensive and defensive maneuvers in air-to-air combat, developed optimum ratios of explosive charge to weight of weapons for air bombing, and attempted to design more effective practices for the combat air patrol in thwarting suicide attacks. One member of the group visited B-29 bases in the Marianas and took part in operational flights to help improve the correlation of submarines and aircraft in air-sea rescue.

As the membership of ORG included more and more specialists on equipment and the analysts who had only general training became familiar with special devices, the group began to assist the Navy in development and testing of equipment — rocket sights, radar detectors, antitorpedo countermeasures, airborne searchlights, depth charges and depth bombs. They also helped to build and test mock-ups of our own and of enemy instruments for training and study.

It is impossible to assess the over-all contribution of the Navy's ORG in outwitting the submarine and the kamikaze, and in devising new tactics for all sorts of naval operations. There is no doubt that the work of this team of combat scientists saved thousands of American lives and many thousand tons of Allied shipping and helped immeasurably in the ultimate triumph of our Navy over the once arrogant naval forces of the Axis. Positive proof of this claim was established when Admiral King requested months before the Japanese surrender that the ORG be set up as a permanent part of the Navy.

This has been done. Morse remained for several months as its Director. He and Kimball and others continued as consultants. Steinhardt is the Director of Research and a nucleus of experienced men has stayed on with the Navy to carry on this essential and highly interesting program. New men are being added and there seems little doubt that the group will once again grow to at least half its wartime strength. The civilian team is now called the Operations Evaluation Group and its services are in great demand.

The techniques of operations research that proved so effective during the war have many peacetime applications, not only to national defense but also to many aspects of railroad operations, to the location and design of highways and the control of traffic, to city planning, to assembly-line processes, to the operations of a large department store, in short, to any large operation in which careful measuring of the effectiveness of individual activities or components in order to discover weaknesses can be carried out on a statistical or analytical basis.

If the Office of Field Service had done nothing more in the war than to foster and strengthen the Operations Research Group, it could rest on its laurels.

There were, however, numerous other projects in which OFS men helped the Navy. The total number was small, but the field-service men were active on a wide variety of naval problems. Some of them are described in the paragraphs which follow and others in later sections of this volume.

The need for improving our methods of detecting hostile objects in the ocean from surface and subsurface craft led to intensive studies of underwater acoustics and marked development in the sound gear carried by our vessels. In addition to the Navy's own research organizations there were several centers of this work supported by NDRC — at Columbia University, Harvard, the University of California, and the Woods Hole Oceanographic Institution in Massachusetts. Continuing liaison with all these groups on behalf of the Bureau of Ships was furnished by a Special Studies Group under a Columbia contract with Division 6 of NDRC. This consisted of a dozen scientists and nearly forty nontechnical personnel under the direction of Dr. Lyman Spitzer, Jr. They functioned as an advisory staff to the Navy and provided independent evaluation and interpretation of many research projects on underwater sound. They kept the various laboratories constantly informed of the needs of BuShips, and prepared summaries of basic information regarding performance of underwater-sound-detection devices for the Navy. The group was thus in position to guide the research effort and to help in the introduction of new equipment.

In the spring of 1945, in accordance with a general plan for the orderly curtailment and demobilization of OSRD research, it appeared that much of the laboratory work on sonar was to be taken over under contracts directly between the Navy and the institutions concerned. But it did seem desirable to continue a group of independent analysts such as Spitzer had developed. Their work was comparable in some ways to that of the Operations Research Group and OFS was persuaded to assume the further sponsorship of Spitzer's Sonar Analysis Group. This was accomplished by means of a "company contract" with Columbia University so that the work continued with a minimum of interruption in the transfer.

From March until December Spitzer's staff constituted an OFS project and was then transferred to direct Navy auspices. The group prepared reports on the transmission of underwater sound, reflection

NAVY OPERATIONS RESEARCH GROUP
(Includes only those affiliated with OFS)

Director
Philip M. Morse

Intelligence Section	*Deputy Director*	*Research Directors*
Abraham C. Olshen	George E. Kimball	Jacinto Steinhardt
		Edward A. Uehling

I B M Unit	*Base Liaison*	*Administrative Aides*
Earl B. Gardner	Foster L. Brooks	Emily B. Mitchell
Robert R. Seeber	Gordon D. Shellard	Dorothy Rawlins

Records	*Aide to the Director*	*Stenographic Staff*
Nathan F. Jones	J. Allan Hauter	Mary E. Palmer
John A. Humphrey		Joy Robinson
Donald A. MacCornack		
H. Alan Steeves, Jr.		

Group Members
(Arrangement in columns according to length of service with ORG,
beginning at the left)

Arthur F. Kip	John B. Lathrop	Reuben Fine
Maurice E. Bell	Edward S. Lamar	Frederick A. Ficken
Robert F. Rinehart	Walter E. Albertson	Norman E. Steenrod
Albert Thorndike	Fred H. Holsten	Arthur G. Steinberg
James K. Tyson	Kenneth V. Thimann	Scott E. Furbush
John R. Pellam	Lincoln R. Thiesmeyer	Egidio Picardi
Joseph A. Neuendorffer	John M. Boermeester	John V. Wehausen
Walter L. DeVries	John P. Coyle	Henry Hemmendinger
Howard H. Hennington	James M. Dobbie	Alex A. Petrauskas
Alan M. Thorndike	Jacques Dutka	Hugh R. Davidson
Arthur W. Brown	Carl E. Thompson	Thielo G. Howland
Sheldon C. Reed	Richard J. Jones	Henry E. Singleton
Ralph E. Beatty, Jr.	Milton Lewis	William F. Read
Arthur A. Brown	Bernard O. Koopman	Herbert C. Rutemiller
John L. Little	Robert J. Best	Martin J. Klein
Ralph E. Traber	David C. Peaslee	A. Ranger Tyler
Charles M. Sternhell	M. Stanley Livingston	Harold C. Trimble
William J. Horvath	Carl B. Allendoerfer	Robert E. Fullerton
Charles Kittel	Roy W. Jastram	Maxwell O. Reade
Charles F. Squire	Jarvis Farley	Thomas E. Phipps, Jr.
Gerard R. Pomerat	Ralph E. Wilson	Harold E. Sawyer

of sound from surface ships and submarines, acoustic properties of ship wakes and of small bubbles in ocean waters, and criteria for recognition of various types of underwater sound. They also studied the effects of temperature and density on the performance of underwater-sound equipment.

THE SONAR ANALYSIS GROUP

Director

Lyman Spitzer, Jr.

Scientific Staff

John M. Aitchison	William Grumbly	Nathaniel Shear
Peter G. Bergmann	Albert N. Guthrie	Aaron Spector
Philip G. Frank	Richard F. Humphreys	Rupert Wildt
Edward Gerjuoy	Jordan J. Markham	Arthur J. Yaspan

Nonscientific Staff

Hannah J. Alexander	Arthur Garry	Jane A. Pelterson
Charlotte Avidon	Ethel Grod-zins	Camille Piccoli
Emily F. Bach	Nettie S. Harmetz	Carolyn M. Reiser
Phyllis M. Behnke	Grace M. Jeffreys	Marjorie K. Reynolds
Henry Birnbaum	Norma Joseph	Charlotte W. Robertson
Marian Butler	Blanche Klapper	Esther Shainer
Olga Catani	Marvin Klapper	Alfred G. Stecker
Hadassah Fain	Lucile A. Krause	Marjorie B. Stecker
Frances Fairbanks	Sol Malasky	Lilyan F. Stolier
Robert L. Farris	Arthur P. McLoughlin	Ethel E. Wagner
Kaye Fink	Jane Murphy	Iona Walker
Evelyn M. Fisher	Geraldine Oberg	Frances L. Williams

In April 1944 certain modifications had been made in the design of FM sonar at the Navy Radio and Sound Laboratory, San Diego, under a University of California contract with Division 6, NDRC. The naval command in the Mediterranean asked that a unit of that equipment be furnished them for operational tests on minesweepers and that qualified technical consultants assist in the testing program. OFS procured the services of A. H. Roshon and J. W. Sampsell from the California laboratories. In company with Lieutenant Commander T. R. Foley they flew to North Africa and installed the equipment. Tests in Palermo Bay, at Salerno, Italy, and in the vicinity of Bizerte convinced the Navy that this equipment should be installed as quickly as possible. Accordingly Roshon and Sampsell flew back to the United States and proceeded immediately to San Diego to expedite the construction and delivery of Service installations.

From March 1944 until July 1945 Lawrence E. Deckinger, mathematician from New York University, worked as an OFS consultant in the Bureau of Ordnance studying the performance of torpedoes, especially those launched from aircraft. He analyzed records available in Washington and at the various torpedo ranges, factories, and training installations, and recommended modification of the testing procedures, made calculations, and prepared tables for use in aircraft torpedo attacks. From a study of operational data he was also able to help in the preparation of tactical manuals for fleet commanders.

In August 1944 the Bureau of Ships asked OFS to supply a statistician familiar with I B M machine methods to assist in a computing project under way at the Cruft Laboratory of Harvard University. An automatic sequence-controlled calculator, popularly known as "the algebraic superbrain," was to be put into operation for the solution of complex differential equations and for other involved mathematical calculations needed in ballistics, the theory of underwater sound, naval gunfire control, and other Navy problems. Rex R. Seeber, Jr., mathematical statistician from a New England insurance company, who had been a member of ORG in general charge of its I B M program, was an obvious choice for this project. He was transferred from ORG and continued on the Harvard project until the end of June, 1945.

In the spring of 1944 the Navy asked for a specialist to accompany carrier-based aircraft squadrons and train maintenance personnel in the use of certain infrared equipment. Brian O'Brien, Jr., was selected for this assignment and served for more than a year. He had been active in the development of infrared devices at the University of Rochester as an employee under an NDRC contract. Although he was exceedingly young for a field mission, he was one of the few men in the United States who knew this equipment thoroughly. O'Brien spent three months on a carrier in the Central Pacific and returned to the United

States with suggestions for modification that would make the equipment more effective. In the ensuing months he was engaged in development, installation, and testing of additional infrared devices preliminary to their use by the fleet.

In March 1945 O'Brien accepted a commission in the Navy and OFS secured Roger E. Harrington from the University of Rochester to continue the infrared projects for the Bureau of Aeronautics. Harrington spent several weeks at the Naval Air Station at Patuxent River, Maryland, during installation and flight testing of the equipment before the surrender of Japan eliminated the necessity for completion of the project.

In December 1943 OFS received a request from the Aircraft Instruments Division of the Bureau of Aeronautics for field men to follow up the introduction and use of airplane instruments and to gather information on their performance in operations for the guidance of the Division. Charles H. Colvin, Director of the Guggenheim School of Aeronautics at New York University, and Dr. W. G. Brombacher, Chief of the Aeronautical Instruments Section at the National Bureau of Standards, agreed to undertake this work. Colvin spent several months visiting research laboratories and war plants in this country where aircraft instruments and navigational equipment were produced and then toured Navy installations in the Pacific to gather data from operations personnel. Brombacher, slated to carry out similar work in the European theater, was delayed for some months because of blanket instructions that no one was to go to England except on the most urgent business. This was a reflection of the operations that led to D-Day and the establishment of our forces on the Continent. In September, however, he was able to visit laboratories, manufacturing plants, Government offices, and Army and Navy installations in the United Kingdom, where he collected much information that would be useful to the Bureau of Aeronautics.

For many months one of the most serious obstacles to successful amphibious operations in the Pacific was the lack of adequate charts and maps. In areas controlled by the United Nations, survey control was obtained by the usual geodetic methods. Areas in the hands of the enemy were so sketchily mapped that many islands never before recorded were encountered, and the records of the Hydrographic Office did not afford adequate mapping data. Our forces had to depend on captured Japanese maps, charts, and geodetic data, and such rough maps and charts as had accumulated in the Hydrographic Office. Nevertheless planes, cameras, and photographers were available in the war zone and could furnish excellent photographs. It was felt that there should be a photogrammetric service in the field to make good charts from these as quickly as the occasion demanded. Trained men with proper instruments could produce these charts more quickly there than they could be made by sending the material to Washington.

Vertical photographs are generally preferable for charting purposes; but there were many occasions when quicker coverage could be obtained from obliques. Often it was possible to get high oblique photographs through holes in the cloud cover when it was impossible to make verticals. Moreover, obliques were more economical of flying time and involved less risk of personnel and planes. But obliques were not being used for charting because means for doing so were not available in the field.

Techniques for making charts from oblique photographs were under development in the Geological Survey, in the Army Engineer offices at Fort Belvoir, and in the Hydrographic Office. In December 1942 the Navy requested that NDRC also undertake development of suitable instruments and more efficient methods for charting from obliques. This problem was studied by Merrill Flood and Associates and the Aero Service Corporation under contract with NDRC. They developed plans for a precise rectifying instrument with a specially designed lens and initiated construction of an experimental pinhole photographic rectifier.

Army, Navy, and NDRC agreed that there was need for securing more firsthand information in order to determine how best to make more accurate charts and maps in a hurry in the field, and OFS was asked to send Dr. Merrill Flood and his associate, Dr. Phillip Kissam, to the Central Pacific for this purpose.

When the Aero Service Corporation rectifier was completed at the end of April and a small rectifying camera developed by the Hydrographic Office had been tested, Flood, Kissam, and Commander Alexander Forbes of the Hydrographic Office, who had been Navy

CHAPTER VIII

SQUARE PEGS AND ROUND HOLES

IMPROVING SERVICE PLACEMENT OF ITS SCIENTIFIC MEN

To THOSE who might question that this was a technological war one need only point out the remarkable increase in technical ratings for enlisted personnel that developed in all branches of the Army and Navy. This was a reflection of the burgeoning of new weapons, new medicines, new techniques, and tactics that came as a result of the co-ordinated attack of American science in a combined civilian and military war research program. There just were not enough technically skilled people in the country to supply demands of the laboratories and war plants and still leave an excess which the Services could draw on to operate and maintain the many new devices. All sorts of technicians would have to be trained — and in a hurry. The story of the big job done by the Services and by the educational institutions co-operating with them to supply this need would fill volumes. But in so large an institution as the Army or the Navy, with administration necessarily distributed and delegated to so many people of varied ability, the ultimate assignments of some of the "ninety-day experts" did not always permit them to use even these quickly won skills to best advantage.

Technicians are, of course, not scientists and engineers. The total available number of these more highly trained professional people was a woefully small part of the whole population. More could not be trained in short order. A technician can be produced in a few months; but it takes six to ten years to develop a scientist. Improper placement of such a man was an even more critical waste.

It was also clear at the outset that there were not enough scientifically educated officers in all grades, either in the regular Army and Navy or in the Reserves. Both recruiting and conscription were necessary to augment the supply. Many technical men enlisted in a patriotic effort to put their special knowledge to work on particular problems. Some were thoroughly happy with their commissions and assignments.

They used their special training directly and constantly right through the war as technical officers. But all too frequently such recruits were frustrated by the lack of understanding, sometimes even the stupidity of officers assigned to command over them. When the original problems had been solved and the scientists wanted to shift to others, some found themselves blocked by rigid compartmentation that eventually and inevitably seems to characterize any organization that is both immense and laden with tradition. Placement officers often knew absolutely nothing about science and made errors of judgment in the assignment of scientists and partially trained science students who were drafted. Some of these scientific and technical people finally achieved transfer to duty related to their qualifications, but only after they had spent months in less logical positions.

The Services themselves were aware of this situation and were constantly taking corrective steps. But the effort seemed small and localized. The organizations were growing so fast that for every revised assignment that might be made, improper ones were developing at the same time elsewhere in the mushrooming Army and Navy. Furthermore, the reasonable position of the Services is that if it has taken several months to train an intelligent man to be an antiaircraft artilleryman and he has been sent to Europe, it would be foolish to call him back or switch him to the Medical Corps just because someone discovers later that he had been a biology major in college and had one year of graduate work in bacteriology. He might be most unhappy about not getting a chance to work on tropical diseases where he thinks he could do the most good; but by the time the request for recall reaches his unit, his battery may be at the front under fire. Besides, if he is ordered back, he must be replaced at once with a man who knows just as much about antiaircraft.

Difficulties of this sort which made it impossible for the Services to guarantee that a man would be placed according to his training in civilian life were fully understood by OFS. It was recognized also that scientifically disciplined men were probably not on the whole any more subject to improper placement than were bankers as a group, or salesmen, or musicians. Yet the scientists represented a much smaller percentage of the population and had skills that could be applied directly to the problems of technological warfare. Wherever it might prove possible, OFS therefore felt an obligation to aid the Services in making the best possible use of a scientist or engineer already in uniform or about to be inducted. This was not to become a major function of OFS, of course; and it could certainly not be advertised, or the OFS office would have been deluged with requests.

The OFS effort along these lines had to proceed largely in an informal, quiet way, through conferences with high-ranking officers about the problem in general, or about specific cases that had come to its attention. Frequently OFS was able to answer an Army or Navy request for a scientist by indicating a properly qualified man right in some branch of that Service, already in uniform, indoctrinated, immunized, and familiar with the military channels. If it was found, as OFS surmised, that his assignment was of lower priority or his skills were not being used to best advantage, and if transfer could be arranged without throwing a whole program out of gear, the Service transferred him to the new activity. Cases of this sort were brought to OFS attention by scientific organizations, by the men themselves, by their friends and colleagues in science, even sometimes by officers who understood the importance of the matter but who were individually powerless to act because someone in the chain of command above them refused approval.

Actually the Army and Navy are fundamentally no more anxious to place or keep square pegs in round holes than are the critics of such a situation, including its victims. But the reluctance of Service offices to move toward correcting an individual case is readily appreciated. It always means paper work for officers who may be swamped with duties that seem more critical because they relate to daily military operations. Endorsements are needed to secure release of a man. Out in a theater it may be necessary to get twelve to fifteen approvals before he can be shifted. His transportation to the new duty must be arranged and a replacement provided. All of this takes time — perhaps so much that it discourages the effort. A commanding officer is pardonably more interested in the "bird in hand." How can he maintain morale and build a co-ordinated team if his men are forever being shifted? Even if the man who has proved able as his ordnance officer was once a good chemist, he has become a good ordnance officer and can not be spared. The man sent to replace him might prove much less capable. No one who has been at some pains to build an organization and weld it into an efficient unit can be blamed for trying to keep it whole. In some cases the element of rank unfortunately also enters the considerations. If the scientist-officer happens to be a Colonel and the officer to whom he would have to report directly on the proposed new duty is only a Major, the request for transfer may well become side-tracked. Then there is always the question of the relative priority of the assignments. A field commander naturally comes to regard his problems as more immediate and urgent than something that has to do with research for future needs elsewhere. Altogether the factors militating against transfers within a Service are so numerous and force-ful that pressure from high authority is usually needed to bring them about.

Generally OFS referred such cases to its major liaison offices in the Services without recommendation, merely noting what seemed to be ineffective use of an individual, and leaving the decision as to what, if anything, should be done about it to those most intimately acquainted with *all* the circumstances. Formal and systematic records of such referral were not kept, but many a soldier or sailor owes the transfer that changed his immediate destiny to the quiet word from OFS to a sympathetic office in Washington. This involved no bribery, no play-ing of politics; it was merely a matter of pointing out a man qualified to meet an urgent need somewhere else. OFS had simply aided the Service in diagnosing that need and in locating and evaluating the qualifications of a man to fill it.

Fortunately for the Office of Field Service the Army had one mecha-nism that permitted special consideration for young scientists who were drafted despite the appeals of OSRD. This was the Enlisted Reserve Corps (ERC). A few men who were already working on OFS projects, or who had the right qualifications to do so when the Draft Boards re-fused them further deferment, were permitted to continue in OFS work after induction by assignment to inactive status in this Enlisted Reserve. This meant that they could be employed by OFS, remain in civilian clothes, and carry on as if they were civilians. But they were subject to call to active duty at any time military exigencies might require. Every six months their cases were reviewed to determine whether they should be left in status quo or called to active duty. Four men who had already served some time in the Army were placed in this inactive list to join the Navy's Operational Research Group. Their special training in mathematics and engineering would clearly make them more valuable in such work than in combat. A Ph.D. who had taught physics and meteorology and had then been with this ORG for some weeks was drafted despite strong representations of OFS. The Army placed him in the ERC at once upon induction and gave him a directed assignment on loan to the Navy to continue this important work. A few men were likewise given this status to work on various other OFS projects. It was a firm policy of OFS, however, that the ERC status should be regarded as the rare exception rather than the rule. It was never appealed to except as a last resort to save an OFS man for scientific work when every argument with Selective Service had failed.

In the spring of 1945 the manpower barrel had been scraped almost to transparency. Selective Service seemed determined to drag every man under 30 into uniform to fill its quotas, regardless of his training or the many months he may have devoted to war research. The War Department had its own problems to hold civilian personnel for its research and administrative work and yet to fill the ranks of the fighting forces. The Army felt that retention of a man in the Enlisted Reserve for Navy work could not be defended any longer. On urgent request from the Navy and from OFS the ERC men on detail from the Army to ORG were released for transfer to a comparable Enlisted Reserve set up by the Navy. This would cover both these individuals and a moderate number of men engaged in other OSRD research activities of special interest to that Service. As the draft pressure increased further, others were added to this Navy Enlisted Reserve. Had the successful campaigns in the Pacific not relieved the pressure, it is possible that a third of the whole ORG might have been forced into this status because so many of its most experienced and valuable men were under 30.

In the late summer of 1944 OFS participated in a systematic attempt to improve utilization of technical manpower that developed in the War Department. During the early months of that year a large number of well-qualified professional scientific and technical personnel had been inducted into the Services. This had handicapped research programs sponsored by the Services themselves. In order to conserve the technical skills of these men and exploit them in the operation and application of new devices of importance to the Army, the War Department ordered the establishment of a Technical Detachment. Men of special skills already in the Army and inductees who had worked on the development of new devices were to be assigned to this Detachment. They could then be utilized in laboratory installations at home or could be organized as teams to aid in the introduction of newly developed implements of war into the theaters. The New Developments Division was assigned the function of co-ordinating this activity and it asked OFS to supply a competent senior scientist as an advisor to assist in the execution of this plan. Dr. Marsh W. White, a mature senior physicist of the Pennsylvania State College, who had extensive contacts with various fields of science beyond his own and with research organizations, was persuaded by OFS to undertake the important task of helping the Army make better use of the scientific talent within its own ranks.

At first it was specified that the men assigned to the Technical Detachment were to be sent rather promptly overseas because the intention was not to militarize the home research laboratories. This ruling was quickly modified, however, so that inductees could be assigned back to research and development where the need for them was really more critical.

At the Reception Centers, draftees having the right qualifications were earmarked as Technical Detachment Potentials by the classification officers. The personnel information on each was then sent to NDD for consideration at the time he was sent to camp. The period of his basic training was controlled by NDD. A committee representing several branches of the War Department looked over his papers. With the immediate needs of the Technical Services in mind, this committee determined whether his qualifications could be used to greater advantage in one of the special branches of the Army or in the Technical Detachment.

At first it was ordered that there was to be no publicity regarding these special assignments. Had this project not been soft-pedaled for some months, the pressure to add men would have been terrific and the program might have been handicapped by strong political repercussions. Gradually restrictions on security were released so that pertinent information on needs could be obtained more readily from the civilian research agencies and from Army technical branches and a better job of placement could be accomplished.

The personnel records of about 2500 men were examined by Dr. White and Lieutenant Colonel Harold W. Lieske of NDD, who was associated with him in this work. About 200 men were assigned to the Technical Detachment and 600 were assigned directly to other technical services in the Army. Dr. White also conducted a quiet campaign of indoctrination among influential officers in the Army to acquaint them with the desirability of giving special consideration to the utilization of scientific and technical personnel. As a result it is possible that the Technical Detachment will become a permanent part of Army organization.

After Germany had collapsed, Dr. White surveyed the Army's needs for technical manpower in the United States and for the final assault on Japan. More than 800 men in a wide variety of skills were needed. Many men of this type whose special abilities had been in use against the Nazis were now bogged down in the demoralizing administrative routines involved in occupation. Accordingly Dr. White went over to Europe with three officers and screened the records of personnel in England and on the Continent in order to select a large number for early recall to the United States and transfer to scientific work. Between 300 and 400 qualified men were located and arrangements made for expediting their return to this country.

It would not be an exaggeration to say that through the work of Dr. White OFS aided in the better utilization of nearly a thousand men and helped to formulate policies and operating procedures that may affect the work of many times that number during peacetime or in the event of another war. Although this project was considered as only a small one in the OFS records, it may prove to be one of those "little things that have enormous consequences."

The story of the Technical Detachment is only one illustration of the ways in which the Services all through the war were continually seeking means to make more efficient use of specialists. This applied not only to technical men but also to personnel in all categories of previous experience. The geologist who spent the war unpacking crates at a

Quartermaster depot may find this hard to believe, but it is true. Tests for aptitude were studied and revised, new techniques in placement tried, special training programs for classification officers proposed. Now that the pressure of combat requirements has eased, much more attention can be focused on the problem, and sweeping changes are in prospect. Steps are also being taken to increase the amount of scientific training in the programs of Annapolis and West Point, and to permit officers of the regular Army and Navy to pursue graduate study in science and engineering. Contacts between civilian scientists and the military, intensified and extended during the war, will continue on a broad scale. There is sound basis for optimism about improving Service utilization of technical men. Perfect placement will probably never be achieved if expansion has to be as precipitous as it was this time; but the outlook for avoiding the square-peg-and-round-hole situation appears constantly brighter.

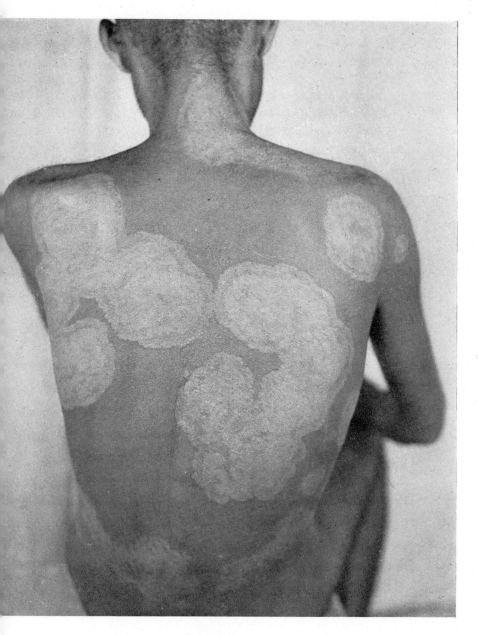

Jungle Rot

Japanese prisoner in the Southwest Pacific blotched with fungus

Forward Echelon

Headquarters staff of the OFS field office in New Guinea

CHAPTER IX

RUST, JUNGLE ROT, AND PSYCHONEUROSIS

THE FIGHT AGAINST DISEASE AND DETERIORATION

THE LOW VALUE placed by the military caste of the Rising Sun on the health, comfort, and life of the individual foot soldier in the front lines was vividly illustrated in the quality of Japanese medical services in the Southwest Pacific. Our combat scientists reported that enemy doctors in the field were incompetent and often did not diagnose correctly the tropical diseases to which their troops fell heir. Apparently their superior medical men, many of whom are known to be especially good, were retained in the home islands.

We, on the other hand, sent some of our best physicians and surgeons to the farthest reaches of the globe and supplied them with the finest equipment of modern medical science. Their difficulty was not lack of skill or failure in diagnosis. It was, rather, their inability to get the latest information promptly from the clinics and laboratories at home. We learned, for example, that the first word officers in the Southwest Pacific theater had about the effectiveness of DDT came to them in a copy of *Time* two months after it was published, rather than directly through channels from their officers in this country. Similarly the research agencies in the United States complained constantly of the inadequate flow of medical information from combat experience to help guide the search for more effective medicines. Without such information how could they devise better procedures to isolate causes and combat infections that were almost as great a menace as were nests of Japanese fighting from the jungle-shrouded caves?

The seriousness of this problem had been brought home to Dr. Compton in his contacts with field officers; but even then a period of several months elapsed before formal request was sent in for the group of experts wanted to survey what had been the major medical problem — malaria. When late in April, 1944, a radiogram from SWPA asked that such a team be sent forward, the Committee on Medical Research was anxious that this mission should proceed with dispatch. Under its sponsorship and supervision our laboratories had been doing intensive research to find new drugs for the suppression and treatment of malaria and were anxious that these be given field tests.

Original plans for the malaria mission called for a team of four outstanding experts. Dr. Francis Blake of Yale University Medical School was asked to serve as leader of the group. He was to concentrate on clinical aspects of malaria and other communicable diseases of special importance to the Armed Services in the Southwest. Dr. James A. Shannon of New York University Medical School was to join the party for attention to the chemotherapeutic aspects. Dr. Fred C. Bishopp, Assistant Chief of the Bureau of Entomology and Plant Quarantine in the Department of Agriculture, agreed to look into the relation of these diseases to insect carriers; and Dr. Robert B. Watson, principal epidemiologist of the Tennessee Valley Authority, was to concentrate on the epidemiological aspects of malaria.

When final plans were formulated, unforeseen developments prevented Blake and Shannon from participating. Bishopp and Watson agreed to proceed alone, Watson attempting to represent the interests previously delegated to Blake and Shannon. The party left just after the Fourth of July.

The over-all purposes of the survey were: to acquaint the Allied armies with malaria research in the United States and to determine progress of similar research in the SWPA; to explore the possibility for co-ordinating work in the theater with that at home in testing new compounds of chemotherapeutic value in malaria; and to consider the administration and effectiveness of atabrine. The men were to find out also whether there was evidence of toxicity from prolonged use of atabrine, and how well the field tests with airplane distribution of DDT for mosquito control confirmed predictions.

For two months Watson and Bishopp toured hospitals, research laboratories, and field stations. They visited Sydney, Melbourne, and Canberra for conferences with the highest authorities in Australian research organizations and with Australian Army medical officers. Then they went to New Guinea for discussions with medical officers and enlisted men. Inevitably they were drawn into consideration of subjects beyond the primary purpose of collecting information on malaria — scrub typhus, fungus infections, the role of various parasites in the spread of tropical diseases, deterioration of supplies and equipment.

They reported that malaria was no longer a serious problem in that theater because of the excellent work of American engineers, sanitation officers, and medical men. In the early military campaigns the casualty rates from this disease had been very high. But a rigid program of draining or oiling swamps, of spraying insecticides, of discipline regarding clothing and atabrine, and of early diagnosis and treatment had licked this affliction. It had now been surpassed by "fungus" disorders as a cause for concern. They were responsible for about one fifth of all medical admissions to Army hospitals in MacArthur's command. Some of them were known to be created by the growth of minute plant organisms; some were the common bacterial infections known as impetigo. Others were flat lesions of the skin, usually of the forearm, known as lichen planus, whose etiology (true cause) has not yet been demonstrated; and some were other skin reactions resembling fungus infections but suspected to be really expressions of allergies. Hardly a person who had been in the theater for a month or two escaped one of these. Moreover, any sort of an open abrasion or contusion proved difficult to heal in the exceedingly humid climate and provided ready entry to infectious organisms.

Bishopp became interested in the infestation of food supplies by insects. He reported the surprising information that in general New Guinea is not as heavily populated with insects as are many places in the United States.

From the standpoint of research in this country the emissaries felt that their mission had accomplished a great deal because they returned with a new viewpoint and many suggestions to guide experimental work along more practical lines. They believed one of their chief contributions to the theater had been in calling attention to a great deal of misuse of equipment because it arrived without adequate instructions or because discipline had not been sufficiently rigid. The importance of systematic training was also evident in the relative rates of malaria. Well-disciplined, old-line, regular Army units had little malaria, while in new, less well-schooled units the rate was high. Bishopp and Watson listed many recommendations for a continuing program of research to be carried out by officers in the theater and made a strong plea that arrangements for co-ordination of this research even within the theater be improved.

In September 1944 the Navy asked OFS to send two specialists to the Southwest Pacific as consultants on the large-scale dissemination of DDT by means of smoke generators that Division 10, NDRC, had developed. Dr. Frank Brescia, physical chemist, and Mr. Irwin B. Wilson, chemist, who had been engaged in the development work on these generators, left for Guadalcanal in November and remained in the Pacific as Navy Technicians on malaria control until April 1945. In February OFS arranged to send Mario J. Goglia, Division 10 Project Engineer on airborne smoke generators, to the Central Pacific to help the Navy install them in aircraft for DDT dispersal.

The seriousness of the fungus problem had already been indicated in Compton's report. For many weeks OFS and CMR had been trying to locate the right specialist to deal with it. This would call for a man trained thoroughly in general medicine who also had a knowledge of fungus sufficient to qualify him as an expert in this line — that is, he must be a medical mycologist. The number of men in the United States who possessed this unique combination of experience was very small. An ordinary skin specialist (dermatologist) would not do. The nation was short of doctors anyway and few could leave their crowded practices without serious loss to the civilian population.

Finally, on the recommendation of CMR, OFS interviewed Dr. Joseph G. Hopkins, medical mycologist of New York City and the faculty of Columbia University Medical School. Dr. Hopkins was enthusiastic and eager to go. He knew his way around with the Army. He was already working on the staff of the Army Hospital at Fort Benning, Georgia, and he recognized the opportunity for furthering research in this country by collecting skin fungi that were perhaps unknown in the cultures then available in our hospitals and research laboratories.

Hopkins was tall, gaunt, and over sixty. He looked wiry enough; but OFS was hesitant to send a man of such unquestioned special abilities out to an assignment that would probably make strong demands on his physical stamina. Perhaps there was a younger man who could take it better. When Dr. Hopkins became aware that the OFS officials were dubious about sending him because of his age, he smiled disarmingly and said that he knew the need was urgent and that few men could be found to fill it. Anticipating this objection he had already had a thorough medical examination and had been pronounced sound. He would go and stay as long as the Army needed him.

Dr. Hopkins spent the month of August getting ready for at least six months in SWPA. He collected new ointments that might prove helpful, conferred with skin specialists, and talked with military men who had returned from that theater. Then for seven months he visited hospitals and battle-aid stations in Australia, New Guinea, and the Philippines, and worked in close collaboration with Major John V. Ambler, dermatological consultant on the staff of Brigadier General Guy B. Denit, Chief Surgeon of the theater. Most of his time was spent in observing typical cases, discussing problems with medical personnel, and inaugurating small-scale tests, particularly for treatment with undecylenic and sodium propionate ointment.

He went out to live with the troops in the field for months at a time and stayed with them while they slugged it out with the Japs. Everywhere he went Hopkins won the confidence, co-operation, and appreciation of the troops. He was an active research man even under the handicaps of forward areas and sent back many cultures of fungi isolated from field cases for study in the home laboratories.

The complexity of the problem he had tackled and the variety of skin conditions which claimed his attention during those seven months is indicated in the list of types of dermatitis discussed in his final report to the Surgeon General: dermatophytosis of the feet, of the hands, of the groin, of the trunk, and of the beard; chromophytosis; fungus infections of the ear; pyogenic infections; diphtheria of the skin; miliaria and "heat rash"; contact dermatitis from plants, from antiseptics, and fungicides; symmetrical, eczematoid, atypical lichen planus; exfoliative dermatitis; blue nails; scabies; warts. Affliction with any one of these came to be known among the foot soldiers by the graphic but nonspecific name, "jungle rot." After the Leyte landings when men had stood, marched, and even slept in flooded rice paddies, it was not surprising that they developed all sorts of strange ailments.

When Hopkins reported his findings and recommendations at a joint session of OSRD and high military officials in the spring of 1945, the chairman of the meeting said that no doubt this work would have many far-reaching results. Dr. Hopkins modestly replied that the only long-term result he could thus far discover was that he had returned feeling at least ten years younger. He was truly a combat scientist of the finest type. Dr. Stephenson says, "He is deservedly the most praised of all the men who were out there"; and this is confirmed by an impressive sheaf of commendations Hopkins received from the theater command.

With the cessation of hostilities in both theaters and the attendant slackening of discipline, the incidence of venereal and related diseases went up alarmingly. Late in the summer of 1945 scabies had become a major problem in Italy. This scourge, which is caused by mites, is generally contracted only through personal contact and its manifestations are often improperly diagnosed as venereal disease. At the request of the Surgeon General's Office OFS dispatched Gaines W. Eddy of the Bureau of Entomology and Plant Quarantine to the Mediterranean to investigate methods used in the diagnosis and treatment of this annoying malady. He spent several weeks in a tour of medical installations in Italy and the rest of his stay at the 300th General Hospital near Naples. Armed with new synthetic materials developed in the United States whose effectiveness would rival the common treatment with benzyl benzoate, he introduced to the theater ideas in the treatment of scabies which had been known at home for some time.

Repeatedly he isolated the causative mites from lesions of patients incorrectly classified as venereal. He also located and removed mites from areas of the body that showed no sign of attack and had therefore not been treated. Unfortunately in too many cases the ointments had been applied only to the lesions. Eddy pointed out that thorough eradication of the mites could only be achieved by bathing the patient and sponging him from the neck down over the entire body with a preparation rubbed in, not merely spread. This practice was not followed because some of the salves had resulted in extreme discomfort. Since the hospitals were crowded and understaffed, sufferers with scabies were handled as out-patients and there was a constant threat of reinfection from contact with the civilian population in which this disease was rampant. Furthermore, a generally sagging morale created by the rapid demobilization of medical officers in the theater militated against co-ordinated attack on the problem.

Unfortunately DDT had not proved effective against the mites. Eddy stated that sprinkling them with DDT powder would be just about as effective as bombarding them with talcum.

As our troops settled down to occupation duties in Manila there was a striking rise in the rate of true venereal diseases, particularly of one variety known as chancroid. The Surgeon General in the theater requested that OFS send out two specialists to study the epidemiology and treatment of this infection. Although the war was over and OSRD had already begun extensive demobilization, Dr. Bush authorized OFS to inaugurate this project with the understanding that the personnel would be transferred shortly to full War Department auspices. Dr. Charles M. Carpenter, Associate Professor of Bacteriology and Public Health at the University of Rochester School of Medicine, and Dr. Robert B. Dienst, clinical bacteriologist of the University of Georgia Medical School, were recruited through CMR to carry out a diligent field study of many phases of this disease. They were accompanied by Lieutenant S. W. Gilkerson, a technician from the Medical Corps.

The team concentrated its work at the 314th General Hospital near Manila. Dienst and Lieutenant Gilkerson devoted their efforts to techniques for isolating the causative organism. After Dienst returned, Carpenter remained to investigate the same problem in Japan.

The work of this mission dealt not only with patients but also, where possible, with their female consorts. Tests were made on 98 "hostesses" in Manila and on 58 "Geisha girls" in Tokyo. Carpenter was also asked to study a peculiarly penicillin-resistant gonorrhea that had been reported. He found, however, that this yielded promptly when the penicillin injections were of adequate strength. Both in Manila and in Japan, Carpenter also studied the results of bacteriological work in connection with leprosy.

Although this mission gathered information of value to a continued research program, it did not by any means solve the problem of chancroid. Carpenter stated in his final report: "There is still much work to be done on the bacteriology and epidemiology of the disease. The methods of laboratory diagnosis are unsatisfactory and little is known about prophylaxis and immunity. Additional research should be carried out because of the unusual opportunities for study of the disease in the Far East and because it is a serious problem facing the Army of occupation."

With our troops deployed in areas having such extreme contrasts of climate as the Aleutian Islands, North African deserts, Pacific jungles, and tropical forests of India and Burma, the Quartermaster Corps faced tremendous problems. It had to provide appropriate clothing that would permit the freedom of action essential to combat, and materials properly protected to withstand the varied environments. It had turned over to American physiologists and medical men many questions about the design of tropical clothing and the physiologic effects of different climates on front-line troops. Dr. Sid Robinson, track coach and physiologist of the University of Indiana Medical School, had been engaged in this work for many months under a CMR contract with that institution. He had persuaded his track squad to serve as guinea pigs by wearing different kinds of tropical clothing in their normal workout training in order to compare their physiologic effects.

Word of Robinson's studies had reached the American and British Operational Research Sections in Southeast Asia. In the summer of 1945 a request was sent through the War Office in London and the British Commonwealth Scientific Office in Washington for Robinson to tour military research establishments in London, India, Ceylon, and Burma. The British authorities provided transportation. Before the trip was completed calls from Australian medical research centers created a change in itinerary. Between the 21st of June and the 3rd of September Robinson circled the globe completely. He flew the 3500 miles from Ceylon to Perth nonstop, and the next day an additional 2000 to Melbourne. As the only Field Consultant to go completely around the world on a single mission, he conferred with literally hundreds of British and American officers and research men. He probably accomplished more to improve liaison between the many agencies interested in matters of tropical physiology than could have been effected through months of correspondence.

*   *   *

Obviously disease in any form is a serious deterrent to the success-ful prosecution of a military campaign. In addition to the loss of man-power from physical disabilities there is an inevitable impact of battle on those complicated structures known as the human brain and per-sonality. The morale of a fighting force may be largely determined by its general health; and the prevalence of illnesses, especially of rare varieties about which little is known, can produce anxiety, discontent, and psychological disorganization.

Napoleon's comment about an Army traveling on its stomach was a pithy expression of the dependence of the will-to-fight on even one aspect of physical well-being. But even if one could eliminate the factor of general physical health and consider only well-fed troops in perfect condition operating in a Utopian absence of illness, there would still be a problem to assess properly the effects of individual weapons, com-binations of weapons, and of the total environment of battle on their sensitive nervous systems, purely apart from the physical damage that the weapons produce.

The mechanical effects of an explosion can be readily observed and measured in rather precise quantities. To determine its psychological ones is quite another matter. Yet it is important to attempt this, at least in a qualitative way, for two reasons — to find out how to increase such damage among the enemy, and how to minimize it among our own men.

The greatest sources of casualties in World War I were tuberculosis and influenza. In World War II they were neuropsychiatric disorders brought on by the complex stresses of a total war that involved ever more terrible implements of destruction. Even though in the early days our Armed Services had made an attempt to screen out those who might collapse psychologically, the percentage of our losses through what is commonly known as "combat exhaustion," "battle fatigue," and "nervous breakdown," was alarmingly high. We had reason to believe that the same was true of the enemy. If we knew more about the actual causes of such casualties, perhaps we could turn this to ad-vantage in planning tactics.

The New Developments Division and other agencies of the War and Navy Departments were interested in the possibility of finding answers to such questions as: What relationship is there between the demoralizing effects of a weapon and its actual lethal effects? Are the implements that account for the largest number of killed and wounded the ones that are really the most feared? Is there a relationship between the kind and intensity of noise made by an instrument of war and its demoralizing effect? Did the multibarrel rocket gun of the Russians known as the *Stalin Organ,* or the screaming bombs the Nazis dropped on Britain really increase neuropsychiatric collapse? Is the kind of wound a weapon produces a primary consideration in the fear it engenders? Would it be more devastating to carry out continuous artillery bombardment for hours, or to use artillery only intermittently, sporadically, and at unpredictable times? Do attacks at night produce greater terror than the use of similar weapons by daylight?

The answers to such questions must come from painstaking observation in the field. The correlations between types of weapons used, methods of their employment, and psychological effects in weakening resistance are exceedingly difficult to obtain. There is little positive knowledge in this subject. Officers hold varying opinions about the effects of particular weapons or tactics, but they admit frankly that these are not too well supported by facts. NDD was anxious to test the theories by sending a mission of top-notch psychologists to the European theater after we had landed on the Continent and were beginning to shove the Germans back through France. Perhaps our ultimate victory might be won sooner if more were known about how to use our weapons and other resources to produce the maximum demoralizing effect on the Germans and break their will to continue the fight.

In July 1944 OFS was asked to undertake this project and procured the services of Dr. Mark A. May, eminent psychologist and head of the Institute of Human Relations at Yale University, and Dr. Hans Reese, neuropsychiatrist of the University of Wisconsin Medical School. For several weeks this team examined documents and reports in the War Department and conferred with members of OSRD's Applied Psychology Panel. Then, accompanied by Brigadier General Emmerick Kutschko of NDD, they left for ETO. The party was attached to ALSOS for administrative purposes and was aided by the assignment of a military interrogator from G-2.

Reese and May made pilot or sample studies in an effort to obtain definitive answers, to check on conclusions derived from earlier work, and to learn the best practical procedures for conducting such field surveys on a still larger scale.

In London they found that the British War Office had been studying the same problem for some time and had developed a plan for similar field missions. Major General Paul R. Hawley, Chief Surgeon of ETO, Colonel Lloyd Thompson, Senior Consultant in Psychiatry, and their staffs expressed the unanimous opinion that the study of the psychological effects of weapons should not be limited to those of Allied weapons on enemy troops. It should also include the mental damage to Allied troops from enemy weapons. Reese and May instigated studies by the Research Branch of the Special Services Division on nonpsychiatric wounded American troops in France, and on neuropsychiatric casualties at the 96th General Hospital in England. They visited prison camps in UK and in France and then went forward with the Armies to interview prisoners as they were taken at St.-Malo, Brest, Boulogne, and Aachen.

The mission of Reese and May could not be considered as more than a preliminary investigation. Although they talked with hundreds of officers and enemy prisoners, the total sampling was inadequate to provide statistically reliable conclusions. The difficulties of correlating information gained from prisoners with details of the operations that led them to surrender were discouraging. Nevertheless, such conclusions as the psychologists could draw indicated trends that might be useful in operational planning. They found that troops fear shells and bombs much more than they do small arms, and that seasoned troops actually acquire a healthy disrespect for rifle and pistol fire. In general, a soldier fears most the thing he is most exposed to or against which he has the least protection. The tank crews fear bazookas; the ground troops fear shelling and mortar fire that comes on them unexpectedly.

Reese and May pointed out, however, that troops tend to harbor considerable awe of a weapon that has somehow gained a reputation for greater lethality than it possesses. Yet they may show little concern over a device that actually produces the greatest number of casualties. In this respect "the relation between fear and actual danger in war may be quite parallel to the familiar relations observed in civilian life. Most people have no fear of . . . the situations which, according to liability insurance companies, produce the greatest number of injuries and deaths" — automobiles, bathtubs, and cellar steps. "On the other hand, a great many people are afraid of such innocuous things as non-poisonous snakes, mice, high places and ghosts."

Reese and May were close enough to the Siegfried Line to see that at that stage in the war our advance across Europe would be no picnic. They had the impression that German morale was generally low but that the Germans would continue to fight on to the bitter end. In an attempt to determine reasons for this they questioned scores of prisoners of all ages. The influence of Goebbel's propaganda was obvious in the replies. When asked, "Realizing that you were defeated, why did you continue to fight?" some stated that they must obey the orders of their commanding officers regardless of the situation. Some mentioned the "menace of the Russians" who were "determined to make slaves of the Germans for generations to come." Others spoke of the time that might be gained for the High Command to bring up reinforcements or put into operation the new secret weapons Hitler had promised. Others were afraid of reprisals against their families. Some insisted that there were SS spies within the Army who had orders to shoot anyone who showed an inclination to stop fighting; and a few even expressed a fear of horrible treatment and mutilation by Allied troops.

In October the team returned to the United States and recommended continuance and extension of this study to exploit the subject to its fullest extent. They suggested that specially trained teams be organized to gather firsthand information in the theater. Taking into account the relation of the pattern of attack to the enemy situation, psychologists would correlate these findings with the general effects of propaganda and psychological warfare. The pace of the Army across Europe proved so rapid, however, that this proposal was not given the high-priority attention it seemed to merit in the fall of 1944 and was never carried out. It was widely believed that the whole psychology of the Japanese was so different from that of the Nazis that things we might learn about creating demoralization among the Germans would not prove very helpful when applied in the Pacific.

Nevertheless, there was an increasing interest in the mounting rate of neuropsychiatric (N-P) casualties among our own troops. It might be useful to know more about the factors in combat that precipitate these disorders so that appropriate measures could be taken to prevent them, or to render more effective treatment.

The studies by the Special Services Division in ETO and England that Reese and May had helped to initiate had set the stage for more extensive work along these lines. Early in April 1945 General Hawley requested that a team of outstandingly able psychiatrists come over to visit the Army fronts in Europe and attempt to discover the immediate causes of N-P collapse. He observed that: "The clinical picture seen at the clearing station level changes within a few days, even hours, as the soldier is evacuated farther to the rear. Because an accurate knowledge of the pathology is necessary to guide and plan the most effective treatment it would seem important to attempt an evaluation of the psychopathology as observed at the forward echelon for the purpose of correlating it with subsequent treatment methods. . . . It is obvious that the psychiatrists in the Army, and particularly the group at combat levels, do not have time and are not necessarily professionally equipped to undertake any such research."

Through the co-operation of Brigadier General William C. Menninger, Director of the Neuropsychiatric Consultants Division, General Borden of NDD, and officials of CMR, a group of five of the country's leading psychiatrists was alerted for early departure to ETO. The mission consisted of Drs. Leo H. Bartemeier of Detroit, Lawrence S. Kubie of New York, Karl A. Menninger of Topeka, John Romano of Cleveland, and John C. Whitehorn of Baltimore. These men had heavy commitments both in their private practices and in consulting services for the base hospitals of the Armed Services at home. Nevertheless they were willing to accept the assignment to gather information they regarded as of inestimable value in further prosecution of the war and in psychiatric research generally.

The Allied pincers were already closing on Berlin. Unless the mission could leave at once there was little hope that the men would be able to deal with exhaustion casualties immediately as they came out of battle. To rush all five of the psychiatrists over the countless hurdles of processing and have them ready to leave on the same plane, taking into account the complications of their exceedingly busy schedules, was a rare, challenge to the OFS staff. But the group took off on schedule only two weeks after the first contacts with them by telephone.

Arriving up front about ten days before V-E Day, the N-P team had only a limited opportunity to carry out its original purpose of observing American boys just after they had broken under the stresses of combat. The plan to separate and operate independently in several parts of the theater was abandoned. Although hostilities had ceased, there was still a vast amount of useful information which these medical men could gain from an extensive tour of battle-aid stations, clearing stations, field hospitals, and base hospitals. Consequently they continued as a group and traveled through France, Germany, Czechoslovakia, Austria, Belgium, England, and Scotland for the next three months. They visited the First, Third, Seventh, and Ninth Army fronts, talked with hundreds of medical officers in the American, French, and British Armies, the British Navy, and the Allied Air Forces, and attended meetings of civilian research organizations. They spent a week in an American hospital for the treatment of psychoneurosis near Liége, Belgium, and went to Buchenwald.

Since they had no responsibility for handling patients and no routine medical tasks, they went as observers and consultants. The advantage they enjoyed as civilians in obtaining information from patients is indicated in a quotation from their final report. This status ". . . enabled us to identify ourselves very readily with either privates or officers, non-commissioned or commissioned men, because we were not, in fact, in any one of these positions ourselves. Furthermore, we escaped some of the features of the situation peculiar to the Army. We were not under any compulsion or obligation to find ways of getting men back to duty. It was our function only to study the conditions without the necessity of serving any utilitarian purpose by which Army doctors are always bound and constrained. We came to our study of psychiatric casualties mentally fresh and without the physical and mental fatigue which was evident in many Army psychiatrists. By travelling from one medical installation to another and by conferring with many doctors it was like seeing the problem through many eyes so that individual blind spots and prejudices were cancelled out. . . ."

Everywhere they went the American psychiatrists were received with the warmest cordiality. Dr. Kubie reported, "There has been not one episode in which our presence was resented or our work obstructed." Colonel Thompson and Colonel Ernest Parsons accompanied them on many of the journeys, introduced them, and made arrangements for their functioning.

Probably no other OFS travelers except Dr. Compton moved about at such high levels. They lunched with the Director General of the French Army Medical Corps and dined on gold service with a Viscount. They spent week ends on quiet visits in the country homes of distinguished British psychiatrists and were special guests at the House of Commons. And they presented papers at a meeting of the section for psychiatry of the British Royal Society of Medicine.

For almost a month they were guests of the British Government and reported that ". . . the courtesy, hospitality, thoughtfulness and thoroughness of these arrangements cannot be overstated. Cars with drivers were sent to our hotel every morning to take us to the appointed places, and we were each provided not only with a carefully specified itinerary and directory, but with a bound portfolio of documents relating to the work and installations to be seen or described or both." Romano visited the Burden Neurological Institute in Bristol to gather information on new equipment used there for electroencephalography (the technique of recording brain waves). In England they discussed problems in selection of officers and witnessed a film of the War Officer Selection Board which depicts the techniques for utilizing psychiatry in selecting officer candidates. The Germans had started this practice in 1936, the British had followed in 1941, but the American Army has not yet adopted the method.

The findings and recommendations of this eminent group are incorporated in a long report, parts of which have already appeared in the public press. Menninger's opinion is that ". . . The scientific fruitfulness of the trip was of a very satisfactory order. But even more important in the long run may have been some of the collateral values of the expedition. One of these was the information gained with reference to the problems of psychiatric education. . . . Associated with this is the good effect which I am presumptuous enough to think our visit had on the morale of some very weary and often discouraged young medical officers, especially psychiatrists.

"Finally, I think the experience of seeing at first hand the devastation in Germany, the confusion and anxiety in France, the social ferment in England, to say nothing of the specific problems of the United

States Army — this experience had an effect upon all of us which cannot but influence our thinking, feeling, talking, planning and working for the critical years immediately ahead."

The mission criticized the confidence our officers placed in the quick and superficial routine psychiatric screening tests to weed out potential N-P casualties. The group emphasized that American soldiers in ETO had done a splendid job and that any remarks about the decadence of our Army were pure nonsense. Our men fought brilliantly even though their motivation for fighting was far different from that of the British who saw their cities blitzed, or of the Russians whose country was overrun. Nevertheless even the strongest of them were vulnerable to breakdown when, through difficulties in applying the military policy of rotation, they were subjected to prolonged strain, or when poor replacement planning sent them into battle without adequate integration into their combat units. The fact that some suffered psychologically under these abnormal conditions is certainly no reflection on their valor or their patriotism. It merely emphasizes the severity of modern warfare and the critical importance of adhering to sound procedures in rotation and replacement in order to minimize N-P casualties.

Although our psychiatric casualties were numbered in the tens of thousands, the work of our Army doctors had been so effective that in one instance 5000 were returned to military duty from a single hospital within one year. The mission felt that probably 95 per cent of all the N-P cases could go back to useful tasks in "normal" *civilian* life. Unfortunately the measure of rehabilitation in the Army during the war is, however, the ability of the individual to go back for more of the same kind of hell — which few can do.

It is exceedingly difficult to get statistical information to support sound conclusions about the return to duty and the subsequent history of an individual who broke down in battle. "Many such patients by reason of their return to combat will be killed or wounded. In two ways this limits their value for the statistical comparison of results. In the first place, it makes it impossible to give a conclusive appraisal of the durability of the recovery under combat stress. In the second place, survivors will constitute a selective sample, since their survival may mean either that the accidents of war have placed them in areas of less severe combat, or else that they may have protected themselves from the full hazards of combat by lagging behind while keeping up appearances. . . . In a war of rapid movement follow-up statistics are tremendously difficult to secure because of the frequent transfer of whole divisions from one front to another."

The mission devoted many hours to considering ". . . how the combat soldier, exposed to internal and external stresses, may suddenly deviate from accepted channels or patterns of behavior in such a way as to render him unfit for duty so that he becomes a casualty." At the battalion aid stations where he is first received he manifests signs of a temporary psychological disorganization out of which more permanent ones may develop. The group felt that the term "combat exhaustion" cannot be used for definitive diagnosis. It should be considered merely as a temporary label and the ultimate treatment should depend on discriminating diagnoses made by trained psychiatrists at the level of the general hospital or the psychiatric hospital.

The occurrence of N-P casualties among our troops varied greatly from battle to battle and the number increased in waves. It was greatest, as might have been expected, in situations where the stresses were most severe. During the Battle of the Bulge and in assaults on particularly strong positions where action was prolonged, the number of men eliminated by psychological collapse was high. When a spirit of victory was in the air, in the closing days of the campaign, severe psychiatric disturbances dropped sharply.

There is considerable difference of opinion among military psychiatrists about the maximum number of days of continuous fighting that even the sturdiest and most stable soldier can endure. One informant ". . . had concluded from his observations that 180 days is such a maximum figure, that to expose a soldier who escapes injury or death to more than this amount of combat is to sacrifice manpower uselessly." Such considerations must be taken into account in determining overall policy about rotation, replacement, and reassignment. The mission reports, however, that ". . . Some acknowledgment of the exigencies of unexpected military situations" must be made. . . . It is obvious that the commander in the field may find his forces in a situation which calls for the emergency employment and expenditure of manpower in disregard of the ordinary principles of training, preparation and integration of the soldiers in his fighting unit. At certain times in the ETO (as in the Belgian Bulge), such desperate and challenging situations have evoked magnificent reactions in extemporized fighting units."

The psychiatrists devoted considerable attention to the methods of treatment in use by Allied medical officers. Their comments about the use of narcosis and other techniques should prove exceedingly valuable not only in peacetime applications in professional psychiatry but also in improving military psychiatric training and procedure.

Our shortage of medical men was serious enough; the scarcity of trained psychiatrists was a major handicap that prevented us from bringing the benefits of the latest knowledge in this specialized field to alleviate the sufferings of many thousands of American soldiers and sailors who were victims of "combat exhaustion." One of the most critical needs, not only of the War Department but also of our civilian population, is the training of thousands of men in psychiatry to deal with the widespread maladjustments that are an inevitable aftermath of so universal a war.

Dr. Karl Menninger is today devoting his full attention to this very problem as the newly appointed manager of the Veterans Administration psychiatric hospital in Topeka. Here scores of psychiatrists will be trained for service in the twenty-one VA mental hospitals and six mental hygiene clinics where more than 50,000 men who are victims of "combat exhaustion" are struggling to peer through the blackout curtain that fell between their minds and the world of reality. In this assignment, which probably pays him only a fraction of his earnings in private practice, Menninger is again working closely with General Hawley, now the chief medical officer of General Bradley's Veterans Administration. Dr. Menninger could take this assignment because the Menninger Foundation in Topeka which he headed, and which holds the same high place in the field of psychiatry as does the famous Mayo Clinic in the study and treatment of bodily ailments, is now the property of the State of Kansas. In May 1946 it was turned over as an outright gift from Dr. C. F. Menninger, who set up the Foundation, from his illustrious sons, General (and Dr.) William C. and Dr. Karl A., and from those associated with them in building that significant institution.

The importance to the nation of this action by the Menningers can be appreciated better in the light of official statistics. They show that about one fifth of our population either has been, is now, or can expect to be in a mental hospital. If Dr. Karl's unselfish decision was in any way influenced by his overseas experience with the N-P mission of OFS (and it is difficult to think otherwise), then it would not be an exaggeration to say that this single project, short as it was and failing to accomplish its original purpose, was one of the most far-reaching in its ultimate effects on our civilian life.

A staff officer who breaks his leg because the front steps of his head-quarters collapse where termites have eaten out the support, or the artillery spotter who sees nothing but a milky cloud of fungus etching the lens of his field glasses, needs no further warning that the world of biology harbors myriads of silent enemies, often microscopic, whose lives may be almost as serious in interfering with his military plans as the fire of enemy machine guns.

In the tropical areas especially, where warmth and humidity favor the life processes of many organisms unknown in other parts of the world, chemical and biological deterioration of supplies and equip-ment was acute. Thousands of tons of materials improperly protected against these depradations, or incorrectly packed, handled, and stored were utterly useless within a few weeks. Naturally this was of greater concern to the American taxpayer than it was to the constantly moving GI who often had to abandon perfectly good stores simply because there was no transportation to take them along.

In SWPA where shipping was at a premium, the invasion of ship bottoms and dock pilings by marine organisms caused enough inter-ference with operational planning so that specialists were needed to survey the situation and recommend preventive measures. Such damage from small oceanic borers is universal and is caused primarily by cer-tain mollusks (shelled organisms) and crustacea (shrimplike animals). It is particularly prevalent in the tropical waters where these creatures can breed all year.

In the winter of 1944 Dr. Charles H. Blake, marine biologist from M.I.T., and Mr. A. P. Richards, biologist of the Clapp Laboratories in Massachusetts, went out to the Research Section to study this prob-lem. They worked with the Maritime Service Laboratory in Sydney and reported that no single method of protection would be successful for all conditions. Many of the boats and barges that showed the worst damage had been built by the Australians without regard for the specifications Americans had set forth to guard against such attack. Blake and Richards recommended the use of antifouling paint, to be renewed every three months, but emphasized that this could only be a temporary preventive because "brush" coats are not effective once they have been broken through with scratches. As a more effective procedure they recommended that planking should be pressure-treated with creosote or copper naphthenate, or sheeted with treated plywood. If these procedures were not practicable, they recommended that certain native hardwoods found more resistant to attack from these marine organisms should be utilized in the construction of ships and harbor facilities.

In May the Army requested that Blake remain in the theater for a few additional months to study the problem of insect infestations in supplies of grain in storage. The chief difficulty seemed to be with flour, most of it procured from Australian sources. Blake visited mills and granaries in New South Wales and Queensland. He compared the conditions of sanitation and of insect incidence found there with those of the warehouses and subsistence dumps. He also studied the attack of insects on meat and fruits, and issued an extensive series of recommendations for improved procedures in storage and handling. One of his discoveries that rather surprised many officers was that the freon bombs in which they had such confidence for minimizing insect hazards were really not effective in kitchens and bakeries and should be reserved for other purposes.

More serious than the attack by insects and vermin on the meat supplies furnished from Australia to the forward areas was the improper loading and handling of ships that carried these foodstuffs. For some weeks there would be a glut of beef and then for weeks there was no meat at all. Sometimes four ships loaded with meat would arrive on the same day. In one case a shipload of meat in a New Guinea harbor was condemned as unfit for human consumption. It had spent two months en route from Sydney, had moved in to unload its high-priority munitions, and then been ordered back out into the harbor for several more weeks. When the unrefrigerated cargo was finally unloaded the meat was spoiled and infested with vermin.

Alert to any problem that involved insects, Blake was also called on by the Signal Corps. Wood beetles were eating the poles of the telephone lines from Lae to Finschhafen almost as fast as they could be replaced and were even cutting through the lead conductors. At Blake's suggestion the Signal Corps slit tin cans, painted them with a protective material, and tacked them on the poles. The damage by beetles was practically eliminated.

The unpleasant climate of northern Australia in winter is suggested in Blake's comment that the only way he could keep warm was to wear heavy woolen underwear and a woolen uniform and then put pajamas, bathrobe, and trench coat on over them. In this garb he spent many hours writing his notes.

Research agencies in this country, aware of the problems that would be encountered under varied weather conditions in different parts of the globe where the war was or would be fought, had devised many protective measures. Before these were applied, large quantities of material had to be shipped ahead to the theaters. It was often some months before a can, or a radar set, or a pair of binoculars, properly tropicalized and packaged at the production plant, reached storage warehouses in the forward areas. In the meantime vast damage might be done to materials not so treated.

Much would depend, of course, on the discipline obtaining in the theaters. Care in handling, proper storage, and appropriate protective routines specified by the laboratories at home and circulated through Army channels could prevent great losses. But it would be too much to expect that a dogface, sweating it out in a jungle foxhole and not knowing at what moment his own life or that of his whole company might be obliterated, would show much concern over the proper ventilation of his clothes. He might well appreciate that rust could quickly ruin his carbine; but he had no idea how long he would need it. If it did not survive the attack by moisture, he could doubtless get another from the Services of Supply. Carelessness of this sort, multiplied many thousands of times, created a picture of widespread decay, and supply officers who know how difficult it is to procure spare parts and replacements were greatly disturbed.

The whole problem of tropical deterioration loomed large in the minds of both Army and Navy personnel at the time of Compton's visit in the Southwest Pacific, when our forces had just gained firm footholds in New Guinea. Concern over it had penetrated to Washington, and a joint Army-Navy-OSRD committee to study all aspects of this problem was organized under the chairmanship of Dr. Gustavus J. Esselen. This step was partially an outgrowth of extended studies carried out under the direction of Brigadier General Georges F. Doriot, Chief of the Military Planning Division in the Office of the Quartermaster General. In March General Doriot had procured the services of Dr. Elso S. Barghoorn, meticulous medical mycologist from the faculty of Amherst College, to survey biological aspects of tropical deterioration.

Barghoorn's review of existing research projects and testing techniques within various branches of the Armed Forces and the civilian laboratories led to a plan of action. This called for establishment of a mycological research laboratory to develop more rigidly standardized tests. It also suggested organization of a scientific commission and mobile laboratory for study of the causes and control of tropical deterioration in combat areas. "Serious deficiency . . . repeatedly emphasized in the entire study . . . conducted in domestic laboratories, lies in the essential ignorance of field conditions, field requirements, and the performance in the field of protective techniques. . . . Much of the time and effort . . . expended in speculation as to how materials are behaving in the field, and research invested in simulated tropical testing, could be more intelligently directed if investigations in the field indicate the need for specific lines of research and demonstrate the correlation of domestic test procedures with field performance."

When the Tropical Deterioration Steering Committee was created, General Doriot released Barghoorn to serve as Technical Aide in the early phases of its activities. The Committee established a Tropical Deterioration Information Center at George Washington University and launched an ambitious program for collecting, abstracting, and correlating information from all sources on chemical and biological aspects of deterioration. The OFS at Hawaii was decidedly helpful in sending information from forward areas to this Center.

In the summer of 1944 OFS received a request from SWPA for a team of specialists to survey tropical deterioration, in conjunction with

Australian scientists who had already done extensive work in this field. Concurrently there was a request to exchange an American specialist in these matters with a similarly trained representative of the Australian research program. It was thought that the American scientist would precede the field mission to the theater, would spend some weeks getting thoroughly acquainted with Australian work and facilities, and would then join the mission in New Guinea as a working member of the team. Dr. Leslie A. Chambers, biophysicist from the University of Pennsylvania, experienced in several aspects of tropical deterioration, was recruited for this assignment.

NDD had assured OFS that Chambers could proceed to the theater as a civilian without special Army appointment, could visit the Australian facilities through the courtesy of the American consulate and the Australian authorities, and would then be issued necessary military credentials and travel orders when he later reported to the Research Section of OFS at GHQ. Unfortunately this did not prove to be the case. On arrival in Australia Chambers was immediately referred to GHQ to report, and found himself in the anomalous situation of an individual in a theater of military operations without official orders and with only verbal and written instructions from civilian agencies. Yet he was to carry on investigations in parts of that theater to which he was not permitted to travel without military orders. It appeared to the authorities that an advance survey in New Guinea would be desirable. Special orders were cut and he was dispatched to do this before going to the Australian laboratories.

Meanwhile in Washington arrangements for the mobile laboratory and mission were going forward. A team consisting of Drs. W. G. Hutchinson, mycologist from the University of Pennsylvania, Herbert W. Reuszer, soil microbiologist on detail from the Department of Agriculture, E. W. Baker, entomologist and expert on mites, detailed from the Department of Agriculture Station in Mexico City, and Barghoorn began elaborate preparations for a lengthy study in SWPA. Reuszer and Baker made arrangements to shift their families from Florida and Mexico respectively; Hutchinson moved his mother, with whom he had been living in Philadelphia, to Providence, and secured a man to take over his work at Pennsylvania. Barghoorn likewise located a replacement to assume his functions with the Tropical De-

terioration Committee. All of the men went through the rigmarole
of processing, purchased uniforms and insurance, and gathered scientific equipment and samples for field testing. They spent some weeks
in conferences with interested authorities such as Dr. Waksman, dis-
coverer of the new wonder drug, streptomycin, and prepared to attack
what had appeared as a serious problem.

The group departed for California on Army orders. While they
were awaiting transportation at Hamilton Field a radiogram from
the theater canceled the mission. The men, the Committee in Washington, and OFS were perturbed. It was apparent that this cancellation
must have had the approval of the Research Section and had probably
been sanctioned by Chambers. But it was not until Chambers returned that the circumstances leading to this disappointing action
were fully understood.

After his trip in New Guinea, Chambers had spent some time with
Australian authorities as originally planned, and had looked into many
aspects of the deterioration of Quartermaster supplies, foodstuffs, and
equipment, and his version of the cancellation was delayed for some
weeks. He explains the matter in his final report. In 1943 initial operations based at Port Moresby had led to extensive loss of supplies and
equipment. This "was sufficient to cause alarm and reports received
in Washington based on data collected during this period precipitated
a belated and somewhat frantic attempt to cope with the situation.
Unfortunately the reports were fragmentary and failed to keep pace
with the progress of field experience . . . it is believed that undue
emphasis was placed on the biological aspects of tropical deterioration"
in the questionnaires sent from Washington.

"Practically all military personnel and Australian scientists who
have been in contact with developments in New Guinea are agreed
that losses from climatic factors are now very much reduced . . . there
has been a great reduction of the overall percentage loss from the dep-
redation of fungi. . . . The current opinion is that ninety per cent
of the overall losses are due to unsuitable packaging and storage and
that the major efforts of the future should be directed toward improvement in design, packaging methods and corrosion preventatives and
toward implementation of protective procedures already demonstrated
to be effective. . . . With the exception of canvas in use and optical

instruments, satisfactory techniques for preservation of material in New Guinea are known." (These observations were strongly confirmed in oral reports to OFS by Bishopp and Watson and later by additional consultants who had been in SWPA.)

Chambers's observations had put him in complete concurrence with the general opinion among officers that it would not be "feasible, practicable or possible to carry on research in the operational area. . . . It was frequently suggested that solutions for the problem might be more effectively sought in other tropical areas, the results of such studies to be fed as rapidly as possible into operational theaters. Frequently officers concerned pointed out that nothing which might be learned by a research group could contribute to the campaign in New Guinea since the material for completion of that operation and for initiating the invasion of the Philippines was either already on hand or on the way. Incidentally, the impending Philippine strike and the enormous strain on transport, communications and human energies which it imposed was a factor in the situation which could not be reported at the time. Now it can be told that the impending strike would have made the mission (had it reached New Guinea) ineffective."

Upon his return to GHQ Chambers had submitted a report through the Chief Quartermaster of the theater, including recommendations that resulted in canceling the proposed mission. These were approved by the Research Section of OFS, the Chief Quartermaster, the Commanding General of the Services of Supply, and the Chief of Staff.

The Quartermaster Corps in Washington and other military agencies had prepared samples for the mission to take to SWPA for exposure and test. After a few weeks it was decided that the group should go instead to Barro Colorado Island in Panama to conduct these tests and to study the fungi of such tropical areas. Baker was unable to participate in this diversion of the project, but the others, under the leadership of Hutchinson, left for the Canal Zone in October 1944.

Barghoorn sent an excellent description of Barro Colorado in a personal letter to one of the OFS staff members: "This is a tropical island *par excellence,* but not one of those palm-fringed coral-sand atolls of the Trade Wind Tropics. There are exactly two coconut palms and the jungle doesn't give them much room for growth. The island and all the country round about, except where cleared by man, is covered with a dense, dark green, tropical rain forest, interspersed with areas of the most riotous jungle you can imagine. The green gloom of the forest, the dripping trees, and the saturated air make this an excellent location for the work we are doing. To have a well-organized laboratory with a jungle twenty steps from the door makes this a particularly good combination. Work is going along very well, although the amount of it has just about buried us the last few weeks. Getting out test samples required stringing several thousand feet of rope and digging four hundred feet of trench on the jungle floor in an equatorial climate.

"One thing has become very clear, and that is that one cannot study this problem by talking to people in well-kept offices and being guided through newly-constructed and excellently-designed warehouses. You have to live with the problem in the jungle where you don't have to look to find it."

Hutchinson remained in Panama until November and concentrated on problems in the protection of optical devices. Reuszer studied bacterial attack on cotton-duck fabrics subjected to burial in the damp soils, and returned at the end of the year. Barghoorn remained to continue exhaustive studies of the relative importance of fungi as agents of tropical decay and to gather representative cultures to augment the collections of American research centers specializing in this subject. He was particularly anxious to determine whether a sequence of organisms might be involved in the normal deterioration. In February he returned to correlate information and consolidate the culture collections at the Harvard Biological Laboratories. Here, under supervision of Dr. William H. Weston, NDRC had established a central repository for tropical fungus cultures. During the spring of 1945 Barghoorn purified and identified almost 1500 cultures he had sent from the Canal Zone.

In April the Quartermaster Corps requested that field research and testing on experimental cotton textiles be increased in scope and extended as a Quartermaster Corps Project in co-ordination with an Ordnance Tropical Deterioration Project at Fort Sherman in the Canal Zone. Barghoorn was released from his responsibilities to Esselen's Committee and loaned to the QMC for this purpose. As a preliminary step in preparation he worked out with Dr. Weston a system for numbering and cataloguing the collections of tropical fungi that now comprised over 5000 cultures obtained from the combined activities of the QMC and NDRC during the preceding fifteen months.

In the latter part of May, Barghoorn left for the Canal Zone with R. T. Darby, civilian technician from QMC, and remained in Panama until December. Upon the cessation of hostilities with Japan and demobilization of OFS he was transferred in October to the pay roll of the National Academy of Sciences under its contract with the Quartermaster Corps for similar studies.

Throughout his long association with OFS Barghoorn was an energetic worker and a prolific reporter. He did not get out to active combat areas but his contributions in the field of tropical mycology were indeed substantial and will be widely used in future research and in the protective measures devised by the Quartermaster Corps.

The medical and biological activities in which OFS participated were but a small part of the fight against disease and deterioration, a continuing battle that is only intensified by the circumstances of war, but one in which the contributions of OSRD's scientists may prove as significant as was their more spectacular work in devising engines of destruction.

CHAPTER X

SCIENTIFIC SLEUTHING

RESEARCH BEHIND THOSE AXIS BOASTS

THE LITTLE German town of Urach was in an uproar. The American Army had swept through and was racing toward Stuttgart. French and Russian slave laborers, now liberated, were rioting, pillaging, and raping. In the midst of the confusion two uniformed Americans drove up to the town hall in a jeep. One was a civilian scientist, but he looked for all the world like an officer and his driver was an enlisted man.

The American civilian spoke to an old German who appeared bewildered by the excitement around him. It was obvious that the American had lived in Germany, knew the language, customs, and idiosyncrasies of the people. The German disappeared into the rioting crowd. In less than half an hour he was back with a dozen of his comrades, the native villagers. They greeted the American as a rescuer and pleaded for assistance and an armed guard.

The "officer" promptly dispatched them to summon the town fathers for a meeting in the village hall. When all were assembled he assumed full charge and commanded them to bring the leader of the French laborers to the hall. When this was done he ordered the man to gather twenty of his countrymen. Soon they were lined up on the village common and the two Americans distributed firearms they had located in the loft of the town hall, swore the Frenchmen into service, and charged them with patrolling the streets and maintaining order. The American implied that he had considerable forces of American troops at his command. As he left the village that night he assured them he would return with an army in the morning to see that his orders were carried out.

The next day, not without trepidation, the scientist and the driver arrived again. Things had quieted down by this time. He improvised reasons why the rest of his troops were unable to come and then pro-

Vortragsfolge

der 2. wissenschaftlichen Tagung der Arbeitsgemeinschaft
»Kernphysik« (Reichsforschungsrat — Heereswaffenamt)
im Haus der Deutschen Forschung,
Berlin-Steglitz, Grunewaldstr. 35,
am 26.2.1942 um 11 Uhr

1. Kernphysik als Waffe   Prof. Dr. Schumann

2. Die Spaltung des Urankernes   Prof. Dr. O. Hahn

3. Die theoretischen Grundlagen für die
Energiegewinnung aus der Uranspaltung   Prof. Dr. W. Heisenberg

4. Ergebnisse der bisher untersuchten
Anordnungen zur Energiegewinnung   Prof. Dr. W. Bothe

5. Die Notwendigkeit der allgemeinen
Grundlagenforschung   Prof. Dr. H. Geiger

6. Anreicherung der Uranisotope   Prof. Dr. K. Clusius

7. Die Gewinnung von Schwerem Wasser   Prof. Dr. P. Harteck

8. Über die Erweiterung der Arbeitsgemeinschaft »Kernphysik« durch Be-
teiligung anderer Reichsressorts und
der Industrie   Prof. Dr. Esau

Challenge to the High Command

*Program for a meeting of German physicists
in 1942, at which possible military applications
of atomic energy were stressed. Nazi military
leaders were invited*

Der Chef
des Oberkommandos der Wehrmacht

Berlin W 35, den 21.2.1942
Zimpfapfer 72-76.
Bernsprecher REXAL.

Sehr verehrter Herr Reichsminister !

    Für die liebenswürdige Einladung zu der wissen-
schaftlichen Tagung im "Haus der Deutschen Forschung" am
26.Februar spreche ich Ihnen meinen besten Dank aus.
    So grosse Bedeutung ich auch diesen wissenschaft-
lichen Fragen beimesse, so werden Sie andererseits Ver-
ständnis dafür haben, daß ich Ihnen infolge meiner dienst-
lichen Belastung leider eine Absage erteilen muß. Ich werde
mich über das Ergebnis unterrichten lassen und wünsche
Ihrer Arbeitstagung vollen Erfolg.

               Heil Hitler !

               [signature]

An den
Präsidenten des Reichsforschungsrats
Herrn Reichsminister R u s t
Berlin = Steglitz
Grunewaldstraße 35.

Polite Brush-off

*General Keitel wished the nuclear scientists
every success — but declined the invitation*

Reprinted from Science Illustrated, May 1946, by special permission

Secret Weapon

RIGHT: The result of experiments by the Nazis on an atomic bomb, under guidance of the physicist Heisenberg, was this aluminum sphere, about two feet in diameter, which was filled with metal uranium...

Armaments Race

LEFT: Shack and bunker at Kunersdorf near Berlin where the Germans carried on experiments with a uranium pile.

ceeded to set himself up as the mayor of the village. Remaining for more than a week, he restored the life of the village, set up rationing of food supplies, found quarters for war orphans who had been roaming the streets, assigned the wounded and ill to hospitals, and regulated the municipal services. Finally the occupation forces of the regular Army arrived.

On the day the American civilian left there was another meeting in the village hall. In an elaborate ceremony the village fathers thanked him for what he had done and presented him with a Napoleonic sword they had cherished for some years as a special trophy of the town.

The resourceful American was Dr. A. Allan Bates, prominent metallurgist from the research laboratories of the Westinghouse Electric Corporation in Pittsburgh and member of the ALSOS Mission. He had come into Urach right on the heels of the Armed Forces in order to talk to the Research Director of the Kaiser Wilhelm Institute for Metallurgical Research in near-by Stuttgart and to examine certain records. For some twenty-five or thirty years the Germans had led the world in metallurgical research, and he wanted to get all available information about their progress. Obviously scientific investigation could not go forward in the turmoil he found on arrival. It was essential to restore some semblance of normalcy. Our combat troops were rushing across Germany so fast that the occupation forces were unable to keep up and there was no one else on hand to take over. Bates did so in the interest of getting on with his work.

This incident illustrates several important features of ALSOS. In the first place, those who could accomplish the most in the least time were American technical men who had not only a broad grasp of their special scientific fields but who also were facile in the language of those they would question and who knew the psychology of Germans well enough to understand their inbred respect for authority. It was not surprising that they mistook Bates for an officer of some importance. The average dogface in our own battalions found it hard enough to distinguish an Expert Consultant from a bona fide officer. The confused villagers doubtless believed he was at least a General; and he made no effort to disillusion them.

Moreover, Bates and his colleagues in ALSOS had to get to their intelligence objectives or "targets" as quickly as possible. If they had not, records might have been burned and equipment destroyed under instructions from Berlin. Or they might have been tossed into hopeless confusion and damaged, either in thoughtless exuberation or in reprisals by displaced personnel. The people our investigators wanted to see would have escaped or would have had time to collect their thoughts and plan systematic falsehoods to put us on futile clues. Consequently ALSOS was organized so that it could operate in self-contained units of civilian and military personnel with their own transportation and with credentials that would provide adequate mobility.

The idea of sending small groups of top-level scientists and engineers on intelligence missions to Europe had crystallized in the War Department in the fall of 1943, months before Bates became a figure in the municipal Government of the Continent, and before OFS was in a position to participate actively through loan of its personnel. Such operations would have to be carried out primarily under Army jurisdiction in the theater; but the subjects on which information about German progress was to be sought were also of critical interest to the Navy and to OSRD.

Ordinary technical intelligence deals with the characteristics and performance of equipment. American military investigators have had long experience in this type of work. But there was some uncertainty as to what would prove the most effective procedure for gathering scientific intelligence. In a technological war information about the enemy's research and development well in advance of the translation of new ideas into large-scale production of more devastating weapons is obviously a first line of defense. It gives us time to produce suitable countermeasures, organize our offensives to interfere with the enemy's research, or even perhaps to beat him to the punch with the very same weapons because our production capacity is greater and we can turn the progress of his science quickly to our own advantage. Consequently the Office of the Secretary of War established an ALSOS Mission as a co-operative venture of the War Department, G-2, General Groves's Office, the Army Service Forces, the Navy, and OSRD. Its primary purpose was to find out the extent of truth behind Hitler's constant boasts of new and more terrible weapons, particularly to learn what progress the Nazis had made in harnessing nuclear energy.

When American Divisions had a firm foothold in Italy and it was possible to take into custody and question scientists, production engineers, and other personnel who had worked under the domination of the Nazis, ALSOS sent a team of American military men and scientists to Rome to explore methods of procuring this type of intelligence and to determine particularly whether the Nazi war machine had made some of its most significant secrets available to its partners in the Axis. Colonel Boris T. Pash was the military leader of the group; OSRD furnished Drs. J. R. Johnson, James Fisk, and Lieutenant Colonel Will Allis; the Navy sent Lieutenant Bruce Olds; and General Groves's Office supplied Major R. R. Furman.

This group returned in February 1944 and the War Department took up with Dr. Bush the possibility of extending such a project on a larger scale to follow up the invasion of Europe. It had become clear that the material encountered by the investigators would be almost meaningless except to scientific people of the highest qualifications. No one knew how long the war would last after our first landings on the Continent and we needed long-range intelligence if we were to devise effective countermeasures to the secret weapons of the Nazis before they were first used against us. The desirability of such a mission was recognized by everyone concerned. It was formally placed in charge of the Assistant Chief of Staff, G-2, again as an Army-Navy-OSRD project. The general plan was to have the activity directed jointly by a military chief (officer from G-2) and a civilian scientific chief who would produce the civilian technical staff as needed and would counsel the military chief on specific scientific objectives. An Advisory Committee, consisting of the Assistant Chief of Staff (AC/S), the Chief of the Office of Naval Intelligence (ONI), the Chief of the Army Service Forces (ASF), and the Director of OSRD, was appointed to supervise the project. They named deputies to serve on the committee — Colonel C. P. Nicholas, Policy and Planning Division, G-2, for AC/S; Captain W. A. Heard for ONI; Colonel E. W. Gruhn for ASF; and Dr. Waterman for OSRD.

Colonel Pash was asked to continue as military chief of this reconstituted ALSOS Mission because of the capable way in which he had handled the earlier venture in Italy. A complement of officers and enlisted men from various branches of the Services were selected to work with him, some of them as military investigators or interpreters and some in administration.[1] In order to guarantee necessary mobility the mission was to have its own transportation, billeting, and other facilities and was to operate essentially as an autonomous body in the theater.

Dr. Samuel A. Goudsmit, internationally known nuclear physicist from the faculty of the University of Michigan, was chosen as scientific chief to work with Colonel Pash. He had just returned from five months in England for the Radiation Laboratory and had earlier traveled extensively on the Continent. As a former resident of Holland he had become thoroughly familiar with the pertinent languages and foreign institutions of learning. ALSOS would look to Dr. Goudsmit in co-operation with OSRD for authoritative advice on all scientific aspects of the work, and additional civilian personnel was to be supplied primarily through the Office of Field Service at his request.

A strong delegation from the Navy was added under the leadership of Commodore H. A. Schade. Later, when the Navy set up its own technical intelligence program in Europe this was withdrawn, and ALSOS continued as an Army-OSRD activity, maintaining liaison, of course, with the Navy both in the field and in Washington. Since the Air Forces were planning to establish a similar mission on their own account they declined the invitation to add personnel.

In ALSOS headquarters at the Pentagon Dr. Walter F. Colby, colleague of Goudsmit in physics at Michigan, provided continuous scientific liaison and worked closely with Major Howard J. Osborn, alert and efficient young chemical engineer who was an officer the OFS men could always count on to straighten out tangles and cut red tape.

When the chiefs of the mission left to establish operating headquarters in ETO it was anticipated that eventually representatives from almost all the Divisions of OSRD would be attached to ALSOS. The number needed and the order in which they would be called would, of course, be determined by the progress of our forces in capturing critical areas. In order to avoid unnecessary delays in dispatching the men, OFS had about thirty of them partially processed to stand by for a call from Europe. Experience showed, however, that

---

[1] Organizational and administrative aspects of the mission were ably handled by Colonel W. M. Adams.

the rapidity with which ALSOS investigators had to move made administration of more than a small group in the theater too cumbersome. Preoccupation with matters relating to nuclear research, biological warfare, rockets and jet propulsion, proximity fuzes, and radar prevented concentrating much attention on other aspects of German research. Moreover, the number of intelligence missions under various auspices increased geometrically after D-Day in Normandy. Several of them were authorized to investigate scientific and technological matters. Goudsmit felt that these other groups might be able to cover Nazi progress in less critical subjects adequately. Consequently, the ALSOS team in the field was never a large organization. Men were attached to it for short periods and for specific purposes. When they had gathered the information wanted they returned at once to exploit it as quickly as possible in our laboratories and war plants.

After the armies had liberated a large part of France but had not yet broken into the Nazi homeland, the situation was much as it had been in Italy. French scientists and technical men were available. French factories that had been engaged in war production under the German invader were in our hands. Thousands of Frenchmen and displaced slave laborers from other countries were milling around, and the underground was vigorously helping us to turn our advances into a rout. We knew that the Germans had made use of production facilities in France. It was doubtful, however, that they had disclosed their research to conquered Frenchmen; but at least we might be able to find in work they had parceled out to the French factories clues about the things they were studying most energetically.

Dr. W. A. Noyes, eminent chemist and Chief of Division 10, who had studied and lived in France for some time, went over to Paris as an ALSOS investigator to look into these possibilities. He reported that the Germans had used the French scientists only in minor ways and that we could not expect to get much useful information until we could set foot on German soil ourselves. He also concluded from conversations with the French that the Germans were loath to use poison gas. He reasoned that they probably had significant developments in this field but would recognize that we must have also. They would therefore be afraid of reprisals. The soundness of Noyes's deduction was amply demonstrated later when our investigators found large quantities of German gas munitions and uncovered secret formulas of new and far more deadly poison gases than had been used in World War I.

In these early days of ALSOS operations when targets suddenly became available more rapidly than had been expected, there was insufficient time to secure scientists from the United States. An appeal to Mr. Archambault brought prompt response and staff members of the London mission were dispatched to join Goudsmit in the exploitation of targets of prime significance.

The Allies were most eager to capture the launching sites of the V-1 and V-2 that had created such consternation in Britain, to locate the factories where these missiles were produced, and to obtain with the greatest dispatch what information we could about German gains in aerodynamics, jet propulsion, and rocket design. These were branches of science and technology in which the Nazis had made spectacular progress and Hitler had threatened to use even more diabolical weapons of the same sort. Dr. C. N. Hickman, physicist from Bell Laboratories, and Dr. C. C. Lauritsen, physicist from the faculty of California Institute of Technology, both leaders in Division 3 rocket development, examined many of the critical localities in France and the Low Countries. In the course of his sleuthing Hickman went into an underground iron mine near Verdun which had been converted into a V-1 factory. A mile and a half from the entrance was a large plant that had operated in three shifts of 2000 people each, mostly slave laborers, under the supervision of about 500 Germans. They were forced to walk to work and were kept on minimum rations. Hickman reported that when the success of our troops made abandonment of this factory necessary the enraged Nazis deliberately massacred scores of 14-year-old workers. Then, unable to evacuate the equipment as rapidly as they wished in the narrow tunnels, they simply dynamited the entrance and left.

The National Advisory Committee for Aeronautics also detailed a team of its top men to study German progress in aeronautics. This group consisted of Henry J. E. Reid, J. W. Ebert, C. Kemper, and R. G. Robinson. They remained in the theater for many weeks and gathered a great deal of information that has already been put to use by American engineers. One of Ebert's reports carries interesting observations on the success of the Germans in hiding their important war research activities. Near Braunschweig he visited an aerodynamics plant and high-speed wind tunnel partially concealed in the woods. This was a center employing nearly 2000. The plant was heavily camouflaged and covered with artificial trees. Over the wind tunnel the Nazis had constructed a concrete platform, coated it with soil, and planted live shrubs and trees. The absence of bomb craters was convincing proof that Allied airmen had missed at least this one important target.

Bates was the first of three metallurgists attached to ALSOS. He was joined in the theater by Dr. Robert F. Mehl, faculty member of Carnegie Institute of Technology, who had gone over with a team of technical men from industry under an understanding that he would join ALSOS for at least part of his time. Later when Bates was called back for critical work in the development laboratories he was replaced by Dr. S. L. Hoyt of Battelle Memorial Institute. Hoyt commented that his investigations uncovered three or four items, any one of which would well repay the time and expense of sending him to Europe. This is readily understood when one remembers that scientific research is extremely fluid and essentially international in character except in war. The stupendous American war production would have been impossible without the use of hard carbide cutting tools that came directly from earlier German research. American airplanes were also constructed in no small degree from alloys originating in German laboratories.

When our Armies had broken across the Rhine and thousands of targets opened simultaneously, a substantial number of scientists were added to the mission. It was then necessary to furnish civilian aid in the technical administration of ALSOS, and Dr. Edwin C. Kemble, physicist from Harvard University, went over to serve as assistant scientific chief and to provide continuity of co-ordination in the headquarters. By the time he arrived ALSOS was in Paris. Burnham Kelly, who had been a Technical Aide in Division 2, also went to Paris as aide to the scientific chief. Subsidiary headquarters were set up at several places in Germany as the front lines swept westward and eventually the mission was centered at Heidelberg.

In November 1944 ALSOS men were in Strasbourg as soon as it fell and found that the Nazis had made no worth-while progress on an atomic bomb. Having been brilliantly successful in securing information we wanted about German work in nuclear physics, the ALSOS team could thereafter devote more attention to enemy developments in such varied fields as subsonic and supersonic air travel, gas turbines, precision optics, malaria research, radar, proximity fuzes, and biological warfare. The reports of ALSOS investigators cover a substantial part of the total record of German scientific progress. Among the achievements of ALSOS was the capture of documents that gave a complete picture of the organization of German science during the war. For obvious reasons, the ways in which Sam Goudsmit's field men went about to secure the information they sought cannot be disclosed. They are part of the rapidly developing doctrines of scientific intelligence that must be regarded as military secrets.[2]

While the Germans had made striking progress in certain fields they were well behind us in penicillin and atabrine research, in radar and radar countermeasures, and in many other fields. There was no general harnessing of scientific manpower for war purposes, and their fundamental research fell off both in quality and quantity during the war years. Many German scientists reported that there had been little co-operation between various branches of the Nazi armed forces in military applications of science and technology. The decadence of German science is further seen in the distinction that arose between "German physics" and "Jewish physics." This perfidious doctrine was adopted by some of the Nazi scientists themselves so fanatically that when a professor of the Kaiser Wilhelm Institute used the word "relativity" in a lecture of Stockholm, he was threatened with the loss of his job.

Dr. P. Osenberg, Director of the *Reichsforschungsrat,* over-all research agency of the Nazi Government, told his ALSOS questioners that up to 1942 nearly a third of the German scientists had been withdrawn for military service. Late in 1943, 40 per cent of the laboratories, universities, and technical schools were without war projects because the German High Command had counted on blitz victories. Not until 1944 did they realize the necessity of concentrating on research and development for military purposes. Then they recalled a large number

---

[2] Consequently an OSRD wag suggested that the title of this chapter should have been — "Sam's Scientific Sleuths Seize Axis Secrets — Sh–h–h!"

of scientists from the fighting units and attempted to rectify the error. But it was too late.

Fortunately our advance was so rapid that instructions of the Nazi High Command to destroy all important documents relating to research were not fully carried out. In many instances the Germans frantically tried to dispose of the material by burying it in abandoned mines and throwing it into wells. Following up a series of clues, Dr. Louis F. Fieser, distinguished chemist of Harvard University, tried to locate the entire library of the German Chemical Society, which was reported to have been hidden in a potash mine. During the search he stumbled upon a sizable cache of small firearms in another mine. Apparently they had been stored there in the hope of a postwar coup by the Nazi underground. But Fieser's prompt tip brought our troops to the site and the secret hoard was seized.

Development of the proximity fuze had been a closely guarded secret even after its first use in combat. We knew that if the Germans had a similar device in production, it could prove horribly lethal to our troops. Moreover, even if the Germans had not yet perfected such fuzes to the stage of an early large-scale use against us but had given the basic secrets to the Japanese, our men might yet face this weapon in the Pacific. Dr. Edward O. Salant, physicist from the Applied Physics Laboratory of Johns Hopkins, went over to probe Nazi progress in this direction. He was later joined by W. E. Tolles of the Airborne Instruments Laboratory and then by Dr. C. R. Larkin, E. P. Ertsgaard, C. C. Klick, and J. D. Sterrett, Jr., sent out by OFS on loan to the Signal Corps in connection with our own use of such fuzes. Whereas ALSOS had become largely an Army show, this group was known as "Salant's circus" because they were all over the theater working closely with the Navy, the Air Forces, the British, and the French. They reported that the Nazis had more than a dozen projects for development of proximity fuzes. There were no models in service, however, and none in mass production. Even if they had given the Japanese their latest information about this device, there was little danger that they could produce it in quantity in time to create a serious hazard to the Pacific forces.

One ALSOS scientist may have been responsible for the Army's success in capturing the major part of the German supply of radium.

Dr. C. P. Smyth, physical chemist of Princeton University and brother of the man who wrote the Smyth report on atomic energy, got on the trail of this invaluable prize and spent several days following clues. They pointed to a certain community as its probable location. Unable to follow it to that town, Smyth notified ALSOS headquarters at once. Within a short time American military authorities had the radium.

Colonel Pash gained an enviable reputation for the speed with which he operated and his adroitness. An ALSOS group was one of the first American units to enter Paris. It had cut across to join up with a French Armored Division and went in just behind the first five French vehicles to enter the capital city. Although turned back four times by sniper fire, the team took its first target that same day. On one occasion before V-E Day, Pash took two officers and two enlisted men with him up over a mountain trail in Bavaria to examine targets in a small village. They were approached by a German officer who told the Colonel that 700 German troops were in the surrounding hills anxious to surrender. Recognizing the disadvantage in numbers and the danger that this placed him in, Colonel Pash replied that appropriate surrender arrangements could be made the following morning. He turned quickly to his own men and gave them orders, supposedly for the disposition of substantial units of his own "army" near by. As soon as the German had retired, Colonel Pash and his men grabbed the information they wanted and cleared out. They were the only element of the American Armed Forces within miles. They did not return to accept the mass surrender; but the bluff gave them time to accomplish their purpose.

In the closing stages of the war the job of ALSOS became primarily one of sifting through documents. The dramatic action of seizing an objective before its value for exploitation was lost had to be replaced by the less glamorous, sedentary tasks of translating and correlating the vast quantity of material the mission had gathered.[3] For this function OFS recruited a number of scientists who had no previous affiliation with OSRD research and development activities but whose familiarity with the languages, the geography, and the people was a useful adjunct to comprehensive knowledge in their individual fields of specialization.

[3] Not including the slightly bomb-damaged Egyptian mummy offered to Dr. Carl Baumann and Miss Mary Bohan, secretary of the Mission, at the ruins of a museum in Berlin.

THE ALSOS MISSION

(Only the civilian participants who held affiliations with OFS, even tenuous ones, are listed)

Scientific Chief

Samuel A. Goudsmit

Advisory Committee	Washington Liaison
Alan T. Waterman	Walter F. Colby
John E. Burchard	Charles F. Meyer
	Richard A. Bloomfield

Assistant Scientific Chief

Edwin C. Kemble

Technical Aide

Burnham Kelly

Investigators

A. Allan Bates	John R. Johnson	George A. Richter
Carl Baumann	Carlton Kemper	Howard P. Robertson
Richard A. Beth	W. B. Klemperer	Russell G. Robinson
Walker Bleakney	Clifford C. Klick	Edward O. Salant
Wallace R. Brode	Gerald P. Kuiper	James K. Senior
John W. Ebert, Jr.	James A. Lane	Harold R. Shaw
Edwin P. Ertsgaard	Charles R. Larkin	Thomas K. Sherwood
Louis F. Fieser	Charles C. Lauritsen	Charles R. Smyth
James R. Fisk	Mark A. May	John D. Sterrett, Jr.
Ralph W. Helmkamp	Robert F. Mehl	Walter E. Tolles
Clarence N. Hickman	Pierre Mertz	Peter Van de Kamp
Thorfin Hogness	W. A. Noyes	H. S. Van Klooster
Samuel L. Hoyt	Elwood C. Pierce	Gregory H. Wannier
H. Thomas Johnson	Hans Reese	F. A. C. Wardenburg, Jr.
	Henry J. E. Reid	

Consultants

Roger Adams	L. Don Leet	Edward L. Moreland
Karl T. Compton	Alfred H. Loomis	Carroll L. Wilson

In the fall and winter of 1944 the Navy developed a plan for pursuing its interests in various kinds of intelligence on scientific, technological, and technical matters, and established a Navy Technical Mission in Europe (NavTechMisEu). This was placed under the supervision of Commodore Schade. NavTechMisEu soon set up a series of head-quarters in England and on the Continent and acquired facilities so that it could operate with the same freedom enjoyed by ALSOS, but over a much larger territory and with more personnel. During the first part of its stay in Paris the ALSOS mission had quarters generously provided by the Navy.

Although ALSOS and NavTechMisEu were under entirely separate auspices, continuing liaison was maintained between these two organizations. Dr. Wallace R. Brode, chemist who had participated in early ALSOS missions on loan from the London office and was later head of the Paris OSRD office, rejoined ALSOS for the purpose of providing this contact with the Navy.

Late in the following summer the Curriculum Standards Division in the Bureau of Naval Personnel asked OFS for two competent senior psychologists who could investigate German methods of selecting and training military personnel. Through the co-operation of OSRD's Applied Psychology Panel, Drs. H. L. Ansbacher and Harold A. Gulliksen were assigned to this duty. They left with Lieutenant Commander D. D. Feder of the Curriculum Division early in August and were attached to NavTechMisEu for administrative purposes. The party conferred with many military psychologists of both British and German Armed Forces, and located the entire files and some training apparatus of the German Baltic Naval Selection Center. They did not confine their activities, however, to tests and training aids used by the military, but secured information also on techniques the Germans developed in industrial psychology.

OFS also contributed to the work of NavTechMisEu the services of Dr. J. H. Wayland, physicist from the rocket laboratories at California Institute of Technology. He left Washington at the beginning of August and spent one month in England studying British advances in underwater ballistics and the design of British equipment for launching large projectiles into water to simulate aircraft drops. He also examined German technical documents that were accumulated earlier by intelligence teams and conferred with members of these groups about the best ways for exploiting Nazi progress in underwater ballistics. The climax of his mission was a ten-day tour of German naval establishments and research centers.

OFS participated in one other extensive intelligence operation in the European theater. This was through the Technical Industrial Intelligence Committee (TIIC), organized in October 1944 at the direction of the Joint Intelligence Committee of the Joint Chiefs of Staff. This policy-making and planning group consisted of representatives of eight agencies including intelligence branches of the Army, Navy, and Air Forces, the Federal Economic Administration (FEA), Office of Strategic Services (OSS), War Production Board (WPB), State Department, and OSRD. Its function was to channel American requests for information about the technological advances of the Nazis, their production tricks, and engineering "know-how" that might help American industry in the continuing war with Japan and in the postwar period.

It is difficult to draw sharp distinctions between this type of engineering and production information (technical industrial intelligence), scientific research and development in advance of production (scientific intelligence), and information about the performance and use of the end products (military technical intelligence). Clues uncovered in examination of any one of these phases of German progress might well point the way for important investigations in other phases. Bush felt that technical industrial intelligence *per se* was beyond the primary interests of OSRD in research and development. Nevertheless, he believed it important for OSRD to contribute to and maintain close liaison with this activity and appointed Dr. Thiesmeyer as the OSRD member of TIIC.

Although it had not been designed as an operating agency with funds and authority to dispatch personnel overseas, TIIC did have the responsibility for finding investigators and arranging for them to hold military appointments as civilian specialists for overseas service. The agencies represented were not equally experienced in processing civilian personnel. With the war rushing to a conclusion in Germany it was obvious that thousands of critical targets would become available at any moment. In order to procure an adequate number of specialists from science, industry, and Government and place them in enemy territory in time to be effective, the processing would have to be centralized in one office. The OFS experience in converting civilian scientists into military field men aided TIIC to develop a processing unit and to design simplified procedures quickly. FEA was asked to finance and operate the necessary administrative facilities in Washington and overseas under general supervision of TIIC. In a few months more than 500 of America's top-notch technical men were gathered into TIIC teams and were rapidly acquiring firsthand knowledge of Germany's industrial potentials.

These TIIC investigators ferreted out the secrets of Nazi scientists and engineers in solving problems in the production of synthetic rubber that had stumped American specialists. These were swiftly applied in our own war production against Japan. American industry will also benefit enormously in the years to come from the vast amount of technological data TIIC investigators gleaned. The progress of the Germans in certain fields of hydrocarbon research, in synthetics and plastics, in metallurgy and machine tools, and in the many-faceted chemicals and textile industries was remarkable but not unexpected. It is now available to our industrialists through the Department of Commerce, which is arranging for publication of TIIC reports as rapidly as they are declassified.

Through arrangements made by OFS several OSRD men were made available to TIIC as investigators — Dr. Robert F. Mehl in metallurgy, Dr. Pierre Mertz in guided missiles, Dr. George A. Richter of Eastman Kodak in cellulose chemistry, and Dr. George A. Carden of CMR in antimalarial drugs.

If TIIC had been set up as was ALSOS within a military organization and with its own facilities so that it could operate more or less independently, its whole program would have proceeded with greater dispatch. No one can tell how much more information might have been procured. TIIC was, however, merely the American co-ordinating unit for a combined British and American intelligence agency established in England by the Combined Intelligence Committee under the Combined Chiefs of Staff. This was known as the Combined Intelligence Objectives Subcommittee (CIOS). It consisted of appropriate

British and American military and civilian agencies, including OSRD. This meant that TIIC investigators were really CIOS men. They had to go through London and follow more elaborate channels than did the members of other intelligence teams operating in ETO. They were joined by similar groups selected from British science and industry, and the field teams operated on a combined basis, their reports being made freely available to authorized personnel in both countries.

In the early days of CIOS, as in the early days of ALSOS, the availability of OSRD scientists in London was a distinct advantage, and many of the first CIOS reports were written by OSRD men. In the theater, where relations are always less formal, members of one team were frequently loaned to another, and heterogeneous groups went out to investigate a particular target. In this way ALSOS likewise contributed heavily at times to the work of CIOS. Differences in auspices were almost forgotten in the common goal of getting as much information as possible for the benefit of the Allied cause.

As vast areas of Germany were opened to American intelligence and a multiplicity of targets suddenly fell into our hands, there was much more to be done than could be covered by any single agency. A large number of separate groups with overlapping directives began operating in parallel, all under G-2 in the Supreme Headquarters, Allied Expeditionary Forces (SHAEF). In addition to TIIC, NavTechMisEu, and ALSOS, there was an extensive Army Service Forces technical intelligence organization, and later one set up by the Air Forces. There was also the British Bombing Research Mission and its American counterpart, the U.S. Strategic Bombing Survey. An early attempt to provide co-ordination between these groups was creation of a Scientific Intelligence Advisory Section in G-2 SHAEF, composed of the heads of the various major intelligence groups. Goudsmit represented ALSOS in this body.

The overlapping of directives appeared superficially to be a great waste and to encourage duplication. Probably in many cases it did. But it permitted a scientist who happened to be the first man on the scene at a large factory, for example, to learn what he could about processes and production while he investigated the research laboratory — that is, to pick up technical industrial information while it was fresh, even though his main purpose was scientific intelligence. Eventually it would get to the right parties. He could not tell whether or not another team would seek out the same target, or whether the information would still be available when they did. This situation led to a great deal of confusion because each group grabbed everything it could while the getting was good, knowing that the total number of investigators in Germany was inadequate to cover all aspects of the technical progress such an industrialized nation had made in a dozen years. The final capitulation had come too suddenly and targets would deteriorate rapidly. They had to be exploited at once. Consequently, the overlapping authority of the many intelligence teams was in reality an advantage to our side.

Some time after V-E Day it became apparent that the most important work of ALSOS had been completed. There were still mopping-up expeditions to cover minor fields for which there had not been time earlier, and there was the stupendous task of translating captured documents. It was clear that much of the work of TIIC could be done in the post-hostilities interval when its investigators settled down in industrial areas and made exhaustive examinations of production records, plant processes, and trade information. The CIOS directive was broad enough to include intelligence in economics, sociology, government, and education, and full exploitation of these fields would require many months. Some of the NDRC Divisions were disappointed that their special interests had not been more intensively covered by ALSOS. They were still anxious to procure information in the fields of their competence. There was, therefore, a decided question as to the future of ALSOS and the extent to which OSRD should continue to send men eastward for intelligence work.

When Waterman left for the Pacific in the spring of 1945, Burchard had become Acting Deputy Chief of OFS and served as Waterman's alternate on the Advisory Committee of ALSOS. In August he left for a survey of the intelligence situation in Europe to determine the future course of OSRD participation in ALSOS and to advise on the monumental problem of correlating all the significant information in vast quantities of documents that were now in so many different Allied hands. In the midst of this study Japan threw in the sponge, and Bush ordered immediate further demobilization of OSRD. On Burchard's recommendation, however, he approved supplying ALSOS with additional scientists for a few weeks, primarily for the purpose of translating documents, and ALSOS continued to operate until October.

On this mission Burchard had traveled at high levels, had conferred with top officials in England, France, and Germany, and devoted himself to major questions of policy. On the return trip he discovered that he had no priority beyond New York. Having been a VIP [4] for thirty days, he stood all the way to Washington in a crowded coach so that he could report to Army bigwigs in the Pentagon the next day.

Long before the Japanese surrender, plans were made for similar intelligence investigations in Japan and China. It was generally suspected that the Japanese were not as far advanced either in science or technology as were the Germans. Nevertheless, it was known that in a few fields their scientific men had done outstanding work in the prewar years. We wanted to know the extent to which Japanese science had been mobilized behind the war effort. Elaborate plans were drawn for a co-ordinated military, technological, and scientific intelligence effort. OSRD was again asked to supply advice on scientific aspects of this venture and to locate scientists who could become effective investigators. The number of men who combined high scientific stature with a knowledge of Japanese language and customs was exceedingly small, and it seemed doubtful that this Pacific venture would approach the scale of ALSOS.

Dr. L. Don Leet, eminent seismologist of Harvard University, who had lived in Japan, and his assistant, Miss Mary P. Collins, were provided by OFS as consultants to G-2. Late in July Leet left for Manila to confer with officers about implementing plans designed in Washington. MacArthur had placed responsibility for co-ordination of all intelligence activities in the Pacific theater under Major General G. A. Willoughby, AC/S, G-2, and scientific intelligence was to be under the supervision of Brigadier General E. R. Thorpe.

Soon after Leet's arrival the strong possibility that Japan was near the breaking point became clear in the theater. It was therefore urgent that a system of exploiting scientific intelligence targets be set up for immediate operation. When Leet left Manila on Sunday, August 12, for further conferences in Washington, plans had been drawn for a small

[4] Very Important Person.

team of OSRD scientists already in the theater to move into Japan along with MacArthur's first troops and proceed at once to the highest-priority targets. It was felt that this group could probably cover the most significant matters in approximately a month and that thereafter further intelligence exploitation of Japan could be carried forward by the War and Navy Departments almost without help from OSRD.

Less than forty-eight hours later Japan suddenly acknowledged its defeat and the plan was put into effect. Dr. Edward L. Moreland, Executive Officer of NDRC, who was in the theater as a special advisor to MacArthur, led to Japan a group consisting of Dr. Stephenson of OFS; David Griggs and Drs. Edwin G. Schneider and Andrew Long-acre, Advisory Specialists to the Far East Air Force; and Dr. Luis Alvarez, nuclear physicist who was then located on Saipan. Dr. Compton had arrived in the theater a few days before V-J to head OSRD's most comprehensive mission in the Pacific. He accompanied the party to Tokyo and returned to Washington a few weeks ahead of the rest of the men.

Compton reported that Japanese science had been poorly organized for war purposes. Many of Nippon's most outstanding research men had been educated in the United States. The Japanese High Command, fearful that this would influence their loyalty, did not give them high responsibilities in war work. The most important secrets were parceled out in such a way that men were commonly asked to work on components of a piece of gear without knowing the nature of its other components, or its intended use. In general, the Japanese were decidedly behind us in technological developments. They had made some progress in the critical field of nuclear energy; but apparently this was not directed toward its use in explosives. Their work had been aimed at developing atomic energy as a source of industrial power. There were such violent jealousies between the Japanese Army and Navy that joint responsibility for research, so common in America's war effort, was impossible. It was also apparent that the Germans had not shared their best secrets with this eastern end of the Axis, although they had aided Japan in training its military units. Late in the war they had attempted to compensate for this mistake by supplying the Japanese with some information about their rockets, guided missiles, and radar.

*   *   *

Compelling evidence of what the Allies accomplished in developing a partnership between civilian science and military users of its products is seen in the experience of the enemy, who made no similar effort. Prominent among the papers brought back by Goudsmit was a report by a leading German physicist on the relation of German science to the war effort. "In my opinion," he declared, "German physics has produced much less in this war than its quality and quantity would have led one to believe." At the war's end he attributed the eventual scientific defeat of the Germans to lack of a central leadership. Decisions about the acceptance or rejection of research projects in physics for military purposes "depended completely on accident. . . . The refusal to stop projects, the continuation of which had lost its essential value, was one of the greatest faults. . . . Liaison between industry and the Armed Forces was not close enough. . . . A roster of all German physicists was not in existence; consequently a perspective of the available forces could not be obtained. . . . The use of physicists in militarily unimportant places must be considered as a monstrosity. . . .

"The final result of all these considerations is very depressing for Germany. We have lost the war of the laboratories despite all the good initial conditions, particularly the great talent of the German people for physics research . . . the principal reason lies in the lack of a clear organization and in the erroneous selection of organizers according to political instead of to objective points of view."

America did not thus fail.

CHAPTER XI

ANALYSTS OF AIR ATTACK

SELECTING BOMBS AND FUZES

Hit THE right targets, at the right time, in the right way, at the right places, and with enough of the right weapons. This is the dream of every bomber crew and of every officer who plans a strategic or a tactical air strike. The goal is perfection — one raid to do the job. But the factors of weather, performance of equipment and of personnel, enemy resistance, and physical vulnerability of the target are so variable that such precision is virtually unattainable. It is no more likely that the average bombardier, squadron, or mission will use just the correct combination of time, location, tactics, and weapons to make a perfect score than it is that the average bowler will make twelve strikes in succession.

The planning of a bombing mission is clearly an exceedingly complex operation and it calls for many kinds of information and for special technical counsel. The natural tendency of a scientist is to control all factors that might influence his experiments as nearly as possible. Every bombing raid is essentially a large-scale experiment. Consequently the civilian specialists who helped guide the planning of our air offensives perpetually urged greater control in the selection of targets, aiming points, tactics, and weapons. And their postraid analyses proved repeatedly that the end results were measurably more effective in raids where this was done.

Decision as to the right time for an attack is influenced by the use the enemy makes of the target, its relation to the whole of his economic and military program, and the relative importance of that single objective in the progress of the war. Sufficient evidence on this point comes from the testimony of many captured German officials and commanding officers that the crippling effects of our assault on Nazi transportation and oil were more decisive in the final result than was any other part of our strategic bombing. They claimed we would have shortened the war had we started after their refineries and railroads sooner.

Selection of the right target is the business of military planners, but they are more confident of their decisions if they have advice from economists and psychologists as well as reports from their intelligence men. Thorough analysis by structural engineers, physicists, plant-process engineers, and architects may be necessary to locate the most vulnerable spot in a major war plant and thus determine the correct aiming point.

Selecting the right weapon is likewise a job for experts. There is always a question whether bombs carrying only an explosive charge or a mixture of explosive and incendiary bombs will produce the greatest damage to a particular structure or area. If it is concluded that a combination of the two will bring optimum results, there is still the problem of the relative amount of each to be included in the bomb load. This will be influenced not only by the individual potency of the incendiary and the high explosive, but also by climatic conditions, by the inflammability of materials that predominate in construction of the target, by the arrangement of electric and gas lines whose disruption by explosion might create fires, and, of course, by the effectiveness of the enemy in extinguishing fires. There are also all sorts of questions about the correct setting of fuzes. Should they penetrate through a story or two before going off, or should they go completely to the ground and then detonate? Or should the bombs have proximity fuzes so they will burst at some carefully regulated distance away from the target and scatter their fragments over a larger area?

The mass of information that has to be channeled to those responsible for ultimate plans is prodigious. It comes from many sources. Some of it represents the work of mathematicians. From the geometry of the target and of the attacking force, the characteristics of the weapons to be used and the intended tactics, they calculate the probability of hits within a particular area and apply the theory of error to these calculations. Some data come from experimental tests in the laboratories, ordnance plants, and proving grounds. These tests are designed not only to reveal the characteristics of the weapons themselves but also to yield experimental results on their effectiveness against objectives prepared to simulate the conditions expected in an enemy target. Some information comes from reconnaissance photographs taken before the raid; and some from analysis of actual damage produced in a previous raid on the same target or on some similar one.

The need for groups of civilian specialists — experts on bombs and fuzes, structural engineers and architects, and men with an analytical quality of mind such as is possessed by the mathematician, the lawyer, or the chess player — to work at the headquarters of each Air Force, providing advice on the many complicated items that should be taken into consideration in day-to-day missions against myriad single objectives, was felt early in the war and led to rapid expansion of Colonel Leach's Operations Analysis Division. Aid in the proper selection of bombs and fuzes was one of the important functions of the Air Force Operational Research Sections. The success of our air power, deriving in no small way from the work of these groups, gave rise to persistent demands that OSRD train and make available additional manpower to strengthen these Sections or create new ones.

From the scientists' viewpoint it was unfortunate that often recommendations that went out from the planners to the operating squadrons were not followed. Many times the analysts of Air Force Headquarters who had painstakingly prepared recommendations calling for the exclusive use of a certain type of bomb were disappointed to discover from postraid reconnaissance photos that the strike had been executed according to their plan, except that a mixture of six different bombs was used and the whole pattern landed hundreds of yards from the target! Efforts to control the experiment had failed completely. When this sort of thing happened, the patient study by top-flight experts of an ORS or a station like Princes Risborough, the exhaustive tests in laboratories and proving grounds, the arduous gathering of intelligence, and the meticulous structural analysis of the target that had been the basis for such recommendations seemed utterly futile. Furthermore, how could one hope to assess the damage done in a raid by one type of bomb, if it was masked by the effects of another?

No doubt there were times when total disregard of the recommendations was a matter of the ignorance, the whims, or just the plain cussedness of officers or crews who preferred to follow rule-of-thumb methods or to experiment in their own unscientific way. There were many who subscribed to the erroneous principle that the quickest way to demoralize an enemy is to hit him "with everything in the book," or that a bomb four times as big will wreak exactly four times as much havoc.

On the other hand, there were also many times when the recommendations simply could not be followed because of problems in supply, in maintenance, or in the behavior of the enemy. It would be useless, for example, to recommend 500-pound general-purpose bombs if the squadron only had 200-pound or 1000-pound missiles on hand at the scheduled time for the raid. And, in any case, the lethal eggs might have to be released far from the proposed aiming points because the intensity of enemy flak and fighter opposition broke up the tight formations. These were factors which the analysts could neither anticipate nor control.

Not long after creation of the Office of Field Service requests from the various Operational Research Sections of the Air Forces began to come in. The first was from ORS of the Tactical Ninth Air Force in Europe. Dr. Francis L. Yost, physicist who had been a Technical Aide in Division 17, NDRC, and Dr. John F. Hutzenlaub, physicist from M.I.T., were sent to work with this Section in the early spring of 1944. The nature of their work is outlined in a letter from Yost: —

"One of the duties assigned to the Operational Research Section was to keep a careful check on all visual bombing operations and to report at intervals on the accuracy and the general effectiveness with which bombs have been laid down on pin-point and other types of targets. This phase of the work deals only with accuracy as such and does not involve damage assessment. . . .

"Strike-attack photos for each aiming operation are studied to get the following data: the percentage of bombs identified within circles of 500 ft., 1000 ft. and 2000 ft. radii concentric with a pin-point aiming point; the distance of the first bomb from the aiming point (if the first bomb can be identified); the dimensions of the bomb pattern; the radial error and the range and deflection errors of the operations. . . .

"These data are also the sort which from time to time have been sent back to OSRD from the different theaters for bombing studies, particularly by the Applied Mathematics Panel. . . . The work itself requires mainly accuracy, common sense and an analytical frame of mind; it is time-consuming and exacting. Recently . . . we have been training a group of men to assess the photos. . . ."

Hutzenlaub reported that on the whole the claims of American pilots on their return from a mission were well substantiated by later checking against the photographs taken on reconnaissance flights. He felt that the work he and Yost had done for the ORS had been effective in helping to establish an evaluation method for checking strategic bombing.

In June 1944 Morris Atkin, structural engineer trained in the OFS indoctrination program at Princeton, accepted an assignment with the Operational Research Section of the 11th Air Force in the Aleutians. At that time the 11th was relatively inactive and was on low priority for new equipment. Its need of a high-powered specialist was open to some question. Atkin had no illusions about the raw unpleasantness of the foggy climate that had been a constant handicap to air operations; but he recognized that at any moment a High Command decision to strike from the Aleutians might change the whole situation and make the need for a man of such special skills immediate and urgent. He was willing to gamble his own discomfort and probable inactivity against the chance to do a critical piece of work.

The Commanding General of the 11th was concerned over an apparent lack of destructive action when bombing was carried out on Arctic tundra and wanted Atkin to investigate whether peculiar or unexpected results should be anticipated because of characteristics of the ground structure. Atkin arranged tests involving the dropping on Agattu Island of various kinds of bombs equipped with different fuze combinations. Strike photographs and measurements made on the ground were used to determine the extent of damage and Atkin reported that "the ground structure does not appreciably affect expected damage. . . . If bombing damage does not come up to expectations, then more is expected of the bombs than they are capable of doing."

He was also asked to study enemy targets assigned to the 11th Air Force and to recommend the bombs and fuzes to be used against them. In October he submitted a report on Japanese targets in the Kurile Islands. He had analyzed the types to be expected, explained the methods of demolishing or neutralizing them, and worked out a list of recommended bomb loadings based in part on results obtained from other theaters concerning the lethal radius of each type of bomb.

Inasmuch as the anticipated offensive using the Aleutians as a springboard had not materialized by fall and the trend of the war in the Pacific gave little promise that it would, OFS recalled Atkin and placed him in the Joint Target Group where his technical abilities could be utilized more effectively.

Experimental work, long-range planning, and analysis of great masses of information from many operations in different theaters manifestly can not be carried out by men attached to a small operational research section located in a forward area. Pressure upon them to answer all sorts of questions that come up in hour-by-hour activities of the command makes it difficult for them even to keep up with analysis of the raids carried out by a single Air Force. They must be backed up by larger groups in rear areas or at home who can conduct more comprehensive studies in the less hurried atmosphere of a testing ground, a laboratory, or an intelligence office. This principle was recognized and followed, as we have seen, in the organization of ORG, which maintained a substantial operations research center in Washington. As the war progressed, it was also adopted by other Army and Navy groups concerned with this whole involved subject of the proper selection of weapons for aerial attack.

Theoretically, for a given target there should be an optimum amount of preinvasion bombardment from the air and from the surface. To go beyond this would not make enough difference to justify the expenditure of time and ammunition. To do less might entail unnecessarily large losses. NDD wanted to determine whether there was enough information in available battle records from the Pacific to permit statistical analysis that might yield data from which rule-of-thumb methods for calculating this optimum could be developed. The problem involved bomb and shell damage assessment, target vulnerability studies, and routine operations research. It had ramifications into casualty rates, N-P effects, psychological warfare, weapons selection, and tactics.

The reduction of an enemy strongpoint was so often accomplished by a combination of fire power from both air and ground forces and through use of so many different weapons that the task of isolating individual factors for scientific analysis seemed stupendous. Nevertheless OFS recalled Douglas A. Nettleton, mature structural engineer, from an assignment at Princes Risborough to supervise a small-scale experimental study of this problem in the Pentagon. He had been through intensive indoctrination at the Princeton Station and had learned some of the fundamentals of operations analysis. Assisted by Mrs. Margaret S. Piedem, statistician from AMP, he reported after several months that the fragmentary records did not supply the information needed for valid conclusions. The problem was too complicated to be handled by anything less than a sizable operations research group. Moreover, it would involve thorough revision in the system of keeping battle records. And the possibility of accomplishing this in the midst of war appeared hopeless. Consequently the project was abandoned.

Men assigned to an operations research center at home needed to get the practical viewpoint that came from temporary tours of duty in forward areas. It was also important that such a group have field representatives to help expedite the flow of critical data back to its analysts. Consequently a continual interchange of manpower developed between the small advanced groups in the theaters and larger groups in the United States.

Many OFS men assigned to work in bomb damage evaluation or in weapons selection had served in both places. To follow the career of each of them would be wearisome. The case of Oswald H. Thorson illustrates the varied nature of the work these men performed. He was a practicing architect in Minnesota at the beginning of the war. In preparation for an assignment with Colonel Leach's Operational Research Section in the China-Burma-India theater, he was brought into the Division 2 indoctrination program at Princeton Station. An allergy discovered shortly before he was to be sent to that area made such an overseas assignment impossible. Instead he continued on the staff of the Princeton Station for a time and was then loaned by OFS to the work of the Navy group under Commander Bitter in the Air Technical Analysis Division. He went to Princes Risborough to acquire greater familiarity with the techniques of photointerpretation as background for the analysis of Navy targets in the Pacific. While he was in England a critical need developed in the ORS of the Ninth Air Force and he spent some weeks on loan from the Navy to the Army Air Forces to meet this situation. Returning to Washington, Thorson was assigned for the balance of the war to the Joint Target Group.

In the fall of 1943 Commander Bitter was in charge of a small group of officers and civilians engaged in analysis of naval air operations, particularly attacks on shipping and shore installations in the Pacific. It was obvious that this activity would increase immensely as American forces moved westward. There would be a greater number of targets and of planes in operation, and the Navy might be called upon for certain strategic operations necessary to reduce large-scale objectives on land. Commander Bitter was therefore anxious to expand the scope of his unit, to take advantage of experience of the Air Forces in the European offensive, and of the availability of specialists from OFS. They could be procured more quickly than could an additional complement of civilians by appeal for an increase in his Table of Organization and allocation of personnel through Civil Service. But the extent and the specific directions of this expansion were not immediately clear.

Bitter was in sympathy with the view that any such organization at home should have its field representatives and the same freedom of interchange between field and home base as characterized the work of ORG. He decided to build the organization with a sizable group of officers — men who would be more welcome in forward areas and could secure the information they wanted more readily, not only in the theaters but also at home.

In the succeeding months OFS supported the growth of this activity through assignment of some twenty-five men. The first of these, and indeed the first personal-services contract employee of OFS, was Dr. W. Allen Wallis, able mathematician who became head of the Statistical Research Section of the Applied Mathematics Panel. Wallis devoted part of his time for approximately a month to consultation with Commander Bitter on techniques in statistical analysis that might be applicable to air operations. Dr. Walter O. Bartky, astronomer from the University of Chicago, came to Washington periodically on a WOC basis at the same time to confer on technical aspects of this work and to assist in recruiting additional personnel. Shortly thereafter Roy W. Jastram, economist from Stanford University who had been with the Operational Research Section of the Air Force in the Aleutians, became the first employee of OFS whose full-time services were made available to Commander Bitter. The late Dr. P. I. Wold, physicist of Union College, and Dr. Newell Gingrich of the OSRD Liaison Office spent part time helping Bitter's group to acquire technical reports from many American and British sources.

As Bitter's team expanded and it became clear that proper evaluation of targets would call for experts in fields other than mathematics, OFS added to this project Dr. James K. Hall, economist from the University of Washington; E. J. Hogan, expert in fire protection from the War Production Board; Julian D. Chase, mechanical engineer from the Smaller War Plants Corporation; Homer U. Pearce, retired engineer who had lived in Japan for many years; J. M. Pearce, radio engineer from the Applied Physics Laboratory of Johns Hopkins and specialist on V-T fuzes; several architects and engineers who had received the Princeton indoctrination in bomb damage assessment; and Marc Peter, Jr., who had headed the American work at Princes Risborough.

It was soon evident that a staff of statisticians would be needed to reduce the raw data pouring into Washington in operational reports to a form suitable for analysis and that men experienced in the techniques of operations research would be needed to guide this work. Dr. Morse was persuaded to loan several senior men from ORG for that purpose who organized a statistical and analytical subgroup and recruited additional men, including Dr. C. B. Allendoerfer, alert and forceful mathematician from Haverford College who had previously worked with ORG; Scott E. Forbush, physicist from the Department of Terrestrial Magnetism; Dr. F. A. Ficken, mathematician from the University of Tennessee; Dr. R. E. Wilson, astronomer from Mount Wilson; Dr. Norman E. Steenrod, mathematician from the University of Michigan; Dr. A. G. Steinberg, biologist from McGill University; and Robert J. Best, chemist from the Rockefeller Institute.

The work of the ATAD group thus fell into two fairly well defined categories, one calling for men to do operations research and the other for specialists in weapons selection and the evaluation of bomb damage. Some months later the personnel of the statistical analysis section were absorbed into ORG but continued to work on naval air problems under the over-all supervision and at the request of the Air Intelligence Group in ATAD.

In the fall of 1944 the interests of the Army Air Forces and of the Navy in establishing a headquarters group responsible for long-range, preraid studies to select targets for the Japanese offensive, and to evaluate the over-all damage produced in our raids, were merged in an organization known as the Joint Target Group (JTG). This was set up under the direction of Brigadier General John Sanford with Commander Bitter as Deputy Director. It consisted of four major sections: Economic Vulnerability, Physical Vulnerability, Production, and Evaluation. Like the ATAD it was a combined military and civilian organization and the major part of the personnel gathered for Bitter's project were transferred to this new and more comprehensive group.

The Joint Target Group was intended to function for the American Air Forces in the Japanese war in a fashion similar to the Princes Risborough Station for the strategic bombing of Europe. Its work would consist of two primary activities — the preparation of elaborate folders describing the targets, and assessment from photographic cover of the results of bombing missions. This would involve study of the physical plant and economic conditions surrounding each Japanese objective, as well as careful structural analysis of the target, and would lead to recommendations concerning the combinations of weapons to be used.

All of the OFS men assigned to JTG were members of the Physical Vulnerability Section. This was, in turn, subdivided into sections on statistical analysis, structural analysis, high explosives, and incendiary bombs. The over-all purposes of this Section were to study the physical characteristics of Japanese targets, recommend proper weapons for their destruction, estimate the quantity of those weapons required, and check results of the attacks against the preattack estimates. When information obtained from these studies was combined with that obtained from economic intelligence, it was possible to lay plans for the air war against Japan.

Marc Peter became general consultant to the Physical Vulnerability Section; Allendoerfer was head of the Statistical Subsection, succeeded by Dr. Carl F. Kossack, mathematician from the University of Oregon; Thorson, Claessens, and Atkin worked in the Structural Analysis Subsection; George Packer, civil engineer who had spent some months under assignment to Bitter at Princes Risborough, was an OFS representative in the high-explosives section where data obtained from bombing raids on British and European structures were applied to comparable Japanese buildings.

By February 1945 the volume of intelligence material pouring into JTG was enormous. The task of screening this, arranging for appropriate routing, speeding up methods of obtaining information from prisoners of war, and evaluating the material received called for supervision by a senior scientist. Douglas Burden, physiographer from the Museum of Natural History in New York, took over the responsibility and brought system into the chaos.

As incendiary raids on Japanese cities began, Robert M. Newhall, chemical engineer who had acquired familiarity with incendiaries during a year of work with Division 11, was added to the subsection on incendiaries. He participated in assessment of the physical damage to urban sections, including study of the effects of the atomic bomb. Eugene H. Gerry, fire-protection engineer who had spent some months at Princes Risborough with an analytical group from NDRC, became affiliated with JTG in May and participated in the work of the weapons analysis group.

In June 1945 Allendoerfer became "Co-ordinator of Research" for JTG and served as its major liaison representative on technical matters with Divisions 2 and 11 and the AMP, with Aberdeen Proving Ground and Edgewood Arsenal, with the British Ministry of Home Security and Princes Risborough, and with other activities concerned in the whole problem of bomb damage evaluation.

Once the Joint Target Group had swung into full operation it became a co-ordinating center for target information and operational reports. Its liaison with OAD was close and the members of the various ORS groups in the Pacific theater served in a sense as field representatives of JTG to feed information from daily operations back to Washington for analysis.

In the Central Pacific the Weapons Analysis Subsection of Marshall's team was also called on for considerable work in summarizing, correlating, and analyzing bomb data. This group was headed by Dr. Nathan M. Newmark, senior structural and civil engineer from the University of Illinois who had been a consultant to Division 2. It included also Norman Dahl, junior civil engineer from the research staff at the Princeton Station, Professor A. G. H. Dietz, civil engineer from M.I.T., and Earl K. Bowen, mathematician from Northeastern University. Dietz and Bowen had both been members of the OFS indoctrination groups at Princeton. These men prepared graphic summary sheets, organized to show in simplified fashion the major effects of various bombs and fuzes. They illustrated the effects of the 100-pound, 250-pound, 1000-pound, and 2000-pound general-purpose bombs, the 500-pound and 1000-pound semi-armor-piercing bombs, and the 1000-pound and 1600-pound armor-piercing bombs. These sheets were distributed widely through the theater and were incorporated in the 7th Air Force Ordnance Officer's Handbook. Some of the sheets were eventually found in use both in the Southwest Pacific and in India. Later, similar summaries were prepared for fragmentation bombs and other special types.

There were other organizations in the Central Pacific, both civilian and military, dealing with similar problems. The subsection of Marshall's team maintained continuing liaison with the Air Force Evaluation Board, the Operational Research Section of the Air Force, and the ORG of the Navy. After discussions with these organizations the ORS group prepared tables to be used in selecting particular sizes of bombs and setting the fuzes for attacks on specific targets. The data included in these tables gave information such as the probable diameter of craters in typical soils; the radius at which men in foxholes, lying prone or standing, might become casualties; the radius of severe damage around a hit, and the distance at which near misses could be expected to damage buildings of various kinds, pillboxes, gun emplacements, vehicles or planes on the ground.

With the chemical experts of Marshall's Subsection, Iglehart, Byfield, and Newhall, the bomb damage experts also carried out tests to determine the best proportion of constituents to use in wing tanks that were to be dropped as incendiary bombs.

As the air offensive in the Pacific gained momentum, Colonel Leach established Operational Research Sections with the 20th and 21st Air Forces and appealed to OFS to aid in supplying men with special training in bomb damage assessment and weapons selection. Maurice Barron was loaned to become a member of the ORS of the 20th Air Force. He went first to Orlando for a period of training with a cadre of officers who were to staff bomb groups in the 22nd Air Force. Then he worked with the Joint Target Group, received additional training in photointerpretation, and became familiar with preparation of target folders. In January he and Richard Burson went to the headquarters of the 2nd Air Force in Colorado Springs to plan and teach a special course in photointerpretation and target analysis.

In March 1945 Barron left for India. In June he became Acting Chief of the Operational Research Section. He became thereby a member of the general staff and attended all staff meetings. He was also invited to be present at meetings of the Mission Planning Committee charged with the responsibility for building up a backlog of priority targets for which appropriate studies had been made. His report on an incendiary attack on the dock and storage area of Hangkow, China, is of exceptional interest because the attack was almost a controlled experiment. Early in July he reported for temporary duty with the 21st Bomber Command on Guam and was transferred two weeks later to work under General Doolittle on Okinawa.

Burson had been made available to OAD in the fall of 1944 and was later assigned to the Operational Research Section on Guam. He assisted in determining force requirements for various bombing missions and in assessing the damage to thirty-three urban areas of Japan laid waste by incendiaries. Shortly before the end of the war he became a member of a committee engaged in studying the entire target system of Japan in order to re-evaluate the priorities of the targets.

In the summer of 1945 Dr. W. J. Dixon, mathematician from the Applied Mathematics Panel, loaned to the Joint Target Group, was attached to the OFS group at Hawaii for administrative purposes, and was detailed forward to work with the Operational Research Section of the 20th Air Force on Guam. He participated in studies essentially comparable with those conducted in Washington. After the first clout with the atomic bomb had virtually brought Japan to her knees, he assisted in evaluating the damage from this new weapon.

After extensive indoctrination by OFS at Princeton and then at Princes Risborough, J. Virgil Proctor, senior civil engineer from the University of Kentucky, was attached to the ORS of the 21st Bomber Command on Guam. He instructed members of the Ordnance and Chemical Warfare Sections on methods for selecting bombs and fuzes and for computing force requirements; aided in improving the methods by which missions were planned, and analyzed results of attacks by the 21st Bomber Command. Early in August 1945 Proctor was assigned to a section of A-3 (Air Force equivalent of G-3) for a special assignment in connection with planning the mission that dropped the atomic bomb on Hiroshima. The effectiveness of his quiet and unassuming manner and the degree to which he had won the confidence of Air Force officers was recognized in the personal commendation he received from Major General Lauris Norstad, Chief of Staff of the 20th Air Force.

In the summer of 1944 when our armies had gained beachheads on the Continent and prospects for overrunning large sections of France and then Germany were bright, it was evident that the long-awaited opportunity would soon develop to examine in detail on the ground the damage created by our air offensive. The late President Roosevelt addressed a letter to the Secretary of War, directing that the Air Forces establish a United States Strategic Bombing Survey (USSBS), which would send teams of observers to Germany to examine in detail the physical, economic, and psychological effects of our bombing, especially in industrial areas. From this study they might draw conclusions that would aid in determining future Air Force policy, not only for the offensives against Japan but for the postwar and possibly for the future period. USSBS was to work in close collaboration with a similar comprehensive group established by the British, known as the British Bombing Research Mission.

Stimulated by the force of this directive from the Commander in

Chief, the Air Forces proceeded at once to establish an elaborate organization. Soon it had a total manpower of over 1000, made up largely of military personnel whose transfers to this new duty were arranged with amazing speed. Men of many types were used, including engineers, architects, photointerpreters, intelligence experts, psychologists, economists, interpreters, drivers, mechanics, and pilots. In the theater the survey teams were equipped so that each could operate as a self-contained unit with its own transportation, communications facilities, and provisions for billeting. Thus they were exceedingly mobile and created little disturbance to the local commanders as they moved from one area to another in the theater.

One subdivision of USSBS was concerned primarily with physical damage. A mature senior engineer of considerable experience and knowledge in the field of bomb damage assessment was supplied by OFS to head this Physical Damage Division. Professor Harry L. Bowman, civil engineer of Drexel Institute of Technology, who had been a member of Division 2, accepted this important responsibility and served also as one of the Directors of USSBS.

A large number of structural engineers in uniform were provided to staff the Physical Damage Division, but Army ranks were short of specialists in fire-protection engineering. Miles W. Brown, OFS man who had acquired a thorough knowledge of incendiaries in studies with Division 11 and had then applied this for many weeks at Princes Risborough, was loaned to USSBS. He spent two months examining targets in France and later almost three months examining the fire damage in Germany. As a fire analyst he was concerned with determining the structure of the targets subject to incendiary bombing, their occupancy or use at the time of the raids, and the density of incendiaries in the attack. He reported that the first two of these items were fairly easy to discover. One could examine the structures directly or question employees and managers of the factories and look over reports kept by the German firms. In some instances, of course, the reports had completely disappeared with destruction of the buildings and only verbal commentaries were available.

High-explosive (HE) bombs create road blocks, break water and gas mains, displace roofing, smash windows, short-circuit electrical equipment, overturn stoves and heaters, shatter furnaces, and ignite hot liquids and gases in chemicals-processing plants. Serious fires can be started by HE alone. Moreover, the explosions will keep the fire fighters in shelters until the fires get a good hold. But the USSBS men found that "the principal weapon for starting fires was the incendiary bomb" (IB), which was "most effective in causing destruction in city *residence* areas." In industrial attacks the effectiveness of IB varied considerably. "Incidents were seen where incendiaries were used on plants using or building heavy machinery and where no results were achieved because combustible material was lacking. However, it was fairly well established that some part of the bomb load should consist of incendiaries in almost all raids. The best mixture of incendiaries and high-explosive bombs for any specific target depended on the combustibility of the construction and the contents." This ratio of HE to IB (HE/IB) was a subject that occupied the attention of hundreds of experts and analysts, both in the preraid planning and in the postraid assessment work, and led to many a bitter professional controversy. The burned-out shells of cities in Japan are evidence that the destructive capacity of the IB gained increasing recognition as the war progressed.

The terrific effectiveness of incendiary bombs was nowhere more evident than at Hamburg, which was hit in a series of four major raids during July and August 1943. The city was carefully divided into areas for attack, and it was Brown's impression that if all four flights had been as effective as the first three, Hamburg would have been utterly destroyed. Both HE and IB were used in the raids. Almost 60 per cent of the city was destroyed and the damaged area covered 30 square miles. Over 12 square miles were completely burned, 300,000 dwelling units were wiped out, and nearly a million people were made homeless. The USSBS teams estimated that "of the total destruction, 75 to 80 per cent was due to fires."

At Hamburg, Kassel, Darmstadt, and Dresden, a fire-storm phenomenon was observed. This occurred when many fires were started by incendiaries over a large area simultaneously. Within a few minutes thousands of buildings were ablaze. The intensity of the bomb fall was so great that it was futile even to attempt to fight all the individual fires. As they broke through the roofs a turbulent column of heated air hundreds of yards in diameter rose miles into the sky. This created a draft from the surrounding open spaces which was sufficient to sweep people along the pavements and suck them into the flames, and to break off or uproot trees three feet thick as if they had been blown down by a hurricane.

These observations are confirmed in a comment made by Karl Brandt, Associate Professor of Surgery at the University of Berlin, Brigadier General in the German Medical Corps, and at one time attending surgeon to Hitler. Brandt had flown to Hamburg the morning after the first night raid in July of 1943. He stated that he could smell smoke in the cabin of the plane fifty miles away and that the heat of the fires was beyond description. It was here that he "first saw stones and bricks burning," and he reported that the updraft was so terrific as to overturn autos and trucks. The shock effect of these RAF raids on the Nazi leaders was great. Albert Speer admitted this to USSBS investigators and said, "I reported for the first time orally to the Fuehrer that if these aerial attacks continued, a rapid end of the war might be the consequence."

In the early winter of 1944-45 H. A. Ricards, Jr., specialist on incendiaries of the Standard Oil Development Company, was attached to USSBS to work under the direction of R. P. Russell, President of the company, who had become a Director of USSBS and Chairman of its Oil, Chemicals, and Rubber Section.[1] After twelve visits to Washington to straighten out details of his processing by the Air Forces as a civilian consultant, Ricards finally left the United States in March. His first assignment in England was to review reports on the costly strategic air attacks that had smashed the important Axis oil center at Ploesti. This review established the fact that earlier reports by various agencies were inadequate and represented impressions rather than conclusions based on statistical analysis of the data. Ricards reported that the information was not sufficiently complete to answer fundamental questions regarding bombing tactics, weapons effectiveness, loss of capacity, loss of productivity, and recuperability. Only selected aerial cover had been available at headquarters in Britain; complete records of bomb stowages were lacking or were in conflict, and information concerning production records was missing.

[1] Earlier Russell was a member of an OFS mission on jungle warfare in the South Pacific.

By the middle of March ground warfare in the Sixth and Twelfth Army groups had taken a most favorable turn. It appeared that supremely vital Rhineland targets would fall into Allied hands very soon. Accordingly, work on the Ploesti reports was terminated and Ricards prepared to move into the field. He helped to work out briefs for field team procedure in order to obtain the data needed for proper analysis of the strategic bombing. The Ploesti survey had revealed glaring omissions that could be avoided in the further work of USSBS.

Late in March it became apparent that one of the most important industrial targets, the main works of the I. G. Farbenindustrie in the Ludwigshafen sector, would fall. Ricards was attached to a self-contained team of fifteen civilian and military personnel who moved up through the Siegfried Line and established themselves in the target area while it was still under fire from across the Rhine. The target covered over a thousand acres and was the biggest chemical works in Germany. On the banks of the Rhine it operated the largest water-pumping station in the world. Ricards stayed in this area until mid-April and assisted in a detailed survey of over three hundred bomb incidents in four hundred acres of the Oppau plant which had been devoted mainly to production of synthetic ammonia and by-products and to the refining of oil and manufacture of synthetic gasoline.

Remaining in the theater until the latter part of June, Ricards visited numerous other targets. He found that German records were generally excellent. Despite the fact that under orders from the *Wehrmacht* a large portion of them had been buried or hidden in the surrounding countryside, they were recovered with the co-operation of German personnel.

Upon his return to the United States and further analysis of the large quantity of data obtained by this subsection of USSBS, Ricards reported to Bush that important results were obtained by the mission, some of which were used effectively in the last phases of our aerial war against Japan.

A great deal of the work of USSBS was, of course, intelligence. Just as ALSOS had been supreme in seizing German research secrets, the interrogators of the Bombing Survey performed superbly in capturing enormous quantities of information about German economy and production and they piled up reams of statistical data on the physical damage created by our bombers. This made possible a realistic assessment of the over-all effectiveness of the strategic attacks that were authorized at Casablanca in January 1943. "The field studies of the Survey checked to a considerable degree the accuracy of photo-interpretation when related to building types and building damage. As would be expected, there were minor errors in detail, but these tended to balance and were of relative unimportance. Several special studies made in advance and later checked on the ground, disclosed a high degree of skill in the work of the photo-interpreters." Thus Bowman's men revealed that the patient work of the experts who helped to plan the raids had not been in vain.

The Strategic Bombing Survey was authorized to send similar teams to Japan after V-J Day for analysis of the damage created by our aerial offensives, including the destruction of Hiroshima and Nagasaki. Although OFS participation in USSBS was virtually withdrawn at the end of the war, Professor Bowman remained as Chief of the Physical Damage Division through an arrangement made directly between the War Department and Drexel Institute. Shortly before the transfer of ORG to the Navy, Dr. J. V. Wehausen, mathematician from the University of Missouri, was loaned by ORG to USSBS and went to Japan to study damage to targets struck in attacks by the naval air arm.

In the attacks on Europe nearly three million tons of bombs were dropped. In Germany alone almost four million dwelling units were destroyed or heavily damaged, leaving about eight million people homeless. The principal Nazi cities were reduced to central cores of hollow walls and piles of rubble, surrounded by suburban rings pockmarked with charred and battered buildings. Rail transportation centers became writhing heaps of twisted rails, and airfields turned into a wilderness of craters. The accuracy of our airmen in achieving these results has, however, been commonly misconstrued by widespread use of the words "pin-point" and "pickle-barrel" bombing. USSBS studies showed that "in the overall, only about 20% of the bombs aimed at precision targets fell within this target area" (a circle of 1000 foot radius around the aiming point). The rest spilled over on adjacent fields, built-up areas, or plants. The accuracy possible in bombing under target range conditions in practice at home could not be approached in battle conditions over Europe. Many factors intervened — cloud cover, fog, smoke screens, industrial haze, weather conditions, enemy flak, and fighter opposition, time limitations on training combat crews, and irregularities in the performance of equipment. Far larger tonnages were carried, perforce, than ever hit the installations they were taken to destroy.

There is little question that Allied air power was decisive in all the theaters of our war. "The German experience suggests that even a first-class military power — rugged and resilient as Germany was — cannot live long under full-scale and free exploitation of air weapons over the heart of its territory." [2] And no small part of our success in capitalizing this third dimension of the conflict must be attributed to the analysts of air attack, many of them from OFS, who worked with maps and slide rules to pick out the right places, the right weapons, and the right way.

[2] Most of these quotations and factual data have been taken from the Summary Report of the USSBS, provided through the courtesy of Professor Bowman.

CHAPTER XII

LESS MOTION WASTED

THE ARMY SIMPLIFIES ITS WORK

G I JOE was shaving — not in the relative privacy of the barracks, but right out there in the open, with officers from OFS, the Navy, NDD, and other branches of the War Department watching every move. They were sitting in the air-conditioned Pentagon projection room and he was on the screen, sweating to do the job with as few wasted motions as possible. He was recording every step in the operation on a "flow-process chart" to see if somehow the whole thing could not be made simpler. Of course it could. He went through the routines once, recording every detail of what he had done. Looking at the chart critically, he saw as well as did the audience the steps that could be eliminated, the ways some could be combined or rearranged to make the operation easier and quicker. Then he shaved again, not just to be thorough, but to show how much simpler and faster even such a mundane operation as shaving could be when you cut out unnecessary details. If you could save five minutes a day at this job, that would be fourteen hundred hours of extra sleep before you turned sixty-five. Worth thinking about.

Joe was an animated cartoon character, dreamed up by Allan H. Mogensen and his colleagues, exponents of a work simplification technique, and by Colonel Kent Lane of NDD, devotee of this doctrine who had managed to introduce it right and left in the Army. Joe was produced by Herb Lamb Productions, Inc., of Hollywood. Their animators had gone to work at the request of OFS to create this Technicolor cartoon film as the culmination in a series of movies prepared to help in teaching the principles of work simplification to thousands of officers, enlisted men, and civilians in the War Department and out in the combat areas. The flow-process chart was the heart of the method — study your job, list on this chart every detail, question the need for each step and the reason it is done as it is, then eliminate the unnecessary items, combine what is left or rearrange into a better sequence, simplify the remainder, and sell the improved procedure to the boss.

All this is rather elementary — common sense, when you stop to think of it. But few people do. They are too ready to accept things as they are, too resistant to change, especially to change suggested by subordinates. It takes someone with the fire of Mogensen to shake them out of their lethargy, make them realize that this unquestioning attitude costs money and time — may even cost lives in war. He had proved the point in industry when he stepped up production at the Lockheed Aircraft plants and yet cut their total personnel by several thousand. This saved some forty million a year. Furthermore, by encouraging the workers there to study their own jobs and come up with suggestions, he collected 40,000 ideas that saved the company nearly twenty million dollars and over ten million man-hours of work. In the production of vital materials for our war that would really count.

Even before the war "Mogy" had convinced industry that work simplification pays off. He was a high-powered consultant to scores of big corporations, and had saved them so much that he was able to set up his own school at Lake Placid to teach men from hundreds of companies to use the methods that had become his stock in trade.

The basic idea of studying a job to make it easier was surely not original with Mogensen. The Egyptians must have had it when they invented the wheel, and they probably learned it from observant ancestors. Textbooks of industrial engineering have devoted chapters to work analysis, time and motion studies, and such matters for decades. Efficiency experts have made comfortable fortunes by coming into factories with their charts, cameras, and stop watches. Making black-and-white records of all the wasted motion, they could show incontrovertible figures to prove what employers could have seen easily enough if they had only taken the trouble to observe carefully. This type of study is known as "experting." It is usually done by a person who knows something about the operations studied; and the changes he recommends in arrangement of workers, sequence of operations, design of machinery, or personnel policy are instituted by management and often imposed on the workers without consulting them. It presupposes that they are mere automatons whose behavior is to be regulated by directive, and assumes that they are either too ignorant, too lazy, or too selfish to study their jobs themselves and figure out short cuts.

Mogensen and his school of trainees approach the matter from a different point of view. They recognize that, once management encourages employees to analyze the details of their own jobs and promotes the "reward for suggestions" plan, the workers will find the desirable changes themselves — perhaps find more of them in the same time at less cost because hundreds or thousands of minds are at work on the problem simultaneously instead of a few expensive experts.

What can be done in industry along these lines can be done in Government, in education, in housekeeping, even in the Army and Navy. It may be harder to get this kind of a work simplification program started among the military because it rests on the principle that the man who is performing a routine knows as much or more about it than does his supervisor, that GI Joe can show the General a better way to shave. Mogensen and Herbert F. Goodwin of M.I.T. and the Hytron Corporation had proved this out in the Southwest Pacific in the spring of 1944. The Signal Corps was bogging down under a flood of administrative detail in communications, and General Akin had asked Compton to send out a time-motion analyst or two. His executive, Colonel S. S. Auchincloss, knew of Mogensen's success in the war plants and had recommended that OFS try to get him to introduce his methods to the Army.

When they returned in June Mogensen and Goodwin were the principal speakers in a room full of brass and gold braid at the Pentagon. Their results in rearranging the message centers in SWPA, eliminating unnecessary travel, and speeding up the handling of communications were so striking that other offices in the War and Navy Departments should hear about them. Colonel Lane had engineered this formal report to high echelons. Lieutenant General McNarney, Assistant Chief of Staff, presided and the audience included General Henry of NDD, Major General W. D. Styer of ASF, Brigadier General Thomas North of OPD, Brigadier General H. M. McClelland of Air Force Communications, Captain Briscoe of the Navy, and other dignitaries.

Mogensen pointed out that at GHQ they had encountered the same opposition among officers as had been true in their experience with captains of industry, the same sort of resistance to change. And their reception at Brisbane had been cool. Nevertheless, adopting the same methods they had applied successfully in industry, they proceeded to sell the concept to top officers in the command at Port Moresby and secured permission to conduct classes, instructing in the method, demonstrating its effectiveness with motion pictures, and persuading the participants to make flow-process charts.

Mogensen and Goodwin emphasized that their approach had not been that of experts. They knew nothing about communications. Their chief purpose had simply been to persuade the individual officer or enlisted man to study his own job, seek out the details that could be improved, and recommend ways for eliminating unnecessary steps.

Improvements resulting from suggestions made in these classes convinced many skeptics. Word filtered back to GHQ. Consequently they were received more cordially on return to Brisbane and were permitted to give a series of similar lectures, an hour each day for a week, to a group of 125 personnel of the Services of Supply. A similar program was instituted at the Base 3 Signal Section where the operations in handling a single message were reduced from 57 to 27 with a 30 per cent saving in time. This was the kind of result that would save headaches and backaches all around, and it was evident that, reproduced in many places, this work simplification scheme might really shorten the war. The commanders had been sold and they wanted a man to continue the good work when Mogensen and Goodwin had to leave to catch up on heavy commitments to war industry.

The keen interest generated at high levels in the Army by the report of Mogensen and Goodwin led to a series of projects in work simplification, and OFS was asked to supply additional instructors. All of them came from industry where they had been applying with great success the methods advocated by Mogensen. Most of them had been trained at his special school. The group included: —

E. E. Brashear	Lockheed Aircraft
D. F. Copell	Wagner Baking Company
Arthur E. Crane	Crane and Company
Harold G. Dunlap	H. P. Hood and Sons
Howard D. Engler	Merck and Company
Franklin G. Farnam	Edo Aircraft Corporation

Frank P. Forrest	Lockheed Aircraft
Sophie Greene (Mrs.)	....
Stephen Greene	Pathé News
W. A. Hoffman	RCA Victor Division
G. A. Hornberger	Diamond Crystal Salt
Sherman Lynch	Sylvania Electric Products
Edwin C. Osborn	Lockheed Aircraft
John A. Peart	North American Aviation
L. E. Richards	Crane and Company
Edward R. Whittaker	Sylvania Electric Products

There was nothing very complicated and technical about this work simplification. It would not require skilled scientists to put it over. But it was a type of industrial engineering that could be of enormous benefit to the Services and it could go forward rapidly in the hands of specialists who knew the technique from working with it in industry and who were skilled in teaching it to others. There were already work simplification programs here and there in the Army. The Service Forces had training manuals and methods and were encouraging their use. But in an organization as big as the Army there was ample room for more than one group of experts to introduce these time-and-effort-saving procedures. Consequently NDD had persuaded OFS to help provide the personnel necessary to capitalize the success of this first venture and then later to place more effective tools in their hands through the medium of movies that showed applications of the method to actual Army problems. Dr. Mark May, OFS consultant on enemy N-P in ETO, who had many years of experience in the production of educational films, and Mrs. Greene, who had helped to run a movie firm in France for fifteen years before the war, served as advisors in the production of these reels.

Copell was an admirable successor to Mogensen and Goodwin in SWPA. Armed with 32,000 feet of movie film from industrial operations, he headed for the theater in May 1944 and stayed with the troops in New Guinea nearly six months. First he gave orientation lectures to all chiefs of technical, administrative, distribution, and special service sections at each base. Almost 2000 officers and enlisted men attended these. Then there were more intensive courses designed to develop instructors within the Army who could carry on and spread the method within their own units. More than four hundred suggestions for improvements came from these classes. They involved over 10,000 individual steps in the operations studied, and almost half of these could be eliminated. Copell estimated that in only half of these projects 750,000 feet of unnecessary travel and 2300 man-hours of work would be saved every day. Cold statistics, indeed, but convincing proof that the Mogensen method pays off.

General McClelland urged introduction of the method in the Army Airways Communications System (AACS); and for many months the work simplifiers were giving courses at AACS installations at home and overseas — Asheville, Selfridge Field, Miami, Presque Isle, Manchester, North Africa. Engler and Hoffman went to HQ of the Second Wing AACS at Casablanca that winter. A single improvement effected by one junior officer more than paid for their trip. He found it possible to eliminate 12,000 miles of unnecessary routing and to cut one hundred minutes off the time required for transmitting one kind of message.

Colonel Lane, Mogensen, Stephen Greene, and Whittaker took the program to the Adriatic Base Command and instructed more than 1000 key personnel at Bari, Leghorn, Rome, and Caserta. A primary objective of this mission was to simplify routine operations so they could be turned over to Italians and the number of Army personnel retained in the theater after V-E could be reduced. Then in the summer of 1944 Colonel Lane, accompanied by Dunlap and Osborn, visited GHQ in the Central Pacific and generated sufficient interest to warrant attaching work simplification experts to the OFS balanced team. Lynch, Crane, and Peart subsequently joined this project. By December a survey showed that many improvements had been made and that the local staffs could carry on without additional instruction.

NDD also sponsored courses in the Pentagon attended by personnel of many staff sections. Twenty officers of the British Army staff were invited and put the doctrine to work in their own units. Mrs. Greene made a survey to determine the significance of this effort to the Military Intelligence Service. Her findings showed that officers who had not been pleased at being ordered to attend the classes not only failed to inspire their subordinates but even discouraged any interest shown by their men. In units whose commanding officers had been open-minded and receptive, on the other hand, the results were astonishing. Without increasing personnel, one group had stepped up by 77 per cent the volume of documents processed; in another branch the time necessary for handling documents was reduced from 2 weeks to 24 hours. Altogether in 11 branches of MIS the savings amounted to 23,119 man-hours a year. Expressed in other terms, this meant that each branch could accomplish the same amount of work with a dozen less people. Such results could not fail to impress Brigadier General C. A. Drake, Chief of the Control Staff in the Military Intelligence Division. All this spelled less paper work, greater efficiency, less nervous exhaustion, fewer errors, and less cost to the taxpayers.

In the summer of 1945 Hornberger and Brashear achieved similar results in the Central Pacific Base Command at Hawaii. This was a division of the Army forces in the Central Pacific, responsible for supplying the operational units and for defense of the Hawaiian Islands. Brigadier General Wayne C. Smith, Chief of Staff, encouraged them to present the system throughout the command. An analysis of procedures used in treating requisitions from forward areas resulted in cutting the time for processing them from 75 days to 48 hours. This item alone would justify the high commendation they received; but they did more. With the sympathetic backing of the top echelons, they provided nearly 5000 man-hours of instruction, and the proposals that developed from this work were designed to save about 50,000 man-hours of work and almost 20,000 miles of travel.

Although the work simplification protagonists were warmly praised for such achievements, the major credit really belongs in the Army itself. Some should certainly go to co-operative senior officers who recognized the potentialities and were willing to permit instruction and then to adopt improvements recommended by their staffs. And the rest belongs to hundreds of junior men and dogfaces who learned to make flow-process charts and came up with labor-saving ideas.

In a war fought over great distances under frequently changing plans, with large numbers of men of varying military background and with tremendous quantities of equipment, a large headquarters is faced with a serious problem to avoid unco-ordinated planning and to eliminate overlap and duplication within the lower echelons. Decentralization of command creates difficulties if there is no central control. Personal inspection by the Commanding General is impossible except as an occasional method, and the reports of staff officers are not always oriented toward control relationships. A headquarters organization is needed to provide statistical information for the Commanding General, the Chief of Staff, and all the Staff Sections.

This need was felt at Army headquarters in Hawaii and in March 1945 the Assistant Chief of Staff, G-1, asked for the services of Dr. Harry Hansen from the faculty of the Harvard Business School to analyze the requirements for such a centralized control section and to design a plan for instituting one. After studying the organization of GHQ, Hansen presented an elaborate report and an organizational pattern for a Control Division in the Office of the Chief of Staff.

Hansen's plan called for a group of about seventy-five officers, enlisted men, and civilians. This Control Division was to be activated on September first. When he left the theater late in August, it was not anticipated that cessation of hostilities with Japan would require changes in the proposal.

In a letter of commendation General Richardson said of Hansen's work: "The lucidity and completeness of his reports were of material aid to the evaluation of the personnel policies. By his specialized professional knowledge and continuous devotion to duty Dr. Hansen made contributions of great value to the Armed Forces in the Pacific Ocean Areas."

Hansen insists emphatically that this study should not be classified as work simplification. It was, rather, the organization of a specific group for a specific task and it would increase rather than decrease the actual number of workers. In its over-all effect, however, it would surely simplify the functioning of the top staff officers. And, while adding personnel through creation of a new unit, it could have the gross effect of lightening the load elsewhere, perhaps even permitting decrease of personnel, because overlap, duplication, and unnecessary steps would be eliminated. Hansen's study was not the sort of work simplification that Mogensen would advocate, wherein the changes are recommended by the workers themselves. It was a type of "experting" in which an analyst recommends new ways of doing things and the changes are then laid down by orders from the top. The difference may be chiefly one of terminology. In any case, the effect of Hansen's study was that here again the Army was going to simplify its work.

One other OFS project had work simplification aspects, although they were not apparent in the original request. When Compton discussed with General Casey in SWPA the need for an "operational research group" in the Corps of Engineers, it had been considered that experts in statistics with some knowledge of engineering would be the proper personnel to constitute such a group. Casey wanted a team of about five men to analyze construction operations and report on the performance of engineer equipment in jungle areas. As Harrison talked further with officers about this project, it became evident that men experienced in heavy construction would be in greater demand for trouble-shooting on the building of airstrips, roads, supply depots, and harbor installations than would true operations analysts.

Finding a senior man to head such a group proved difficult; but in the meantime OFS located J. A. Russell, youthful geologist who had spent many months supervising heavy construction in the jungles of South America. He had also been in charge of several hundred natives on gold-dredging operations in the interior of Mindanao in the Philippines. Russell left for the theater, expecting that he would soon be joined by additional engineers and analysts, including a mature senior group leader. He was sent rather promptly to forward battalions in New Guinea and was asked to rate the efficiency of the various units. This assignment placed him at considerable disadvantage because he was a civilian, not much older than many of the men whose work he was to evaluate. Moreover, the officers to whom he reported were short of personnel. Recognizing his experience in directing construction operations, they placed him in charge of enlisted men in functions that were essentially those of command. Russell behaved admirably in this awkward situation and won the full confidence of engineer headquarters; but it was evident that he would have to be shifted because, quite innocently, he was affecting the morale of tired troops up front.

His position was occasionally precarious in other respects also. One day while he was working on an airstrip at Hollandia a Jap bomber roared overhead and laid a string of bombs in a straight line extending right to the position where he had sought cover. If the enemy had not run out of bombs just short of him, Russell would have been the only gold star in the flag of OFS.

Meanwhile J. P. Becich, mechanical engineer who had just completed a large construction job in Mexico in the employ of the W. A. Bechtel Company, was sent out to join him. He and Russell had worked together for Bechtel and, although they were both rather young, they had solid backgrounds of practical experience with heavy construction in jungle areas. It appeared that they would make a first-class combination in the field.

One of the most serious problems they encountered was the great quantity of automotive equipment out of service for want of spare parts or lack of trained technicians in the battalions who could make repairs without waiting for assistance from maintenance units. In collaboration with officers, Russell and Becich revised the standard lists for supply of spare parts. They were then recalled to headquarters and wrote engineering manuals to promote more efficient operation of automotive construction equipment. They were relieved to be working at last in less embarrassing positions where chronological age was not such a significant consideration.

Finally OFS was successful in its attempt to find a senior engineer who could undertake the type of work assigned to Russell and Becich without engendering discontent among the troops, a man whose maturity and broad experience might be useful in a great variety of day-to-day problems. Joseph W. Farwell, construction engineer from the Baldwin Locomotive Company, went out to head the team of "operations analysts" for General Casey. On the day he arrived in the theater Becich already had orders for return to the United States and Farwell took up the evaluation of engineering units. By the time of his first report it was obvious that the original idea for a five-man group of analysts had been abandoned and plans to add personnel were canceled.

Russell accepted a commission in the Seabees and remained in the theater. Farwell continued alone as a special advisor to engineer headquarters. He inspected units at the rate of a battalion per day for almost a month. This carried him from Hollandia to Taclobán in Leyte. There he suffered an injury to his ankle and, although he tried to stay on the job, the medical officers threatened that he might be permanently disabled if he continued to use the weak ankle over the rough terrain of the Philippines.

Although the project had departed widely from its original purpose, there is ample evidence in Farwell's reports that the daily counsel of an experienced senior man repeatedly proved useful to engineering brigades filled with relatively inexperienced junior men. His success in diverting a river in New Guinea to provide the needed gravel for an airstrip would alone have warranted sending him to SWPA.

It would take a room full of statisticians working through reams of reports from Italy, North Africa, Hawaii, the Philippines, Miami, Asheville, and the Pentagon to tabulate the years of labor, the thousands of miles of travel, and the tons of red tape that were probably eliminated because, with the guidance of industrial experts from OFS, the Army simplified its work. Much of the story must come from results achieved after these men left, when hundreds of the officers they trained became instructors and tried to maintain the momentum and the wholesome spirit of job analysis. Even then, one could not assess the total contribution this made to the war effort because there would still be the intangible saving of wear and tear on people's dispositions that cannot be measured. But no algebraic superbrain is needed to calculate the total saving possible if all 10,000,000 men in uniform had learned the simple lesson portrayed by the cartoon GI Joe and saved five minutes shaving every day. That alone comes to over 300,000,000 hours a year.[1]

Perhaps even more significant will be the improvements brought about in our civilian life if the many officers and GI's who were exposed to the work simplification training remember to carry over its principles into their peacetime work and see to it that there is less motion wasted.

[1] Even allowing for a few lazy ones and a few with beards, the calculation shows 304,166,666 hours a year. And, of course, 833,333 hours more for leap year.

Ersatz Transportation
*An Army DUKW crossed the Danube at Donaustauf, Germany, after
other means of crossing were destroyed*

Vision with Infrared

Infantryman about to demonstrate the sniperscope, designed for use in the dimness of the jungle and at night

CHAPTER XIII

DUKW'S, WEASELS, WATER BUFFALOES, AND PENGUINS

THE TRUCKS THAT WENT TO SEA

A GROUP of young Naval Reserve officers stood on the deck of their ship. It was anchored about a mile off shore. There was no sight of the launch that was to take them to the pier, and they could see precious hours of shore leave vanishing. Two were due back to stand the midnight watch.

A small, odd-looking craft was chugging along in the waters near by. The boat was a squarish affair manned by a single civilian. It seemed to move somewhat more slowly than a power launch — but perhaps it would do. When it came within shouting range the officers hailed it and soon they were on their way to shore.

Suddenly they noticed that the craft was not heading for the pier but had turned toward a broad, shelving beach. The boat continued to approach the white crescent.

All at once the front end of the small craft tilted out of the water and it crawled right up across the beach — on wheels! Then it turned, accelerated, and rolled down the coastal highway at the speed of an ordinary Army truck.

The driver smiled at their amazement. He was pleased with this chance to give an unforgettable, practical introduction of the DUKW,[1] an amphibious conversion of the standard Army 2½-ton, six-by-six truck. Developed by Division 12, NDRC (Transportation), and the yacht-designing firm of Sparkman and Stephens, and built by General Motors in 1942, it was equipped with a watertight, welded steel hull. It could develop 90 horsepower and had six driving wheels for travel over land. In the water a three-bladed propeller, 25 inches in diameter and with a 14-inch pitch, was its motivating force. This new amphibian

---

[1] Taken from the General Motors code: D = 1942, U = utility, K = front-wheel drive, W = two rear driving axles.

turned out to be our most effective means for getting supplies from ship to dump, railhead, or transfer point ashore.

The man at the wheel was Roderick Stephens, yachtsman, junior partner of Sparkman and Stephens, specialist in the handling of small boats — the one man who knew more about this new contrivance than anyone in the world. He suspected that the officers, like hundreds of others he met, could not distinguish the DUKW from the numerous types of launches and landing craft that were emerging from the drawing boards and factories to help our military forces come ashore in many harborless waters. He had avoided the route to the pier deliberately. An object lesson in the capabilities of this vehicle was always more telling than pages of description in an amphibious training manual.

Before he and Palmer Cosslett Putnam, engineer, yachtsman, and dynamic idea-man of OSRD, dreamed up the DUKW, Stephens had been engaged in the development of an amphibian made from the quarter-ton jeep. Although he felt the design job was only moderately satisfactory, an order for 12,000 of these vehicles created pressure to rush into production. They started coming off the assembly line without hatches, or with their hatches insecure, and with many other faults. The production men had no experience with boats and knew little about making a seaworthy craft. It was not surprising, then, that soon the Army scrapped the amphibian jeep — chiefly because of "bugs" in its production. This experience proved that someone should follow a new vehicle through from the initial design to its ultimate use in combat operations. When Stephens turned his attention to the DUKW he was determined to stay with it to be sure these difficulties were not duplicated.

Although the DUKW had to be sold to the Army, the Marines, and then at long last to the Navy, after top-ranking officers in all the Services had turned thumbs down on it, hundreds of DUKW's were used in the Allied offensives in North Africa, Sicily, Southeast Asia, and then in the landings at Normandy. They proved themselves in these critical operations largely because Putnam and Stephens had been to these theaters with their coworker, Dennis Puleston, English-born writer, yachtsman, and naval architect, had lived with and trained the crews, had taught green men how to load and unload and how to drive these amphibians in through surf, across treacherous reefs, bringing supplies and ammunition right up to the front.

Puleston had likewise been concerned with the DUKW program from its inception. Before the war he had spent many months sailing, had cruised around in the atoll-dotted waters of the South Pacific. He knew the channels, the reefs, and the shore lines in the far-off places of the world — well enough almost to negotiate them blindfolded. In the two years since Pearl Harbor he had worked with our new amphibious equipment in the Ellice Islands, the Solomons, the New Hebrides, New Guinea, and India-Burma. It was he who prepared the DUKW companies and then landed with them under fire at Arakan. With a back broken in six places when a Jap shell hit too close, he talked his way out of the hospital and went to England to plan amphibious phases of the main landings on the Continent. Yes, more than that, to work from dawn to midnight with crews that arrived less than two weeks before D-Day, until his eyes were hollow and his nerves were raveled.

Here and there a DUKW had capsized in the hands of an inexpert driver and an impression had got around, especially in the Pacific where many more amphibians would be needed to take our men ashore, that the DUKW's were not seaworthy. Nevertheless, they had done so well in Europe that more were ordered and a systematic program for training amphibian truck companies was established in this country. But the theater to which an individual unit would be assigned was seldom known. Moreover, warfare in the Pacific was far different. The drivers would have to go in over coral reefs and sand bars, would have to carry and unload men, supplies, munitions, and weapons on open beaches. They would have to take in 105-mm. howitzers under conditions that could not be duplicated here at home, and to unload a varied cargo from all sorts of vessels. The driver training could surely not be very realistic so far from operations. The men would be simply slaughtered if they got no more than that.

Consequently Stephens was one of the first members to sign up when OFS was creating the balanced team for General Richardson in Hawaii. He would set up schools closer to the battle fronts, train instructors, analyze DUKW operations, and keep a sharp watch for modifications that would adapt the equipment even better to an island-hopping war. Although the DUKW had been devised primarily for the task of handling cargo, it was adapted to many other uses by the various fighting arms. When a pilot was forced down in a shallow lagoon, or out among the coral reefs where other types of craft could not navigate, the Air Force called for a DUKW to rescue him.

The knowledge of our men in forward areas about the DUKW and about other special amphibious vehicles designed by Division 12 was appallingly meager. Stephens knew that he could not handle the whole job alone. He asked that Puleston take over the training program as soon as he could get away from operations on the Continent.

When Stephens went to POA, the amphibious truck companies, fearful that a 105-mm. howitzer might make the DUKW top-heavy and unstable, were cutting down its body to accommodate this weapon. Stephens secured permission to put one in a DUKW, had the mount manufactured and installed without cutting the hull of the DUKW, and climbed in. Then he put it through paces in the surf off Oahu. In spite of the rough sea and heavy breakers the craft remained afloat and executed unbelievable maneuvers in Stephens's practiced hands. Brigadier General M. B. Bell drove by on the beach road. The sight of a DUKW cutting capers off shore caught his attention. Here was a 105 mounted on an unmodified DUKW that was riding the waves without shipping water despite the rough going. He stopped the jeep and signaled the driver of the DUKW to come ashore. He expected to issue a stern reprimand to the foolhardy young fellow who took such chances with valuable Army equipment.

Stephens landed the DUKW and presented himself respectfully at the side of the General's jeep. He explained the situation so effectively that instead of reproaching him General Bell invited him to lunch at headquarters. They would discuss the matter further. Then he called in a large group of officers in command of amphibious units and had Stephens give them a lecture on what a DUKW could and could not do and how it should be handled under the varying conditions they might expect in Pacific operations. The General then ordered the officers to spend two days with their DUKW companies and report back, this time to Stephens, what they found the amphibious vehicles could not do, and to discuss with him their ideas for improvement in handling.

After that Stephens put on a series of demonstrations. He showed that a DUKW could be loaded safely to a total of approximately 7500 pounds, including the operator, his assistant, spare gasoline, and a machine gun. He helped to write doctrine for unloading operations from LST's carrying DUKW's, and aided in establishing organized schools to teach drivers the correct procedures for maintenance and cargo handling with DUKW's.

When Puleston arrived in August 1944, he assumed the responsibility for most of the training aspects of the DUKW program with the famous 10th Army and the other Services. There were amphibious bases at Kauai, Maui, and Lanai; but Puleston succeeded in setting up a DUKW maintenance and training school at the Waimanalo Amphibious Training Base on Oahu which became the main focus of these activities. He aimed not only to develop expert drivers but also to assist the amphibian truck units in preparing for their missions in every respect. He helped to procure the equipment, spare parts, and tools they would need; made certain that all the DUKW's were in excellent operating condition and equipped with the most recent modifications; and studied the performance of the vehicles during training to observe mechanical failures or weaknesses that might be corrected in the field or at the production plant. By the middle of the following summer he had trained eleven Army amphibian truck companies, four amphibian truck battalion headquarters, three Marine Corps DUKW companies, and many other units using DUKW's in the Artillery, Signal, and Air Corps. All the DUKW units that landed at Iwo Jima had been rehearsed under his patient and thorough tutelage.

Puleston's training emphasized such things as surf and coral driving, loading and unloading artillery and cargo, and an intensive program of DUKW maintenance. Its over-all purpose was to assure the complete readiness of a DUKW unit to perform its assigned mission in an efficient manner and with the minimum casualties immediately upon arrival at the scene of operations.

A commanding officer of an amphibian truck battalion on Okinawa who had observed the contrast between DUKW companies from Waimanalo and those that had not been in touch with these OFS specialists wrote: ". . . It was outstandingly noticeable that certain ones showed evidence of better training. They were up or nearly up to strength in personnel; they had more vehicles on the line daily and their vehicles reflected better and more efficient maintenance. They had all of their authorized equipment available and in good condition. They had a much larger supply of parts than the other companies, and their vehicles were complete and up to date with all the latest modifications. . . . The other companies were short of personnel, spare parts, equipment and training; and in some cases it was necessary to spend three to four weeks to train the men, secure the necessary parts and prepare the vehicles for water operations. . . . It is enthusiastically recommended that all DUKW companies and personnel who are to operate in the Pacific receive this training at Waimanalo before being sent out to perform their assigned missions."

With the training effort safely in the hands of Puleston, Stephens turned his attention to modifications. Among these was a propeller guard designed for DUKW's. It was tested, and by September was in use on six or seven hundred of the vehicles. It was designed to prevent damage from coral reefs, floating debris, and wreckage. Stephens devised similar protection for LCVP's and LCM's, which likewise became standard theater equipment, and was instrumental in designing, testing, and installing a ramp rail for LST's and a ramp curbing guard for LVT's and DUKW's. He also suggested an improved field weld, and returned personally to Detroit to see that the same weld was made on the production line so that the later vehicles would have it. This small change would make a great difference. Stephens knew that if the field commanders had to depend on the long line of communications, this modification might never reach the Pacific.

While he was on the mainland Stephens urged that the Army bring out a modified manual for DUKW training and maintenance. When they seemed hesitant to put the responsibility for this job on anyone in particular because they knew so few people who were really competent to do the job, he asked for a stenographer. He sat up all night in the Pentagon dictating copy for the manual and packing into it the many months of his experience with DUKW crews all over the world. He stayed with it day and night until he had seen it approved by the higher echelons. Then he left for the theater with a copy of the manuscript. When weeks elapsed and no official printing reached the theater, he took his manuscript to the local command and had it mimeographed. The men who landed DUKW's on Iwo and Saipan owed much of their safety to Stephens and his rump manual; they would have owed nothing to the official counterpart that arrived after these shows were over.

In the spring of 1945 it was evident that the same sort of training and consultation was needed to bring about efficient use of the M29-C or Weasel. This cargo carrier had originally been designed by Putnam and developed under his continual goading in a crash program. It was intended for use on light snow in the Allied invasion of Norway, but was later adapted for operations over mud in many other parts of the world. The Weasel was a multipurpose, track-laying vehicle, designed especially as a light cargo and troop carrier for use in areas impassable to other heavier means of transport. Because of its light weight and large track area that gave it low unit ground pressure it could be operated successfully through marshlands or over soft sands, across mud or silt, through jungles, and on snow. It could carry a total load of 1000 pounds of cargo and personnel, and could be used for portage operations across slow-moving streams or in quiet water.

When Marshall called for a Weasel expert to work with Stephens and Puleston, the Studebaker Corporation, which had built this wonder vehicle, sent Homer M. Williams, mechanical engineer who knew how to operate Weasels in his sleep, to join the amphibious section of ORS-POA. With Puleston he set up a ten-day course in driver training at Waimanalo, which then became the center also for all Weasel training. Two hundred and fifty men were given a thorough going over and then became instructors in their own units. Williams demonstrated the Weasel for officers of the Ninth Corps Headquarters and the 98th Infantry Division. When the Ninth Corps moved forward, he spent three weeks with the Fourth and Fifth Marine Divisions and the Fifth Amphibious Corps and set up training programs on Maui. At the request of CWS he demonstrated that the Weasel could carry the 75-mm. recoilless gun, the recoilless mortar, and the Navy-type smoke generator. Then with Stephens he rewrote the basic manual for the Weasel, "Carrier, Cargo, M29-C — Its Operations and Uses." Like his colleagues, Williams was in fatigue clothes almost constantly. He worked long hours and was continually alert to discover modifications that might make his equipment easier to handle, more effective.

During the campaign at Okinawa and the surrounding islands Puleston went forward to train DUKW companies sent directly from the States without benefit of the special schooling at Hawaii. While he was studying the use of DUKW's in the Ryukyus, he found himself helping to capture Japanese troops, an experience shared by few of his colleagues in OFS. Asked to make an informal survey of DUKW operations during the garrison phase at Okinawa, he found them far below par. He pointed out, for example, that in the summer of 1943 twenty-five DUKW's, at Guadalcanal had hauled 1200 tons from a single ship in twelve hours; in 1944 an amphibious truck company exceeded 2500 tons in a day; and at Taclobán in April 1945 twenty DUKW's hauled 1847 tons in 24 hours. The companies at Okinawa, on the other hand, were hauling at rates as low as 200 and rarely more than 800 tons per day. Cargo handling was one of the weakest spots in DUKW operations. One reason for this was that Army authorities did not realize what could be accomplished. They had set a low level of work as the maximum achievement. This limit was not usually exceeded until ORS members pointed out what DUKW's could really do.

Without personal criticism, Puleston outlined in detail and quite frankly the reasons contributing to this poor performance, and made numerous suggestions for remedying the situation. There were several causes for inefficient operation. Ships were frequently not ready for unloading when DUKW's were assigned to them. Too often the arrangement of the cargo on these ships had not been made with the unloading operations in mind, and it was necessary to alternate DUKW's with other cargo carriers. This involved changing tackle on the ships as various types of carriers came alongside. Ships were anchored too far off shore; there was improper supervision at the supply dumps where cargo was dropped, or inadequate provision for relieving thoroughly fatigued drivers. The Colonel in charge was so impressed that he ordered close study of Puleston's report and immediate application of his recommendations.

After training two companies at Okinawa, Puleston went on to Manila, helped to select the site for amphibious landings on Korea, and prepared five companies for this mission. At the end of August he arrived at Jinsen, Korea, not far by his travel standards from where he had been when the Japanese attacked Pearl Harbor. At the outbreak of hostilities he had been on a pleasure cruise in a small vessel. Caught in Shanghai and unable to come back across the Pacific, he had made his way homeward via Siberia and plunged into the early stages of DUKW development with Sparkman and Stephens.

There was yet another amphibious vehicle that became important in late stages of the Pacific war. This was the LVT or Water Buffalo. It differs from the Weasel chiefly in size and can carry up to 10,000 pounds. Fully loaded it exerts a ground pressure of 8 pounds per square foot. In the water the speed of the Water Buffalo is 6 miles an hour, and it can negotiate breakers up to 18 feet in height. In the summer of 1945 when Marshall urged that two LVT specialists be attached to ORS, 5 models of this conveyance were in production and a new one had been projected. The Food Machinery Corporation of California, builders of LVT's, reluctantly agreed to release Clarence G. Taylor, a key engineer involved in the proposed new model, for a short interval and to send with him for a longer period Joseph R. Krone, Jr.

When Taylor and Krone arrived at Pearl Harbor there were no units in training with LVT's. Although about 1000 of these carriers were lined up in a vehicle pool, they were inactive. As had been true of the DUKW and the Weasel, few officers realized the full potentialities of the Water Buffalo. It would take weeks of work such as had been done by Puleston and Stephens and Williams to show them what it could do — and the invasion of Japan was not far off.

A series of delays had prevented the Buffalo experts from getting to the theater in time to assist with the operations at Okinawa, but arrangements were made with the Marine Corps for Taylor to go forward and review the use of LVT's there. By the time he arrived, the landing operations had been finished and the island itself was in our hands. He did, however, manage to see four LVT's in action.

Meanwhile Krone worked with the Fleet Marine Forces on Maui, the Second Armored Battalion, and a series of amphibian truck companies. He found that approximately 85 per cent of the LVT equipment needed some kind of modification or corrective maintenance.

He helped an Ordnance Company to provide ballast holes in the ramp, taught them how to prevent rust and corrosion, and introduced methods for controlling track skids. Most of the Water Buffaloes in the theater lacked the modifications that had already been made in more recent models. Machines that were badly needed up front were piled up in supply dumps or at the ports of embarkation, and old defective models were in use. Newer ones, the "bugs" removed, lay in stock piles in this country.

All of the amphibious vehicle specialists of OFS made the same discouraging reports. When new models of vehicles came off the production lines they were sent to embarkation depots and parked, sometimes seven or eight hundred strong. When ships were available, the older models were cleared out first. Consequently there would be a five- to six-month lag before an improvement in the factory became available to operating personnel in the field. No wonder the GI's in the theater and in training ports at home were skeptical of the stories told them by the technical men from industry and from the development laboratories about the performance of the newer models. They commonly regarded these men with disdain as "feather merchants." In one instance specialists sent to a training camp in this country were ordered to leave the post, simply because they had suggested that the governor on an amphibious vehicle be set in a position not specified in the standard operating procedure of the Army.

Once when a manufacturer discovered a defect during production he sent representatives to the embarkation depots immediately. They fixed all of the conveyances on hand; but two hundred had already been shipped overseas. Thereupon the company dispatched corrective devices for these two hundred to the theater. But in no case did they catch up with the original vehicles. This is the sort of thing that made research and development men, manufacturers, and OFS field-service teams turn prematurely gray; and it gave rise to unwarranted prejudices in the minds of fighting men because the equipment they received had been defective.

Shortly after the end of the war, Stephens was asked to address a large group of high officials in the Army, Navy, and OSRD and to tell his story of the development and use of the DUKW. He spoke with feeling of the unforgivable delays that had occurred in getting up-to-date training manuals into the hands of operators. He cited an instance in which an adequate manual, prepared and approved, did not even appear in print for nine months. Almost a year later a large ship-load of copies arrived in the theater. By that time the manual was obviously obsolete and the equipment dispersed. The officers who received the shipment could see no earthly value in attempting to distribute the manuals, and simply stacked them in a warehouse where they may be still.

With complete candor Stephens rammed home the point that continual transfer of Service personnel who have acquired certain proficiency with equipment is a wasteful procedure. After the successful use of the DUKW in Normandy and in crossing the Rhine, officers who had become somewhat expert with this vehicle were shifted to duty not in any sense related to amphibious operations, and green men replaced them. Commonly these replacements knew less about DUKW's than did the men under them, a situation which could not fail to reduce morale. Stephens urged that hereafter the Services make an effort to train some men as specialists in the handling of such equipment and keep them with that equipment throughout their Service careers, just as has been done with radar.

Sometimes the failure of a vehicle can be attributed to a rather simple cause, but it takes months for word of this to be broadcast to all interested units. Stephens pointed out that in the early development of the DUKW there was danger that the whole program would bog down because the DUKW got stuck in sand on the beaches. Experiments showed that this was remedied when the tire pressure was lowered. And the designers put automatic controls in the DUKW so that tire pressure could be changed without stopping. Yet in place after place he would encounter DUKW operators totally unfamiliar with this elementary fact. DUKW's were stuck in Normandy as were other wheeled vehicles. Even as late as the invasion of Leyte an order went out that tires of all vehicles should be inflated to approximately ten pounds more than normal pressure — to allow for leakage if the vehicles were shipped around the ocean for some time before they were used in actual landings. Theoretically, according to the directive, by the time they were needed the tire pressure would be about normal.

As late as 1945 decreasing tire pressure for navigating beaches had not become a universal practice.

Although Stephens was usually blunt, he was also always constructive. Men of every rank recognized the splendid job he and his colleagues had done in improving the operation of the DUKW, the Weasel, and the LVT. He knew what he was talking about. Indubitably he had personally saved hundreds of lives and hundreds of thousands of dollars worth of precious equipment. His comments were therefore received with enthusiasm; and some days after his talk at OSRD the Navy requested that he give a similar detailed oral report to a large complement of officers of the Navy, Marine Corps, and Coast Guard.

In the spring of 1945 when landings on the China coast were being planned it was evident that still another amphibian would be needed. We had nothing that could move in quickly across the broad tidal flats of a huge delta and land troops, ammunition, and supplies. There the problem would be water only a few inches deep, or slick mud and silt that could not support the heavy DUKW's and Buffaloes and Weasels, could not even take our shallow-draft swamp gliders. There would be no underwater obstacles like jetted rails sticking up in the soggy silt to stop our shoreward progress; but these muddy areas were broad and the assault waves would have to cross them swiftly, or they would be mowed down by enemy fire.

The Navy's effort to solve this problem was centered at Port Hueneme on the California coast where such conditions could be found along the shore line. COMINCH asked for help from someone who would know the "soils" of deltas, and OFS sent Dr. Arthur B. Cleaves, one of the country's foremost engineering geologists, chief consultant on the Harrisburg Turnpike, who had later studied drainage on jungle airstrips and foundation problems in Mexico. He had just gone down to Fort Pierce, Florida, as a special advisor to the Joint Army-Navy Experimental and Testing Board (JANET) on various aspects of amphibious operations; but this mud-bottom problem was right up his alley and JANET would likewise be keenly interested in its solution.

At the Acorn Assembly and Naval Training Detachment at Hueneme Cleaves helped in the design and testing of an amphibian named the

PENGUIN. It was a shallow, lightweight sled, equipped with auxiliary treads and powered by an aircraft engine. It weighed less than a ton and could skim over water at the speed of an auto and go across mud flats, through sloughs and tule grass with ease, carrying men and supplies and towing extra loads. Fortunately we never needed to use this "vessel," but it would have traversed terrain impassable to all the types of amphibious vehicles we had yet devised.

This was only one of the many accomplishments of Arthur Cleaves during his two years with OFS, which are detailed in other portions of this book. Energetic, affable, alert, and persistent, he was one of the most successful of the OFS men in working with the military. For his contribution to the development of the PENGUIN, Navy Secretary Forrestal wrote: —

"Applying your comprehensive technical knowledge with resourceful initiative, you worked tirelessly in connection with the mud tests conducted by the Acorn Assembly and Training Detachment and were largely responsible for the solution of difficult incidental problems.

"By your keen enthusiasm, tactful cooperation and brilliant professional abilities you have contributed essentially to the development of urgently needed equipment, vital to the success of the war effort. Your diligent efforts are deeply appreciated."

DUKW's, Weasels, Water Buffaloes, and PENGUINS — as different from a sailor's idea of what a ship should be as was a Spanish galleon from the modern battlewagon. Yet the men who manned them — bluejacket, Marine, and dogface — learned to respect these sturdy, amphibian craft, and often they owed their lives to the combat scientists who designed, worked with, and fought for the trucks that went to sea.

CHAPTER XIV

FROM TEST TUBE AND EASEL, DAM SITE AND ZOO

ARTISTS OF SABOTAGE, DEXTEROUS CHEMISTS, AND VERSATILE ENGINEERS

D R. WILLIAM M. MANN, Director of the National Zoological Park in Washington, was made a Field Service Consultant and accepted leadership of the first group of specialists OFS sent to the Pacific. He seemed a natural choice for a mission to study the arms, equipment, and tactics most effective in combat under tropical conditions and over jungle terrain. He had an intimate knowledge of the South Pacific islands, could converse fluently with the natives, and was familiar with the meteorological and topographic conditions. His competence in entomology and zoology would be useful in dealing with medical and Quartermaster problems, especially those relating to insect control.

As a deputy to Mann, OFS sent Arthur Cleaves. He also had wide experience in the tropics — in the jungles of the Amazon and the thick forests of the Andes and Antilles. Moreover, the acquaintance with radar and with techniques used in operations analysis that he had picked up during several months of indoctrination with OFS would enable him to sound out theater needs along those lines.

Since Mann and Cleaves would only be able to provide leadership and general coverage of some of the Army's problems, OFS added to the team Dr. William A. Fowler, rocket expert from California Institute of Technology, and R. P. Russell, Vice-President of Standard Oil Development Company and specialist on thickened fuels, flame throwers, and chemical munitions.

This jungle-warfare project was the first OFS field mission under Army Ground Forces sponsorship. The New Developments Division had just become the major liaison office for OFS matters and was feeling its way in relations with the theaters on the use of civilians.

General Henry was anxious to get the group off to a good start, and asked General Kutschko, Deputy Director of NDD, to accompany the party, assist them in liaison with GHQ, and discuss with the South Pacific command the desirability of expanding the group to become an operations analysis staff, as had been intimated in General Harmon's conversations with Dr. Compton.

Taking with him a long list of questions from the Quartermaster Corps on commissary supplies, on packaging, storage problems, and deterioration, Mann moved around the theater inspecting QM stores and talking with supply officers. He lived with troops of the 93rd Division who were then moving to Bougainville, went to New Zealand and Guadalcanal, and returned to Washington late in April 1944 with answers to the elaborate questionnaire General Doriot of QMC had given him.

General Kutschko and Cleaves tried to stimulate theater interest in creating a team of operations analysts who might tackle problems in combat operations, communications, and transportation. But the officers were concerned with more immediate matters of equipment, particularly the use of rockets, flame throwers, and smokes.[1] Because these weapons were of increasing importance also in the Southwest Pacific, Fowler and Russell went on to New Guinea to acquaint MacArthur's forces with these developments of Divisions 3 and 11 and to determine rather specifically how much and what kind of civilian aid was needed in the field.

Fowler was an admirable advance agent for the rocket laboratories. He helped to install new equipment that had just arrived, brought officers up to date on developments at home, and returned with many recommendations based on the first SWPA experience with rockets in combat. Finding the military men already rather proficient in their understanding of this new ordnance but eager for expert help, he advised that OFS send out only consultants who knew the subject inside out.

Rockets had been spectacular in supporting the landings at Hollandia, even though the support batteries were improvised from the limited number of rocket projectors, gun-landing boats, and amphibious ve-

[1] This was doubtless a reflection of the visit General Borden had made to this theater several months earlier. He had come as a Colonel of Ordnance to study the Japanese defenses and the feasibility of using rockets against them.

hicles that could be furnished from local resources. It was evident that with a larger supply of rockets and with trained crews the beaches could be cleared even more effectively.

Until an injury sustained in a plane crash shortened his mission, Russell toured the combat areas and studied technical problems involved in the use of flame throwers, incendiaries, and smokes. He concluded that many important possibilities were not being realized because insufficient technical personnel were available in the theater. There was a general lack of knowledge of British and American developments, and communications were so poor that information about theater improvisations was not spread from one theater to the other, nor back to development groups on the mainland. Moreover, it seemed obvious that tests should be made in the field under actual combat conditions.

After his teammates left the theater, Cleaves stayed on alone in New Caledonia as the Acting Chief of a nonexistent group of "operations analysts." He remained in this anomalous status for many weeks and he was far from stagnant. He could see all sorts of needs and never missed an opportunity to point out to the theater staff how OSRD might help. While waiting for negotiations between OFS, NDD, and the theater to culminate in the dispatch of additional personnel, he aided the officers at GHQ in compiling an excellent manual on jungle warfare. Then he turned to a variety of theater problems which might be solved with aid from OSRD. He suggested development of a mortar shell that would burst above the treetops and scatter an impermanent dye to mark our front lines in the jungle. This would warn our pilots and keep them from bombing our own troops. Carrying theater endorsement, this suggestion was received at home with great interest and NDRC developed such a dye.

It was also suggested that mortar shells loaded with the radar countermeasure known as "Window" might be fired by our troops. This would put a hail of aluminum strips in the air above our men. Their positions could then be spotted with the Signal Corps Radar 584 (SCR-584) and relayed to the pilots. Cleaves thought that the same thing might be accomplished to greater advantage with rockets similarly loaded; but he pointed out that officers in that theater did not consider the use of radar for front-line identification favorably because so often the radar did not operate properly in mountainous and heavily forested terrain.

Although attacks utilizing rockets were in their infancy, Cleaves urged that data sheets on rocket damage, similar to those prepared by Division 2 for ordinary bombing, should be set up and standardized. He became interested also in the effects of fatigue on radar operators, especially those in Marine units, and urged the Marine officers to request OSRD help in studying this problem. Unfortunately, in the allocation of scientific aid the Marines were a stepchild throughout most of the war, not because they did not need it or because the scientists were hesitant to work with them, but because their requests had to be filtered through channels where they frequently were blocked.

Cleaves also proposed a radar device that might prove useful in the rescue of fighter pilots downed in Pacific waters. Then he became absorbed in problems of tropical deterioration. Through his efforts, capsules of cresatin, a substance that would release a volatile material to impede the growth of fungi that etched the glass and destroyed the efficacy of optical instruments, were eventually sent to officers of the Marine Corps in the South Pacific and to OFS headquarters in Oahu and SWPA.

Cleaves was, of course, constantly on the lookout for opportunities to use his special training in the war program. Discovering that a geologically trained Major in the Engineers had already undertaken geological studies in the South Pacific, Cleaves saw that this project might profit from greater interest at GHQ, from the presence in the theater of top-notch civilian geologists who could be procured through OFS, from more active support by the War Department that would be implied in sponsorship by NDD, and from the easier flow of technical information that was permitted to civilian specialists operating at staff level. He succeeded in stimulating keen interest among the senior theater officers in the importance of extending this geological work to cover the mineral resources, ground-water conditions, and geological structure of New Caledonia and the adjacent territories. Although the theater had become relatively inactive so that there would be little occasion for direct application to immediate military problems, the proposed study had broad implications in the occupation of this region.

This comprehensive proposal would require a sizable staff of geologists and military men to carry it through. There were many professional geologists already in uniform. To have them transferred to this project would take months; OFS could secure the ablest ones in the country and have them in the theater in a few weeks. Consequently the Commanding General asked that an additional geologist be sent forward to work with Cleaves in implementing the plan, and OFS assigned Dr. Marland P. Billings, outstanding structural geologist from Harvard University, to this mission. Unfortunately, however, soon after he joined Cleaves in New Caledonia the War Department decided to refuse further support in operational areas to field research that could not be turned to immediate usefulness in military operations, and the whole project was canceled.

By this time activity in SPA had been reduced to staging operations and it became clear that this theater was to be reorganized and incorporated into the Central Pacific command. Cleaves and Billings were recalled promptly. Billings returned to Harvard and Cleaves spent several months in the Pentagon examining air-strike photographs from postraid reconnaissance over France and Germany to aid the Strategic Bombing Survey in selecting targets that would prove suitable for ground assessment of bomb damage.

In January 1945 Cleaves was assigned to JANET and, after helping to develop the Penguin, he was again involved in a project that utilized his experience in geological engineering. The Navy wanted to select and train a group of specialists in soil mechanics who could go in as an advance reconnaissance unit on amphibious operations against large delta areas and secure samples of the silt and soil. Analyzing these in mobile laboratories, they would determine the trafficability of these materials, would find out what types of vehicles and loads could be supported by the saturated muds. It would be a costly business if our men were mired way out and could not even wade ashore. Cleaves chose the equipment needed by such a team, helped in the selection of personnel, and then supervised their training. From Fort Pierce they were to go to Narragansett Bay and finally forward to extremely hazardous operations on the China coast. The training was to have been completed by mid-August 1945 and Cleaves would have been en route again to the Pacific. But the Japanese capitulation obviated the need for this mission and he remained at Fort Pierce to write a comprehensive summary of the purpose and methods of the Beach Trafficability Unit he had organized.

A similar example of varied challenges to the technical breadth and personal adaptability of a combat scientist is seen in the series of projects undertaken by Dr. Albert G. H. Dietz. A structural engineer on the faculty at M.I.T., his special interests have been in wood and plastics technology. Although his knowledge of foundations and structures was brought into play in some of his OFS assignments, Dietz also tackled problems far removed from this field.

His career as an OFS consultant began when he enrolled as an indoctrinee in the first course to train bomb damage analysts at Princeton under OFS sponsorship. Then from mid-September until Christmas, 1944, he was Cleaves's predecessor as a consultant to the JANET Board at Fort Pierce. Its major function was to develop means for clearing enemy beaches of obstacles to landing operations. One of the methods JANET was investigating was a barrage of rockets from various types of landing craft. Examining the patterns of their demolition, Dietz calculated the effectiveness of this technique and arranged for aid from AMP in analyzing the results. When JANET experimented with a linear demolition charge to be propelled shoreward, Dietz came up with suggestions for changing its design, and called on OSRD's Division 5 to devise a guiding mechanism that would control its motion. He helped the representatives of Division 6 to demonstrate and evaluate an underwater-obstacle locator, and later took the device to Hawaii where the success of preliminary trials resulted in a Navy order for 300 of these items.

After he had aided JANET with arrangements for a three-day demonstration to show top-level Army, Navy, and Marine representatives the work accomplished at Fort Pierce, Dietz left for Oahu to head the Weapons and Analysis Section of Marshall's ORS. Working with one of the communications men, he converted the underwater-obstacle locator, already accepted by the Navy, into a satisfactory depth finder or fathometer for use in water from four to fifty feet deep. This unit proved so successful that the Naval Combat Demolition Training and Experimental Base immediately requested development and procurement through Navy channels. Dietz also computed the effect of roll and pitch on the accuracy of rocket fire and helped to develop simple, automatic switches that would prevent release of a rocket until the ship was fairly level. With his associates in the Section he experimented with infrared devices to determine whether or not they could be used in recognizing our own planes in night operations; demonstrated experimental models of night-vision binoculars that OFS had sent from Division 16 for test; participated in trials of a glide torpedo; helped to modify a mine detector; demonstrated the new infrared rifle or machine-gun sight known as a sniperscope; and took part in various aspects of the flame-thrower program.

An especially adventuresome mission was that of Maurice P. Coon, New England artist who turned his talents to camouflage and spent almost a year in the forests and hinterlands of India, Burma, and western China. Having aided in the development of a camouflaged agent developed by Division 19 that would be useful in sabotage, his objective was to train fierce native tribesmen to manufacture this material in small quantities and to direct them in using it behind the Jap lines.

He lived with the natives and taught them to drive jeeps and to use the modern weapons we had furnished. Most of the time he worked with men from OSS, but was occasionally sent on missions by himself. In both British and American planes he crossed and recrossed the rugged terrain — once in a plane that hedge-hopped over the ridges to bring food to a Chinese garrison cut off near Mandalay. On another occasion when he was in a C-54 going over the Hump, the big plane was pursued by five Jap Zeros and dropped suddenly from 20,000 feet into the treacherous air currents of the Himalayan valleys to elude them. While he was journeying up the Irawaddy River the Japs strafed and bombed his party for three hours, and 125 were killed.

Everywhere there was torturous heat and humidity, the deadly cobra and the krait, or the ever-present leeches, creatures about an inch long and of pencil thickness. They would extend themselves five or six inches and slide in this elongated form through the eyelets of one's shoes, or into the ears or nostrils at night.

Coon's mission was highly successful; but he paid a heavy price for the rare opportunities he enjoyed as a miracle man in these remote and fascinating areas. Wracked with virulent malaria, he had to be recalled after weeks of hospitalization in Burma.

Division 19 was also active in producing other special weapons for sabotage, the disposition of enemy sentries, and patrol operations at night. Dr. Compton had described some of these to the Alamo Scouts, and they asked that a person thoroughly familiar with them bring models to SWPA for demonstration and test. In April 1944 OFS arranged to send Leonard V. Sloma, mechanical engineer from a Division 19 contract laboratory at Northwestern University. Production models of some of the equipment were not ready, however, until late summer, and Sloma spent the fall months in the theater pointing out the merits of these insidious devices and gathering comments that would guide the further research of Division 19.

The Scouts had to be exceedingly mobile and were consequently unwilling to add this special equipment to the loads they carried. Moreover, not trusting the lethality of some of these special weapons, they were unwilling to substitute them for their carbines. They were, however, greatly interested in gear that Sloma told them about which was under development by OSRD for signaling and communicating over short ranges in the jungle. They requested that a specialist bring models of these items to the theater for demonstration.

In April Ralph M. Showers, electrical engineer from a Division 19 contract at the University of Pennsylvania, headed for SWPA with a trunkful of special apparatus. This included an induction field transceiver, designed for identification and signaling in dense jungle when light weight and radio silence are necessary, an electronic locator for buried supplies, equipment for signaling under water over short distances between small ships off shore and shore parties, and several types of infrared signaling devices. He also took a canister locator, a device to be attached to parachute packs so that their descent could be traced easily by the weird sirenlike noise it made. Showers demonstrated these items not only to the Alamo Scouts but also to many units of the Sixth and Eighth Armies. This resulted in requests to Washington for a supply of the infrared devices and the jungle transceivers to be tried out in actual operations. The equipment was not received in the theater, however, until almost the end of the war and the operational tests were never carried out.

The efforts of NDD and OFS to introduce flame throwers mounted on tanks to the Central and Southwest Pacific met with greater success. These weapons actually got into operations and their effectiveness was illustrated when one of these tanks in SWPA succeeded in "flushing" 8 Japs who were killed by the accompanying infantry. This broke enemy resistance and made possible an advance that resulted in killing 32 more of them.

When early in August 1944 chemical engineer Abbott Byfield, Technical Aide of Division 11, and R. Lannert Iglehart, mechanical engineer and flame-thrower specialist from Shell Development Company in San Francisco, joined the balanced team in Hawaii, the Commanding General of the 4th Armored Group was anxious to have a flame thrower that could be used as an auxiliary on an M-4 tank. He was not favorably disposed to vehicular-mounted flame throwers because they displaced the primary armament of the tank, but he was interested in a periscope-mounted flame thrower developed by the Armored Board at Fort Knox that had not yet been sent to the theaters. At the Army's request the ORS men built an essentially similar device in the theater and demonstrated it successfully. Since it was apparent that, to be available in time for projected operations, these flame throwers would have to be built in Hawaii, a group of Army, Navy, and Marine personnel was immediately set up to do this.

Meanwhile Iglehart and Byfield were also drawn into a development program under the Chemical Officer of the Central Pacific Base Command. He favored the vehicular-mounted flame thrower but the Tenth Army required that the flame thrower itself be contained in a standard 75-mm. barrel, or in a tube that would simulate it so that the silhouette would be the same as that of a regular M-4. When the design for such equipment was approved, Iglehart returned to the mainland to expedite shipment of material and supplies for the construction of this equipment, and then returned to Shell.

During the winter of 1944–45 NDD arranged to send the flame-thrower tank to the Philippines for operational trials. A demonstration team of one officer and four enlisted men took the equipment to the field, and George W. Engisch of Standard Oil Development Company arrived as an OFS consultant to follow up the exploratory work of his chief, Russell. The party left by boat at the end of February with four flame-thrower units mounted on M-4A-1 light tanks and got to Manila early in April.

Assigned to the 13th Armored Group of the Sixth Army, the equipment was sent into the hills to work with other light tanks and the 27th Infantry. This first use in combat demonstrated that the means of communicating with the ground troops had to be improved in order to develop co-ordinated attacks and that it would be difficult in any case to use such tanks in the irregular terrain. The flame throwers were kept alerted but were not used again in operations until late that month. Then in May they were transferred to the 34th Division but were not used because of impassable terrain. Nevertheless demonstrations were continued and the results showed that this was a potentially powerful weapon against Japs entrenched in caves and bunkers.

Lieutenant Colonel Henderson of NDD was very effective in the tank flame-thrower project. Visiting the theater in May and June, he stimulated considerable interest in this development and then returned to expedite shipment of additional units to the operating command. Late in June, 15 units of a somewhat different flame thrower mounted on the M-4A-1 tank were shipped to the Sixth Army, along with 6 mobile servicing units. A team of 6 officers and 21 enlisted men was created to instruct theater personnel in operation and maintenance. The equipment was to be used in the next major combat operation.

In July J. O. Collins, also of Standard Oil Development Company, flew to Manila to replace Engisch. Unfortunately the ship carrying the equipment and the maintenance crews suffered a major breakdown, put in to Guam for repairs, and did not arrive until after hostilities had ceased. Although Collins's mission was thus disrupted, he spent his time in the theater to good advantage, talking with officers of various units about mechanized flame throwers and aiding in the investigation of similar weapons captured from the Japanese. He learned from the 13th Armored Group that, although they had expended over three thousand gallons of fuel, the equipments Engisch had introduced had experienced no major mechanical difficulties.

* * *

Flame-throwing tanks served their purpose on more than one occasion; but they were never used extensively, partly no doubt because they were excellent targets and the casualty rates were too high. The troops in the Philippines were more anxious to use poison gas. Our forces had sufficient gas munitions in the forward areas, and arrangements for supplying more had been perfected so that chemical warfare could have been carried out very speedily. There is no doubt that in individual cases we could have saved innumerable American lives by using poison gas. There was strong pressure on the War Department both at home and in the military ranks overseas to do so. Many people found it hard to believe that roasting an enemy alive with flame throwers, or burning him out with incendiaries and phosphorus explosives, was any more moral.

On the other hand, if America had precipitated the use of gas in the Philippines campaign, the Japs would doubtless have retaliated on the defenseless Chinese. There is some opinion that in land operations the defenders often have an advantage because gas masks restrict vision and the protective clothing the attacking forces have to wear is cumbersome. Enemy troops in pillboxes and caves have less difficulty because they do not have to rely on great mobility. It may be true that considerations such as these, as well as a fear of retaliation, prevented us from starting gas warfare. Certainly the Japs knew that our defensive preparations were excellent and our equipment superior. They were not prepared to defend themselves against toxic munitions. Only the troops in the field and essential workers on the home islands had been supplied with gas masks. Since most of their civilians did not have protective clothing, they must have recognized that chemical warfare would have been extraordinarily effective against their civilian population. Consequently they refrained from starting something that would certainly backfire.

Yet there was always the possibility that we might need offensive or defensive measures, and our Chemical Warfare Service in the Southwest Pacific kept on its toes. In midsummer 1944 OFS received a request for a group of experts to work with them and with Australian research men in studying the behavior of chemical warfare agents under the unusual conditions peculiar to tropical regions. A mission of senior chemists headed by Dr. Wendell M. Latimer of the University of California visited the Australian laboratories and numerous Army installations in New Guinea. The party included Dr. Willis C. Pierce of the University of Chicago, who studied the performance of gas mask canisters, Dr. Paul G. Roach of the University of Illinois, whose specialty was smoke munitions, and Drs. Joseph H. Werntz of the Du Pont Company and Carl G. Niemann of California Institute of Technology who participated in extensive field tests of impregnated protective clothing. Although liaison with the Australians was maintained, the work became primarily an American undertaking.

The investigations of this group culminated in a comprehensive conference on chemical warfare held at Oro Bay, New Guinea, in October under sponsorship of the Services of Supply. Dr. Noyes, Chief of Division 10, in company with Major General Alden C. Waitt, Chief of CWS, and a staff of high-ranking officers, flew to New Guinea to attend. Latimer's team led discussions on the nature of persistent and nonpersistent agents, American impregnated clothing, characteristics of masks and canisters, methods of protection employed by the Japanese against gas warfare, smoke munitions requirements, and the effects of meteorological conditions on the use of gases and smokes. Chemical Warfare officers told of combat experience with smoke munitions, flame throwers, and the 4.2-inch chemical mortar.

As a result of this conference General Waitt proposed to MacArthur that a research team of civilian and military personnel be set up. They would be called the Far Eastern Technical Unit (FETU), and would carry out a continuing program of tests of chemical warfare agents and countermeasures. The FETU was established in February 1945 under the direction of Lieutenant Colonel John D. Reagh. It consisted of ten officers of CWS and three civilians procured from OFS. These were Dr. John W. Zabor, chemist from Northwestern, who visited the theater for a few weeks and helped to establish procedures for testing and sampling, William Shand, Jr., mathematician from the Division 10 laboratories of California Institute of Technology, and Robert K. Brinton, chemist from Northwestern.

For the first five months the FETU was based at Oro Bay and carried out tests of gas and smoke bombs and mortars in order to assess the functioning of these munitions under tropical conditions, particularly in kunai grass and primary forest. This was intended to supplement the similar munitions research carried out by groups at Dugway, Utah, and in Panama. In June the FETU moved to the Manila area where its principal function was to study the effectiveness of chemical munitions, particularly toxics, if they were to be used against Japanese underground defenses. Arrangements were made to isolate an area on Corregidor where typical Japanese underground defenses of many types were available. Before the investigations were started, however, the Japanese signed the terms of surrender and the FETU was deactivated.

There is not much question, however, about what the outcome of these tests would have been. Latimer had made a theoretical analysis of the operations against Biak, assuming that chemical warfare had been used, and concluded that the attack would not have lasted as long and would have produced fewer American casualties. In collaboration with Major M. B. Strauss of the Medical Division, CWS, in Hawaii, Dr. Stanford Moore, Technical Aide in Division 9 who joined ORS in June 1945, made a similar assessment of the potential value of gas warfare against a strongly defended cave on Okinawa. This had been a bitter engagement and was well reported in Army documents. The detailed report of Strauss and Moore was reviewed by some of the officers who had been present during that battle. Again it was the same story. Japanese defenses were inadequate, the cave was not gasproofed, and our casualty rate could have been reduced materially.

Moore was the final emissary from the chemical Divisions of NDRC to the balanced team at Fort Shafter. Armed with the latest information on toxic munitions that might be of value against the Japs, he was sent out by the Project Co-ordination Staff in CWS and would have gone forward to R/S in Manila for a month had the war not ended in August.

The chemical engineers of Marshall's ORS were an active and productive group. After Iglehart left, Byfield stayed on until December 1944. At the request of the Chemical Officer, Seventh Air Force, he assisted in an extensive series of tests on fire bombs and served as consultant on types of fuels to be used in jettisonable fuel tanks that could be used as incendiaries. He converted tables of chemical requirements into forms more readily applicable to Air Force use, and studied the deterioration of certain types of mustard-filled bombs.

Just before Byfield came back to the States, Robert M. Newhall, chemical engineer trained in Division 11 on incendiaries, flame throwers, and thickened fuels, arrived in the theater. The flame-thrower program had reached the production stage by that time, and Newhall maintained close contact with the 43rd Chemical Laboratory which was particularly interested in the proper method for mixing fuels. He helped to develop a standard operating procedure for mixing in the field and worked with Air Force, Navy, and Marine units that were experiencing difficulties with the fuel for jettisonable tanks. Newhall also surveyed the deterioration of equipment, stores, and materiel, considered the problem of marking front lines by chemical methods, and studied the use of barrage balloons to protect shipping and airfields. When Ostlund, one of the electronics men, left the theater, Newhall stepped in to assist in testing an underwater-mine detector Ostlund had developed from a land-mine detector. Although young, he thus demonstrated qualities of a combat scientist by pinch-hitting on problems out of his own special fields of chemistry and chemical engineering.

CHAPTER XV

HUNTING BY FORMULA AND FLYING UNSEEN

DEFENSE AGAINST FIGHTERS AND FLAK

CERTAINLY average duck hunters are seldom aware of the principles of physics and mathematics that will control whether they go home empty-handed, or with a full day's limit. Through trial and error they learn to judge how much to lead the ducks that come from different angles at different speeds, and they find out the killing range the hard way. Members of the "sitting-bird club," who hold their fire until the ducks have landed among the decoys, will usually declare that their skill in aiming and the pattern made by the pellets of shot are the important factors in determining their bag. Even if they shoot only at birds in flight, they are not likely to consider that the problem of getting a lethal hit is infinitely simplified because their own position in the marsh is stationary.

But the gunner in the blister of a bomber found out very quickly that the technique of firing was entirely different. The enemy fighters sometimes came in steep dives at speeds ten times as fast as ducks. He was dumfounded to learn that under certain conditions it was even necessary to follow rather than lead the target — that is, to aim behind it, of all things — in order to get a hit. He would surely never have tried that deliberately. But the mathematician could show him why it had to be, taking into consideration the courses and speeds of his own ship, of the target, and of his ammunition. Furthermore, his "blind" was also in motion — two or three hundred miles an hour, perhaps on a course suddenly changed in an evasive maneuver. He could not afford to experiment, to learn by trial and error. His life and the lives of his buddies were in the balance. Yet there was no time for elaborate calculations. These were made in advance and rule-of-thumb procedures based on them. This was a job for top-notch mathematicians. Scores of them were needed to keep the charts and tables up to date as our speeds and tactics and the operating characteristics of our guns were changed.

Gunnery for weapons that are flexible, that can be moved and pointed by the gunners, requires continual, painstaking study. The factors that will influence the probable number of hits under a particular set of conditions are infinitely complex, and it takes an expert to eliminate errors in the data.

At the end of the war an Air Force textbook on the theory of flexible gunnery was in preparation. Its author, Dr. Edwin W. Paxson, crack mathematician from OFS and the staff of the Jam Handy Corporation in Detroit, says of his intentions: "By whatever god has cognizance of caliber 0.50 projectiles, the book is going to be theoretical. The ultimate consumer at the present time is the gunnery officer specialist. It is not intended that the book supply him with a reference manual of procedures on the daily aspects of his job. This function is competently fulfilled by standard Service publications. Instead, the intent is to furnish meaty matter for continued professional study. . . . The (research) material developed by Service establishments and various Divisions of OSRD should be so summarized, simplified and applied as to be of maximum usefulness to the Air Force gunnery officer in the active theater and in the training command."

The book is based on highly theoretical considerations and intricate mathematical formulas developed in the quiet atmosphere of a research office. Yet it is realistic because the author went to Europe and had firsthand contacts with American and British gunners who did a magnificent job in ETO, and made a thoroughgoing survey of the doctrine of flexible gunnery used by Goering's airmen.

In December 1943 General Grandison Gardner, Commanding General of the Army Air Forces Proving Ground Command at Eglin Field, Florida, asked that this able mathematician and conscientious reporter be attached to his staff as a special consultant. In this capacity Paxson was concerned with initiation of new ideas in aerial warfare. He became a member of a technical planning committee that devoted its attention to such problems as radar jamming, bombs terminally accelerated by rocket propulsion, and aerial drag bombs. As a high-powered specialist on the staff of the Commanding General, he was also consulted on many other matters — heat flow in cold-weather hangars, harmonization of fighter's guns, and the optimum flight path for a B-25 firing a 75-mm. cannon with radar control.

After a few months the planning committee was dissolved and Paxson turned to his original specialty in airborne fire-control equipment. He initiated an extensive program for comparing the performance of typical American gunsights against attacking fighters. Involved mathematical procedures were necessary to reduce the camera records to aiming errors and hit probabilities. The Navy and NDRC were also concerned in this program, and the methods were refined for further use both at Eglin Field and at the Patuxent River Naval Air Station.

Until his trip overseas Paxson devoted about 80 per cent of his time to the OFS assignment and carried heavy commitments with the Special Devices Division of the Navy's Bureau of Aeronautics. Jam Handy was producing training devices for aerial gunnery under contract to the Navy, and Paxson was the chief mathematical consultant in their design and utilization. In August General Gardner released him to work with the Applied Mathematics Panel in determining the optimum flight formations for the B-29 and assessing the radar fire control of that plane. Then in the spring of 1945 Paxson began work on the comprehensive textbook. This eventually took him to all the available laboratories and establishments in the non-Russian zones of Germany where he questioned scientists and examined documents to acquire a broad picture of the state of aerial gunnery training developed by the Nazis. Alert, dynamic, a forceful expositor of applied mathematics, and a tireless traveler, Paxson was considered a Good Joe by the officers and GI's whom he helped to educate in the continually revised doctrines of flexible gunnery.

The Army airfield at Laredo, Texas, was the focal point of the entire Air Force for training the men who operate the flexible guns.[1] A Research Section of the Central School for Flexible Gunnery at Laredo experimented with training devices and studied techniques for evaluating the aptitudes of indoctrinees while they were undergoing instruction. The officers of this Section were primarily psychologists. They needed the help of a physicist and a mathematician to keep them in-

---

[1] OSRD-trained Dr. George W. Taylor who headed this activity pioneered this training program by preparing a manual while he was still serving as a key member of an operational analysis unit in North Africa.

formed of progress in the development of equipment and to answer the numerous technical questions posed by the trainees. OFS provided Dr. Donald P. LeGalley, faculty physicist of the Philadelphia College of Pharmacy, and Dr. Vernon G. Groves, mathematician from the teaching staff of Michigan State College.

LeGalley maintained liaison with the Applied Mathematics Panel, the radar laboratories, Aberdeen Proving Ground, and other agencies concerned in problems of fire control, and followed developments in radar pertaining to gun sights for flexible guns. At the request of the Air Technical Service Command, Wright Field, he designed approach courses for use with a trainer developed at M.I.T. Groves kept in touch with AMP, the Jam Handy Corporation, the Patuxent Naval Air Station, and Bell Aircraft Corporation on various phases of flexible gunnery training and fire-control devices. The diversity of his reports indicates that Groves was active in many technical aspects of the Laredo program — Jam Handy trainers and films, gun-camera films and film assessments, plans for a B-29 trainer, firing rules for the stripped B-29, bullet dispersal probabilities, ballistics of the frangible bullet, offset guns on fighter aircraft, and testing programs for various gun sights.

The mathematical and physical factors that affect the performance of antiaircraft guns, though exceedingly complex, are simpler and more nearly comparable to those that limit the success of the stationary duck hunter. General Marquat, commander of the 14th Antiaircraft Command in SWPA, was eager to have experts analyze the performance of U.S. antiaircraft guns and predictors and study the evasive tactics of Japanese planes. In August 1944 Dr. Sidney Darlington, physicist from Bell Telephone Laboratories, arrived in the theater to work with antiaircraft batteries in New Guinea. Concerned for several months with corrections in 90-mm. fire, necessary because of meteorological conditions, he wrote training circulars on this subject.

At the time of the Leyte invasion General Marquat reported that Japanese planes customarily accelerated when they were first subjected to antiaircraft fire. This resulted in lagging bursts and a technique was needed to counter this maneuver. In consultation with a radar expert from the Radiation Laboratory sent out as an Advisory Specialist from the Secretary of War's Office, Darlington developed a modification of the M-9 antiaircraft predictor that would correct for these lagging bursts.

In November he moved to the Philippines and studied the evasive tactics of Japanese planes by means of motion pictures. Cameras were co-ordinated with the gun directors so that they would record the bursts from antiaircraft fire. But by the time of the Lingayen landing in Luzon the Japanese air forces had been so completely whipped that the antiaircraft companies to which this apparatus was assigned never had occasion to fire on a Japanese plane. In fact, Marquat's reply to inquiries about his research needs was: —

"Have the Japs send us more planes to observe."

The effectiveness of Darlington's work as a combat scientist is indicated in the commendation he received from Marquat: "Your recent exploration of the subject of . . . enemy airplane evasive action, including the development of the required equipment, is of great value to the present and future military service. . . . I hereby go on record as especially desiring your return as a military technical advisor to my command at any time in the future that this may be considered advisable by the War Department."

In the summer of 1945 when the problem of Baka bombs, Japanese equivalent of the German V-1, was critical, Marquat was anxious to take advantage of European experience in adapting the mobile ground radar, SCR-584, to tracking and antiaircraft fire control. On the British coast when a row of these sets succeeded in spotting the buzz-bombs as they rose over the Channel, the AA batteries shot most of them down before they reached their objectives in London. Marquat asked for two radar men and OFS sent Robert S. Levine, who had been at the Radiophysics Laboratory, and Dr. R. H. Caston, Radiation Laboratory physicist who had spent some months with ORS in Hawaii. Using available lightweight radar, they began a project of tracking the trajectories of the Bakas.

The terrific casualties we were suffering from Japanese mortar fire posed an even more pressing problem. This called for concerted action by the scientists and the military men. Mortars had first proved devastating on a major scale at Cassino in Italy. Then in Germany they had been a serious hindrance to our advances, but in the hilly Philippines they were an outstanding obstacle to rapid progress against the Japanese. The mortars were small, highly mobile, and cleverly camouflaged. They were extremely deadly and very difficult to find. After firing a few shots they would be moved or withdrawn into caves. Conventional range finders could not be used against them because of the rugged country; and human spotters were vulnerable.

One of the most precise of several methods that science proposed for meeting this problem was a modification of the SCR-584 so that it would track the mortar shell in the air and project its trajectory back to the firing point, all in about 20 seconds. One serious drawback in this technique was that the 584 was frequently too cumbersome to be taken into the rough topography where much of the difficulty with mortars was encountered. While the research men and engineers were rushing to bring out new, more easily portable equipment, however, our troops were being cut down by the dreaded mortar fire. Consequently Caston and Levine were also drawn into this problem. They developed a board for plotting mortar trajectories and installed it in a modified SCR-584 for operational tests by units of the Sixth Army. Special crews were then assigned for training in the techniques of mortar location by radar.

In the summer of 1945 R. F. Thomson of the Radiation Laboratory joined the radar group in Oahu and spent some weeks demonstrating the use of the MTI (moving target indicator), an attachment added to radar that indicates only the moving targets by cutting out echoes received from all fixed targets. He was particularly concerned with the addition of this device to the 584. In the demonstrations at Hawaii moving ships were discernible in the harbor, and planes taxiing on the airport could be followed down to a speed of about twenty miles per hour. The sets were also placed aboard an LST and were used to spot planes that dropped "Window," the strips of aluminum that would reflect radar signals and make it difficult to tell which echoes were coming from planes and which from these strips. In August Thomson moved to Clark Field, Luzon, for similar demonstrations. They generated a great deal of interest and the headquarters staff asked that this

MTI modification be widely installed. Marquat's Antiaircraft Command planned to use it in spotting Baka bombs and suicide planes in Operation Olympic, the invasion of Japan.

Fortunately for our side, the Axis was well behind us in the development of automatic radar tracking and antiaircraft fire control. Consequently we could rely on deceptive techniques and evasive tactics to defend us from the enemy's antiaircraft batteries. In the "carpetbag" flight from England to France, when American airmen were dropping supplies at night to the French Underground, our losses were reduced by 50 per cent. This impressive result could be attributed to a new camouflage paint developed by Division 16 of NDRC. Efforts to camouflage night fighters and bombers by painting them a flat dull black had not proved successful. In a searchlight against the night sky they showed up practically white. Then the OSRD experts developed an enamel with a high gloss and containing black pigment. Applied as a top coat to our planes, it produced a remarkably efficient specular reflection in the searchlight beam; and this rendered them virtually invisible. Moreover, the paint was glossy. Its skin friction with the air was less than was that of the dull coat; and this made for increased air speed.

Repainting bombers and fighters would take only forty-eight hours when the enamel was simply applied over the ordinary dull finish. But the RAF decided that attrition of its night-flying squadrons was so high that repainting of planes already in service would not justify such operational delays. Nevertheless, the AAF arranged to fly one plane at a time from each field to a modification center for this treatment. Soon reports from the Operations Analysis Sections indicated that this anti-searchlight camouflage provided a greater degree of invisibility in combat than did the standard, dull black, night camouflage.

Word of the effectiveness of this glossy skin in permitting pilots to avoid a searchlight "fix" spread throughout ETO. One Colonel stated that its influence on the morale of his pilots was so good that he would advocate use of the new paint even if in reality it had no genuine camouflage value.

In March 1944 the Air Forces in the Pacific theaters and in the China-Burma-India (CBI) area asked for shipments of this paint and suggested that experts be sent out to instruct field personnel in applying and using it. One of the manufacturers asked to supply the material was the Ault and Wiborg Corporation of Cincinnati. OFS arranged with this firm to loan three of its specialists for field service — Edward F. Burke, A. Todd Selbert, and David J. Stedtefeld.

These men were rather young and the Selective Service situation was tight. Only after several months of pulling and hauling with Selective Service and the War Department were they finally able to leave the country — Burke to the 11th Air Force in the Aleutians, Selbert to the 14th in India-Burma, and Stedtefeld to the Far East Air Force in the Southwest Pacific.[2]

They discovered to their dismay that the material purchased by the Army and shipped to the Pacific theaters was not the enamel obtained from their own company. Instead, a lacquer type of paint was being used. This was less desirable, they were sure. Although it meant they would have to help the Army to use a competitor's products, they were certain that their own firm would approve anything they might do to reduce the losses of our planes and pilots.

Burke's assignment was to convert the B-24 Liberator from the standard official, olive-drab and gray camouflage enamel. Lacquer cannot be applied successfully over enamel. Yet since it was the only material with the special gloss available in the theater, the standard dull finish of the Liberators had to be removed and then a prime coat of zinc chromate applied. To eliminate all traces of wax that remained after using a paint remover, the ship had to be steam-cleaned and washed. Three coats of lacquer were necessary to get the proper depth and gloss on the finish, and then a coat of straight lacquer thinner to remove overspray and lap marks. Once the B-24 had been prepared for painting, it took five days to apply the prime coat, the lacquer coats, and finally the insignia and identification. Burke reported that the total job could not be accomplished by a crew of four or five men in less than two weeks, unless enamel rather than lacquer were used, or unless only those parts of the plane that would be exposed in level flight to a searchlight beam were treated with the anti-searchlight camouflage.

Selbert proceeded to India. With officers of the 10th Air Force, the

---

[2] Had it not been for Colonel Leach's willingness to have these men work with his ORS teams in the various theaters, they might never have gone.

British Bomb Group stationed in India, and the Strategic Air Forces, he selected Bangalore, India, and a site in Assam in China as the best places for painting the planes. Some would be done when they returned from combat across the Hump for maintenance at Assam, and others could be painted before they left the replacement pool at Bangalore.

Selbert remained with the 14th Air Force for several months, and plane after plane was given the new finish as the target areas changed and there were more missions over searchlighted territory. The treatment proved so successful that it was planned to give it to all the B-24's in the theater and to apply it as they came off the assembly lines at home to all new B-24's destined for that area.

When Stedtefeld arrived in the Southwest Pacific he learned that the camouflage paint had been shipped to the theater before he left California; but it had apparently been lost en route or at the port of debarkation. Nevertheless, he was a combat scientist and would do the best he could with whatever might be available in the theater. Proceeding to several depots in New Guinea and the Netherlands East Indies, he located substitute materials that could be used and ordered more by air from Wright Field.

Stedtefeld had brought with him several small demonstration panels. Some were painted the ordinary dull black and others had the new glossy coat. One night he stationed himself a hundred feet from officers and members of Colonel Leach's ORS. When he asked them to tell him by flashlight how many panels he held in his hand, they were constantly confused, unable to see the panels painted with the new camouflage. This vivid demonstration created genuine interest at once and paved the way for wide application of the new technique in SWPA.

The officers of the 13th Air Force were intensely interested in the possibilities. They furnished planes for test runs to determine the value of this paint at low-level altitudes. A ship treated with the glossy camouflage was flown following an ordinary untreated plane, first at 10,000 feet, then at 3000 feet, and finally at 500 feet. Our searchlight operators had no difficulty in spotting the ordinary plane, but they could not locate the camouflaged one at any of these levels except when it flashed a flicker light used for signaling. Even with this momentary identification, the officers claimed it would have been impossible to fire a gun at the camouflaged target with any hope of success.

Stedtefeld also created interest in this glossy paint among naval officers. When Captain C. B. Jones, commander of Fleet Air Wing 17, wanted to try it on Catalinas, Stedtefeld obtained enough of the material to send him for experimental tests. Then there were conferences with other officers who wanted to try this protective coating on PT boats.

Confident that there was enough material in stock to continue the job of finishing night planes for the 13th and 5th Air Forces and that theater personnel had sufficient knowledge of the requirements to accomplish the conversion satisfactorily, Stedtefeld returned to the United States. His mission had involved about 40,000 miles of flying. He had lost thirty-five pounds in the field because of bad food and dysentery, and he knew what it was like up front. Japanese bombers frequently interrupted his work. They came in on nuisance raids during the test runs; and nine times on Christmas Eve they dropped their bombs close to his field headquarters.

The paint specialists from OFS left the theaters before the full value of their work could be seen. But there is no question that they were directly responsible for saving the lives of many American and British airmen and for keeping numerous planes in the air months longer than they would have been otherwise. The truly patriotic attitude of Ault and Wiborg in encouraging these men to remain and do their best, even though its products were not directly involved, is a splendid example of the co-operative spirit OFS encountered repeatedly in its dealings with American industry.

Though the men in our fighters and bombers and our AA battery crews may once have hunted for sport, they were shooting this time for survival. Using formulas, charts, and equations, the field-service experts in physics, mathematics, radar, and paint taught our gunners new techniques of aiming to knock the foe out of the sky, to demolish Jap mortars and Bakas, and to deal with the dread kamikaze. And they proved that by flying unseen we could baffle the enemy's hunters.

CHAPTER XVI

WIZARDS OF ETHER AND WIRE

THE ELECTRICAL EYE-AND-EAR SPECIALISTS

THE Germans pulled out of Paris in too much of a hurry to leave the havoc we expected. But they did throw the largest long-distance telephone switchboard in Europe out of order. At the Paris long-lines repeater station they put sand in generators, wrecked transmission and test equipment, and left the entrance cables and terminal blocks in a confused mess.

The Signal Corps pitched in at once to straighten out the circuits, repair the damage, and re-establish communications channels in and out of the city. While they were puzzling over the main frame cables, the jack wiring and adjustments for French types of repeaters, in walked Robert A. Fox, experienced communications engineer from radio station WGAR in Cleveland. He had just "hitch-hiked" to Paris in an Army truck to join an OFS team of radio, radar, and communications men attached to the Signal Corps. Fox was tired, but this was no time for complaining. He worked day and night aligning circuits, tracing out terminations, preparing charts and drawings to guide the military engineers and GI's, until the station was back in operating condition. Then he helped design plans to extend the long-distance service into Germany as the armies advanced.

Fox was not the only member of the OFS group who found himself working on technical details and on assignments far different from those anticipated when the team was organized in Washington. This was one OFS project completely altered by circumstances in the theater. It had originated when the Operations Analysis Division of the Signal Corps proposed an analytical study of the new, complicated radio and radar equipment that had been sent to ETO in such great quantities. Lynn C. Smeby, Dr. Everitt's Deputy in the Operational Research Staff of the Signal Corps, asked OFS to supply a team of engineers who had sufficient familiarity with Army equipment to determine whether or not the potentialities of this new gear were fully realized in combat and to give counsel and instruction when necessary. These specialists were to prepare staff studies and survey the technical feasibility of new operational uses for Signal Corps equipment. From theoretical analyses and operational results they would submit recommendations for improving existing systems and would furnish an engineering-consulting service on problems concerning radio, propagation, and electronics.

The Signal Corps selected Royal V. Howard, Vice-President in Charge of Engineering of Universal Broadcasters in San Francisco, as leader of this group of "operations analysts." Late in July he left for Europe accompanied by Dr. Karl R. Spangenberg, electrical engineer from Stanford University, and Ozro M. Covington, radar engineer from the Holabird Signal Depot in Baltimore. Later the group was expanded by the addition of Lucien A. Farkas from the Signal Corps Laboratory at Camp Evans, Eugene G. Pack of Station KSL in Salt Lake City, Carl C. Bath of Holabird, and Fox.

By that time our troops were recapturing miles of territory every day and the fronts were fluid. Conditions of defensive warfare and the static lines that would permit analytical studies existed no longer. Operations analysis in the true sense of the word was now impossible in forward areas. The greatest need was for specialists to service equipment, or even to teach the GI's how to use it. Recognizing that this was urgent and that there were simply not enough high-grade technicians available in the theater, Howard's men took off their coats and went to work, helping out wherever they could and often performing functions that in civilian life they would have assigned to subordinates.

Moreover, arrangements for their attachment in the theater had somehow miscarried. Instead of reporting at staff level to the Supreme Headquarters Allied Expeditionary Forces (SHAEF), the group was reconstituted as the Operational Analysis Branch of the Technical Liaison Division in the Signal Section of the European Theater of Operations, U.S. Army (ETOUSA). In this lower echelon they were received with great courtesy but some astonishment. The officers were amazed that men of this high technical caliber should be thus assigned. The theater had only asked for technicians and was apparently unaware of the more ambitious plans in Washington. The military were friendly and co-operative enough; but this kind of a setup inevitably meant longer channels for the civilians and a bigger job of selling their recommendations.

While the team was still stationed in London its members began to function almost as individual consultants on a variety of theater problems. Although they were all working under Howard as group leader and co-ordinator, the original concept of a panel of analysts who would collaborate on one problem after another had to be abandoned. Spangenberg and Howard studied the use of British "S-band" equipment for communications across the Channel. Then Spangenberg and Farkas joined a CIOS team of investigators and visited many critical targets in territories rewon by the Allied Armies before Spangenberg returned to the United States in October. Pack worked on problems in the use of very-high-frequency equipment and facsimile until illness forced him to leave the theater. Howard looked into possibilities of adapting infrared photography for tactical purposes in Ground Force operations. Several men of his team were called on also to help train the troops in using the SCR-584 for tracking and shooting down the buzz-bombs.[1] This solution to the V-1 problem resulted from exceptional teamwork between the British and American military and technical men; and in this feverish effort the staff of BBRL played a leading role.

Finding a deplorable lack of understanding of this massive radar set among the military operators because their experience with it had been meager, the Howardmen trained operating units on the job and assisted in all kinds of repair work. In the defenses of Antwerp they adjusted 60 sets in 6 weeks.

Working with the 584 had its hazards. The AA gun batteries were commonly crowded in concentric circles so close together that there was real danger of knocking the robot bombs down on the batteries themselves. Howard was uncomfortably close to several near misses, and injuries suffered in these brushes with sudden death eventually forced him to turn over leadership of the group to Farkas.

---

[1] While in London and later on location in the field, they had vivid experiences with the German V-1. Thinking of signs in America which say "This theater can be emptied in two minutes," Howard wrote that he was tempted to put up a sign in his quarters reading "When the buzz-bombs come over, this bed can be emptied in one second," — and he affirms that often it really was.

On one occasion an AA battery fired 26,000 rounds in 24 hours and brought down only one or two of the buzz-bombs. But after the OSRD experts, including Bath and Covington, had been in the field checking the equipment and training the men, 97 per cent of the bombs were exploded in the air or forced down long before they reached their targets.

At first the men in the field were suspicious of these OFS specialists. Only after they had ascertained that the team really knew the equipment were they amenable to instruction. The experience of the group in teaching operators showed that a man does not remember an adjustment procedure unless he has actually performed it on the equipment at least twice.

Working close to the front lines with the First, Third, Seventh, and Ninth Armies, the Ninth Air Defense Command, and the First French Army, Howard's team checked spare components, made necessary repairs, distributed modification kits, and provided technical consultation. Frequently they encountered enemy fire. At one point while he was tracing communications channels, Fox even found himself between our own and the enemy lines and under fire from both directions. Nevertheless, the group survived without casualty. Yet they remarked that a good stiff course of military training could have taught them plenty about how to handle themselves and would have saved them many anxious moments. Although these men probably spent more time in and close to the front lines than any other OFS field team, they swore that the aimless shots of exuberant Frenchmen on V-E Day were a much greater hazard than the organized fighting.

In the rapid advance through France and again in the later plunge across Germany during the last weeks of the war, moves of 20 to 50 miles several times a week were not uncommon.[2] The mobility of our AA gun batteries was remarkable. Important objectives such as supply points and forward headquarters were given AA protection within a few hours after they were set up. When early-warning radar equipment was not available, 584's were used for this function. That may be why Goering never found it economical to use precision or

[2] This OFS group traveled east with Patton's Army and reported that first he would order only rations, ammunition, and fuel to be shipped forward; then only ammunition and fuel; and, finally, only fuel.

formation bombing on targets defended by American AA gun units. The Nazi planes were forced to employ violent evasive action and thereby lost a large part of their effectiveness.

Improper handling and storage of spare parts for radio and radar equipment was a senior-grade headache until Bath and Covington succeeded in establishing a special warehouse for radio and radar repair, directly under the supervision of specialists. In the rush to bring adequate supplies across the Channel and up to a front that was moving so fast, confusion had been inevitable. Proper transport was often not available and the drivers of trucks could not be expected to appreciate the delicacy and critical importance of the scientific equipment they carried. Trucks frequently had to be unloaded in a hurry at the nearest supply dump. It might or might not be sheltered. Under sustained damp weather, the wooden boxes housing the precious cargo of spare parts warped so badly that they were no longer watertight and the swollen drawers became immovable. Many times the boxes were handled roughly, dumped off trucks or unloaded from trains and placed haphazardly in warehouses. Finally Covington and Bath managed to sort through the warehouses personally, collected the spare parts, and rationed them to special radar depots on the Continent.

French manufacturers of radio and radar equipment could save us valuable time and shipping space by supplying the Signal Corps with parts and components. But American signal experts who also knew the language were needed to study the extent of this potential help and carry on the negotiations. Since Farkas had been brought up in France, he undertook a survey of radio manufacturing facilities in the Paris and Lyons areas, set up a consulting and testing service on prototypes of radio and radar submitted by French manufacturers, translated patent résumés, trained radar men, and prepared instruction manuals for operators and maintenance crews of the First French Army.

Through deliberate procrastination the French manufacturers had avoided delivery of much signal material to their Nazi masters. Our technical men proceeded to adapt many of the undelivered items to our own purposes. Fox helped to convert a 60-KW mobile unit ordered by the *Wehrmacht* but never turned over to the Germans. He also built a 1-KW teletype unit and installed an RCA console that reestablished broadcasts back to the United States. In accomplishing all this Fox spent a great deal of his time procuring from Army supply channels many items needed in making the modifications. Often this necessitated searching personally in supply dumps and warehouses.

Here was a man with some twenty years of experience in the equipment design and development field, a specialist on radio transmitters in the medium, high, and very-high-frequency ranges. In the ETO he was operating essentially as a technician and maintenance man and running technical errands. In December the Army decided that this constituted a decided waste of competent technical manpower and that he might be used to greater advantage elsewhere in the war. Fox returned to the States with a personal commendation from Brigadier General Carroll O. Bickelhaupt, Director of the Communications Division, expressing warm appreciation for his personal resourcefulness and initiative. A few months later he was establishing communications facilities as a member of Marshall's team on Okinawa.

When Farkas, Covington, and Bath returned the following summer, the Signal Corps asked that OFS keep the group intact for a few months more, so that they could aid in obtaining operational and propagation characteristics of a new system of microwave relay links between San Diego and San Francisco. Consequently, at the close of the war they were helping to install, maintain, and repair new equipment on the west coast and were making tests of field strength.

One day in the spring of 1944 two American tanks went out over forested, rolling terrain behind the lines in Europe. Each had new radio equipment and their orders were to maneuver, establish radio contact, and then practice a joint operation. They were gone for some time when suddenly observers were startled. The two tanks nearly collided as they approached from opposite sides of a low ridge. If this had been a combat operation and the gunners were at all "trigger-happy" they might have shot one another.

An OFS radio and radar man was on hand to investigate — Harold S. Balmer, astrophysicist from the Museum of Science and Industry in Chicago and staff member of the Radiation Laboratory. He found that the tank crews had removed parts of the radio antennas — they proved inconvenient in getting in under trees — and, to make matters even worse, the men had brought along the wrong crystals for operating their sets. The incident is another demonstration of the importance of making civilian specialists available to keep our troops supplied with up-to-date knowledge about the complex equipment arriving in greater and greater quantities.

Balmer also cited an example of the superb discipline in military matters displayed in a unit of the 9th Pathfinder Troop Command to which he was an advisor on the use of radar in big transport planes. On D-Day one of these ships was unable to gain the altitude needed to clear a coastal ridge. Orders came back to jettison parachutes and all unnecessary equipment. They obeyed to a man and each remained calmly in his seat until the pilot crash-landed near a destroyer and gave the order to leave the plane.

Balmer's primary mission was to demonstrate that there would be little mutual interference of the radar equipment we planned to use in the invasion. Given the probable disposition of the various sets for Operation Overlord, the landings at Normandy, he allayed the fears of operations officers of the 8th and 9th Air Forces that one piece of equipment would limit the effectiveness of its neighbors.

The 9th Air Force had another radar specialist from OFS. Donald J. S. Merten of the Sperry Gyroscope Co. had gone to ETO with Balmer and worked for a short time with the ORS of the 9th. Then he was released to become a personal technical advisor on radar to Major General Hugh Knerr, Deputy Commander of the Strategic and Tactical Air Forces. Merten was a key liaison man with research and development agencies, the manufacturers of radar gear, and the Army Technical Services.

In the hazy weather over Europe during fall and winter months the ability to come in and take off by radar was the dream of many a pilot — and blind-landing systems are one striking development in the radar field that holds great promise for commercial aviation. Merten flew back and forth across the Atlantic several times, even after he was injured in a plane crash, to expedite the use of automatic bomb-release mechanisms and to bring the latest information about and equipment for radar-controlled landing to the pilots who returned from strikes deep into Germany and frequently found that the ceiling was zero.

*   *   *

With less than six weeks to go before the mighty armadas of air and surface craft would head for the beaches of Normandy, the British Admiralty and the American Navy were anxious to have the help of experts in radar countermeasures (RCM). The Nazis had spotted hundreds of radars along the vulnerable coasts of France and the low countries. Unless we jammed these sets, the enemy could see our invasion fleets long before they approached within striking distance, could send out dive bombers to harass us, and could operate their coastal artillery with ghastly accuracy.

On April 30th OFS was notified informally that 16 RCM men were needed in Europe "the day before yesterday" to install new equipment and make the finishing preparations for this phase of the imminent invasion. The cable was of the greatest urgency and the interest was top-level. Consequently the project had the full backing of both War and Navy Departments, and major credit for expediting the military arrangements should go to Dr. Edward L. Bowles, physicist from M.I.T., who became the chief consultant to the Secretary of War on radar and RCM for air operations. Two RCM men, Drs. Orville Sather and Paul S. Hendricks of the Columbia Broadcasting System, were already in process for duty in Europe. Several weeks earlier OFS had drawn a contract with CBS to procure them when the Navy's initial estimate of its needs came in. There would be no time to line up fourteen more and put them through the formalities of affiliation with OFS. The Radio Research Laboratory (RRL) of Division 15 agreed to furnish them directly and the whole group was detailed to its Branch Laboratory in England (ABL-15).

On May 6th, one week after the request and a month before D-Day, eleven of these specialists were over the Atlantic, and the rest followed during the succeeding week. The installations had to be made in a terrific hurry and the operators were distressingly green. Nevertheless the equipment withstood gunfire without serious damage and our RCM crews threw the German radar men into utter confusion.

Some weeks later the Admiralty sent a letter through the State Department to thank this country for the swift and efficient help it had supplied in a time of great need. The staffs of Bowles's office and of OFS, who had fought red tape to get the RCM team off, could not resist a vicarious touch of pride in the statement: "The work done by this group was of the highest order, and in addition their personal qualities made them fine ambassadors of their country in every ship and base they visited."

Technical advances in electronics during the past few years made it possible to represent the information received from many kinds of search gear aboard our line vessels on continuously moving diagrams on fluorescent screens. As the number of types of radar, sonar, and radio-detection apparatus placed in various positions on shipboard multiplied, it was essential that the information received from these sources be fed to a central location. Here the visual records could be translated quickly into an interpretation of the tactical situation and then into commands for offensive or defensive action. In this Combat Information Center (CIC) the disposition and movements of enemy and friendly air, surface, and subsurface craft were plotted or represented on screens so that officers could see them almost at a glance. The CIC therefore became the nerve center of the ship. Its size varied with the size of the ship and the number of search and detection equipments that had to function simultaneously. Its location in the vessel was determined by the operational needs and by the construction of the ship.[3] In a large task force the information filtered through instruments in the CIC's of smaller ships, was interpreted and relayed to the CIC's aboard larger command vessels so that the whole force could operate as a co-ordinated unit.

Creation of the CIC was a direct outgrowth of our prodigious expansion in the use of radar. Since a radar set can "see" great distances through darkness and fog, the radius of the area a single ship could control was greatly increased. When several search radars and several fire-control radars had been placed in different parts of a vessel to perform complementary functions, it seemed sensible to establish a radar plot and evaluation center. This would supply necessary information to the Captain, and to the navigation, gunnery, and air departments. It was then logical to feed into the same center information from sonar, from visual lookouts, and from radio communication with other co-operating units in the task force. The CIC became thereby

---

[3] Consequently the proper design and best location aboard ship for a CIC became subjects for heated debate.

the one place where a complete picture of navigational and combat information could be obtained, including the success of our forces in intercepting or sinking the enemy.

As in any complicated communications system, the effectiveness of the CIC was influenced not only by the performance of equipment, but also by the efficiency of the personnel who operated the instruments. And this was affected by their experience and training, by the noise and confusion present in the space in which they had to function, by the speed of their individual reflexes, and by the arrangement of the maze of plot boards, status boards, remote PPI's, radio outlets, telephone circuits, and instrument panels that constituted the modern CIC. Several major branches of OSRD were therefore drawn into the problem of providing proper equipment and helping the Navy to devise the optimum operating procedure for the various sizes and types of Combat Information Center. Divisions 13 (Communications), 14 (Radar), 15 (Countermeasures), 6 (Subsurface Warfare), 17 (Physics), and the Applied Psychology Panel were all involved in various aspects of this problem.

It soon became plain that a careful study ought to be made of the CIC in capital ships where the demands on this co-ordinating ganglion would be heaviest. In the fall of 1943 Commander D. C. Beard, Liaison Officer for COMINCH with Navy projects in sound control undertaken by Division 17, initiated a request to OFS to provide a group of sound-control experts and communications and radar specialists to study the organization and operation of CIC on medium and large warships. Dr. Leo L. Beranek, physicist from the Harvard Psycho-Acoustic Laboratory, was selected as leader of a group to conduct such a survey. The group consisted of Dr. H. W. Rudmose-Jones, physicist and communications engineer associated with Beranek at Harvard, Dr. Albert Tradup and L. A. Yost, physicists of the Bell Telephone Laboratories, and Dr. Richard Blue, physicist from the Radiation Laboratory. Drs. W. S. Hunter, Chief of the Applied Psychology Panel, and Harvey Fletcher of Bell Laboratories, Chief of Section 17.3 under which the Harvard sound-control work had been prosecuted, were appointed as OFS consultants to keep in close touch with the CIC Survey.

Ideally such a study should be conducted during task force operations when the ships are under multiple attacks from air and sea. But space is at a premium in such circumstances. There is no room for "visiting firemen" with their scientific gadgets, whose function is only to observe. Every man is needed to do the fighting. As an alternative, the Navy arranged that members of the group would go on the initial shakedown voyages of a new cruiser and a new aircraft carrier. During practice exercises in the South Atlantic they could secure a fair sample of the problems that might be encountered in actual fleet operations and could then translate their findings into changes in design and training at the Naval Radar Training Center at St. Simon's Island, Georgia, where a mock-up CIC room for use in training CIC officers was under construction.

In November the group visited training stations on the eastern seaboard to become more familiar with various types of Navy equipment and to talk with officers in charge of training. Then in December Beranek and Yost went to sea on the cruiser, and in January Rudmose-Jones and Blue boarded the carrier. Installing a battery of dictaphone recording machines on each ship to monitor the battle telephone lines, the intercommunications circuits, and some of the radio circuits in the CIC, they obtained a detailed account of the conversations that took place during battle practice. These records were carefully correlated in time. The recordings were transcribed and assembled in such a way that the relation of simultaneous events would become readily apparent and the time delays in relaying information around the ship could be evaluated.

Unfortunately, since only one ship was operating on the shakedown cruise, the relation of this vessel to others in a task force could not be studied. The problems were really oversimplified because only one surface or air target was fired on at a time; whereas a strong enemy attack would doubtless have involved firing on many targets simultaneously. Moreover, knowing in advance what was scheduled to occur, the commanding officers did not need to call on the CIC for much information or evaluation. The inexperienced crews used excessively long messages. Failing to enunciate clearly in standard commands and oral codes, they had to repeat themselves needlessly. Messages were not put through the communications circuits with dispatch. Altogether it was not possible to tell very much about the ability of the CIC to handle maximum loads under conditions of surprise attack from several quarters at once and with other craft co-operating in the engagement. Nevertheless a good deal was learned about the performance of personnel and equipment in and associated with the CIC. This would prove most useful in a continuing program of research, development, and training.

Amplifying the information they had secured on the shakedown trips by interviews with Navy personnel who had combat experience, the OFS specialists then devised a typical battle problem which could serve as an assumed basis for measuring the loads to be carried by various telephone lines and the duties required of personnel in the CIC. From an analysis of the results obtained in actual experience and in this hypothetical case, the Survey group reported that the CIC on carriers, battleships, and cruisers as developed at that time would be adequate for limited operations only and that means to relieve congestion on battle telephones during a complicated engagement must be sought.

The work of this panel of OFS experts was formally completed in May 1944 when they submitted a summary report recommending an extensive and long-range research effort that would involve various Bureaus of the Navy, laboratories of NDRC, and manufacturers. Thereafter, although OSRD personnel continued to work on improvements for the CIC, OFS was concerned only incidentally when some of the radar specialists in ORG studied CIC problems.

Some months later OFS was concerned about the sloppy diction of the average American. Under combat conditions, carelessness in speech was a serious problem. An order misunderstood can cost lives; and repetition of messages wastes precious time. It is bad enough in the Navy, but in the split-second operations of an air crew, delay might mean disaster.

Psychologists and the manufacturers of voice communications equipment were working intensively on this problem in the spring of 1945 when the Far East Air Force asked for a team of experts in this field. They were to bring to the theater the latest techniques in training and to give courses in speech to personnel who handled the radiotelephones and the interphone systems in planes. The Signal Corps organized a team consisting of an officer, two enlisted men, and three civilians. It was headed by Dr. Don Lewis, Assistant Director of their Operational Research Staff, and OFS supplied Drs. George P. Moore, speech pathologist, and Henry M. Moser, psychologist. These scientists had been on a project of the Applied Psychology Panel at the Voice Communications Laboratory of the AAF at Waco, Texas.

Working with the 5th and 13th Air Forces and the Combat Training Replacement Center, this team instructed approximately 4500 men at seven training installations on New Guinea, Samar, Morotai, Palawan, Mindoro, and Luzon. A Marine Air Group also took the course at their own request. What all this meant in terms of missions completed and casualties avoided can only be imagined. It does not appear in the technical reports, of course. One must read it between the lines of the letter of appreciation from Major General H. C. Ingles who said that Moore and Moser "performed their duties with skill and dispatch."

To recount the experiences and accomplishments of all OFS specialists in radio, radar, countermeasures, and communications would take several volumes. Even a résumé of high lights in the story will make a long chapter. These men comprised nearly a third of the total scientific staff of OFS. They were dynamic, mobile, tireless, and many of them were still in their twenties. Because the equipment with which they worked was used in so many aspects of the war, their activities were diversified. In the race of the "Scientists Against Time" the laboratories were turning out new gear continually. Only by using each improvement to greatest advantage could we retain the decided lead we had over the enemy in radar and RCM.

The needs of the war in Europe were well in hand. The London Liaison Office of OSRD, the British Branch of the Radiation Laboratory, and the American Branch Laboratory of Division 15 supplied a great deal of technical help and provided facilities for modifying equipment close to the front lines. Moreover, Bowles established an Advisory Specialists Group of men exceptionally competent in these subjects and sent them to ETO as supersalesmen and top-notch advisors to introduce the latest models. Their part in the war was of outstanding importance.[4]

---

[4] Liaison with Bowles and his men was excellent. Most of his experts were also drawn from RL and RRL. Although they went to the theaters under different auspices, the teams from OSRD and from the War Department worked in close conjunction.

The story of OFS contributions in radar, countermeasures, and communications is largely a story of the Pacific — of Marshall's team and the groups attached to the Research Section in SWPA.

From the beginning the Radar, Communications, and Countermeasures Subsection was the largest subdivision of the balanced team at Oahu.[5] Until the summer of 1945 it was headed by Dr. Niels E. Edlefsen, mature and affable senior staff member from RL. The majority of the personnel of this Subsection were transients loaned for a few months, since the research and development effort at home could spare men for brief periods only and since, to keep up to date, specialists must return frequently from the field. Some were attached to ORS for short missions, or merely for administrative purposes and correlation.

Listed in the order of their arrival in POA, the group consisted of:

NAME[6]	TRAINING	SOURCE
Henry W. Royce	Electrical engineering	RL
Evert M. Ostlund	Radio engineering	Federal Tel. & Radio
Ralph H. Caston (Dr.)	Physics	RL
William B. Sheriff	Electrical engineering	RL
William W. Farley	Physics	RRL
John P. Nash (Dr.)	Mathematics	RL
Charles W. Oliphant	Geophysics	RRL
Donald E. Kerr	Physics	RL
Robert A. Fox	Communications engineering	Station WGAR
Thomas M. Moore	Electrical engineering	RL
Harry M. Lindgren	Radio engineering	RL
M. Clifford Francis	Electrical engineering	Bell Labs.
Myer Kessler	Biophysics	RL
James M. Wolf	Biology	RL
Lloyd M. Jones	Radio engineering	RL
Halford R. Clark	Physical chemistry	Eastman Kodak
Robert F. Thomson	Physics	RL
Baldwin R. Curtis (Dr.)	Physics	RL
Leroy L. Blackmer (Dr.)	Physics	RL

[5] The balance was not a numerical one. ORS was really a panel — balanced in the sense that it included technical strength in most subjects of crucial importance to the forces under Nimitz and Richardson.

[6] The Signal Corps also detailed Lieutenants Samuel Feinstein and Harold Gruen to work with this Subsection.

The Radiation Laboratory developed an air-transportable, early-warning search and fighter-direction radar for low- and high-altitude coverage. Known as MEW, it was installed on Oahu and was a key unit in the defense of the Hawaiian Island Area against further air raids. In order to test the effectiveness of this set at various distances and altitudes and under different conditions, the Army and Navy carried out simulated attacks and Edlefsen's team analyzed the results. Throughout its history ORS was concerned with radar defenses of the Islands; but, as the front moved westward, its experts went forward to help establish adequate radar defenses of the newly won island arcs and to assist the military in making spectacular use of radar and countermeasures equipment as offensive weapons.

When the capture of Saipan was imminent, Edlefsen studied topographic maps, aerial photographs, and three-dimensional models to locate the best sites for placing MEW. The siting of radar is a complicated problem. To secure coverage of the widest possible area the equipment should be placed on a high hill so that its beam is unobstructed by the adjacent terrain. Yet great engineering skill may be required to get a large piece of apparatus to such a location through forested, undeveloped country. While the fighting was still in progress Edlefsen went to Saipan to check on this aspect of siting the MEW. It is a massive piece of equipment, weighing well over 50 tons, and requires 30 to 50 operators. In December Royce was sent to Saipan to help install MEW at the site Edlefsen had chosen. Bad weather, high winds, rain, and clouds made the job exceedingly difficult and unpleasant. Nevertheless, on New Year's Eve the set was in operation in time for the Japanese air raid expected with the full moon.

Later Royce and Blackmer helped the 7th Fighter Command install and operate another MEW in a hurricane-proof wooden building on the top of Mount Suribachi. This was to serve as the basic early-warning and fighter-control radar for Iwo Jima, and the height of the Jap aircraft was to be determined by the AN/TPS-10 set known as "Little Abner" that was brought to Iwo by Moore. Little Abner was particularly useful in regions where reflections (known as "ground clutter") from buildings and other objects in the immediate vicinity of a radar set interfere with its operation.

Under certain atmospheric conditions radar beams are trapped and bent so that they follow the earth's surface instead of being transmitted in straight lines. Consequently, one day the radar operator may see reflections of coastlines or ships way over the horizon and the next day, or even a few hours later, the range of coverage is normal and these reflections disappear. Such phenomena are said to be due to anomalous (abnormal) propagation of the radar pulses. When peculiar behavior of this sort created difficulty with the MEW on Saipan, Kerr, Nash, and then Kessler went forward to investigate.

Although some of the radar men of ORS were consultants on many problems, the majority went to the theater as advisors on specific pieces of equipment. Caston and Sheriff helped install a radar used by the 90-mm. gun batteries for coastal fire control against waterborne targets. They effected changes that would make one of these units mobile, and then trained Army personnel on Oahu to use it. In April 1944 this set was shipped to Iwo and Caston remained with it until September. Some idea of the complexity of operating the equipment is contained in a statement in his final report: "Much work must be done to integrate radar computers, guns and battery personnel into a smooth, efficient, working combination. . . . Accurate fire-control does not end with accurate radar." Later Caston went to Manila to assist in adapting this equipment for use against suicide boats and kamikaze in Operation Olympic.

Jones helped the Air Transport Command at Hawaii develop a system of ground checks for IFF equipment and then went to Guam to work on airborne radar. Nash, Kessler, and Oliphant became involved in the problem of identifying our own front lines by radar. Using the SCR-584 to spot Chaff-filled rifle grenades and small mortar shells fired by forward artillery observers, they staged a successful demonstration of this technique for Artillery and Marine officers. Then Kessler assisted with the installation and testing of a stable-base-mounted, height-finding set on an LST. Thomson stopped en route to Manila to demonstrate the MTI (moving target indicator). Fox helped install a base telephone system for the island command on Okinawa.

At the request of the Sixth Night Fighter Squadron ORS men made modifications of an airborne set designed to detect other aircraft. This proved so satisfactory that seventy-five such sets were ordered immediately and it was suggested that thereafter all of the production models carry this same modification.

Many of the miscellaneous problems in which ORS provided informal assistance to the Navy lay in the field of radar. In co-operation with the Pacific Fleet Radar Center, ORS experts designed a special circuit that would reduce the ground clutter disturbing radar operators on a destroyer. When this was tested, the aircraft over the near-by land area could be tracked easily in the radar of a ship close to shore. This would have been impossible with an unmodified receiver. When it was found that much of the radar equipment on destroyers was in need of attention, Wolf taught the officers and men improved test and maintenance procedures. ORS specialists also solved some of the difficulties encountered by submarines in detecting enemy surface craft by radar.

The work of Frank Pease, radar expert from RL who was assigned to the Commander Amphibious Forces at Pearl Harbor, is elaborated in another section of this volume. Not formally a member of ORS, he maintained close liaison with its radar group and called on them for help in demonstrating and introducing techniques for precision navigation with radar. He reciprocated by assisting ORS with the development of a fathometer for work in demolition of underwater obstacles and on problems in the use of certain ultra-high-frequency equipment.

After the demonstration of the precision navigation equipment, Admiral Nimitz recommended it as the most suitable device yet developed for this purpose and suggested its universal adoption by the Fleet. The Navy then planned to equip more than two thousand vessels with this contrivance, including battleships, cruisers, destroyers, minesweepers, and minelayers, and most of the surface craft above the size of an LCT that would be used in amphibious operations. The wisdom of this move became even more obvious when it was discovered that the same equipment could be adapted for gunnery direction and spotting in offshore bombardment.

In the fall of 1944 Farley made an over-all survey of RCM activities in POA to determine the needs of the theater for civilian help and for new types of equipment from the laboratories. He visited the Fleet Radar

Center, participated in evaluating biweekly RCM exercises held on Oahu, and talked with RCM officers of the Navy's air and subsurface commands, with Artillery officers, Signal officers, and Air Force representatives. On his return at the end of November he recommended strongly that a man with radar training who was thoroughly familiar with anti-jamming should become a permanent member of ORS.

Late in January Oliphant became the ORS specialist on RCM. He helped get equipment from the States, evaluated RCM training programs, and gave on-the-spot counsel on miscellaneous countermeasures problems. Working with the Night Air Combat Technical and Tactical Unit, he taught operators of GCI (ground control of interception) radar the possible use of Japanese jamming transmitters or confusion reflectors to hinder Allied night interception. Oliphant was also an active consultant of the Hawaiian Antiaircraft Artillery Command which operated all the searchlights and radar-controlled AA batteries in the island area.

The Air Forces, in collaboration with Division 15, developed a special plane known as a Ferret to fly reconnaissance missions and seek out enemy radar sets. It had all sorts of gear designed to detect, locate, and then jam the Jap radar. If jamming proved difficult, the Ferret gave the position of the enemy set to a "radar-busting" plane which went in and destroyed it.

In the spring of 1945 when the Pacific Command asked that a specialist in this Ferret development come forward to acquaint personnel with its potentialities, H. H. Benning, electrical engineer of the Bell Laboratories, was chosen for this assignment. Oliphant also helped in the test flights of the Ferret and spent several months with an air countermeasures analysis group on Guam. He was succeeded by Francis, who had been occupied at ORS in Hawaii with anti-jamming training, VT-fuzes, and analysis of captured Japanese VHF (very-high-frequency) equipment.

The quality of Japanese radar, although always inferior to our own, was steadily increasing. In the late months of the war it became evident that the Germans had finally given some of their technical information to the Japanese. Radar-controlled antiaircraft fire was, of course, by no means as concentrated over the enemy's Pacific installations as it had been in Europe. Whereas the Germans sometimes had one radar set for three or four antiaircraft guns, in the Tokyo area the Japs had one radar set for every ten. Nevertheless, the morale of American fliers was considerably strengthened by the knowledge that Japanese radar could be systematically jammed.

The RCM specialists of ORS studied transcripts of Jap broadcasts intercepted at Guam to determine whether such data would help us to analyze the enemy's air-warning system. They studied countermeasures to Japanese navigational aids and drew up summaries of RCM developments made in the theater to distribute to all organizations handling countermeasures equipment. And at many schools in the Hawaiian area they trained our troops to operate and maintain RCM equipment or to indulge in the entertaining and profitable pastime of devising countermeasures to the Japs' countermeasures.

Clark was actually regarded as a member of the Weapons and Analysis Subsection because he came to the theater to demonstrate several devices created by Divisions 16, 17, and 19. Among these, however, was infrared equipment for use in signaling. This provided a simple and inexpensive answer to the problem of identifying our front lines. The ground troops needed only to attach infrared filters to their flashlights and the beams from these, though invisible by ordinary means, could be picked up at once by simple equipment in low-flying locator planes.

He also brought models of the sniperscope that Klopsteg had introduced to the theater and Sloma had demonstrated. This was a combination of a telescopic sight and an infrared flashlight. Attached to the barrel of a carbine, it enabled the soldier to see and fire at an enemy at night up to a range of 75 yards. On Okinawa this device had paid off handsomely. Over 300 Japs infiltrating our lines were wiped out in a single night. When the Army wanted to increase the range of this infrared sighting mechanism, Clark suggested that it be mounted on a truck with a sufficiently powerful flashlight to increase its range to 250 yards.

Captured documents prove that the Japanese were working on infrared developments, but apparently they did not have such equipment in the field. We used it so late in the war that they had not yet seized any of ours. But, if they had, in the few remaining months of the war they could not have taken advantage of our progress and produced similar weapons in any quantity to use against us.

The work of the OFS experts on radio, radar, countermeasures, and communications in the Southwest Pacific falls into a more coherent pattern.[7] It was concentrated in three groups — a wave propagation survey, a staff of radar men at the Radiophysics Laboratory, and a panel of technical advisors on radar countermeasures.

Dr. Compton outlined to Dr. Charles R. Burrows, physicist Chairman of the OSRD Wave Propagation Committee, the proposal that an American team work with Australian scientists and the Allied military forces to establish a comprehensive study of anomalous radar propagation. While negotiations to undertake this were in progress, Harrison, head of the OFS Research Section, discussed the situation with Signal Corps units and found that they needed help on the propagation of radio over short distances in jungle and mountain terrain — important, for example, in the operation of walkie-talkie sets. The Army also wanted experts who could determine the best radio frequencies to use during different portions of the day.

Burrows pointed out that his Committee had helped the Signal Corps in Panama carry out an intensive study of jungle attenuation of radio waves and radio-frequency prediction. He believed that these results could be translated to the SWPA experience — or, at least, that the Army personnel who had done the work in this hemisphere would be the best ones to undertake it in the Pacific. His recommendation was favorably received and a Signal Corps team from Panama was sent to the theater to bring firsthand information, instruct Army personnel, and do any further experimental work that might be needed. This group, which consisted of Major E. H. Felix and three civilians, was attached to the OFS Research Section.

Major Felix found from experiments on jungle attenuation in New Guinea that conditions were, indeed, sufficiently similar to those in Panama so that the data from home could be applied directly. Since

[7] At least until the summer of 1945 when RL and RRL began feeding specialists to the Far East Air Force for a wide variety of wholly separate projects.

the command could be guided by Australian groups working on this same problem, it was unnecessary for the U.S. team to deal with it further.

Conferences with personnel of the Ionosphere Station at the Radiophysics Laboratory brought out the need for studies of noise levels in various frequency bands at a network of observation stations. Felix's group set up a noise-measuring station at Darwin and operated it for about a month. Then they turned it over to the Australians and organized a series of lectures for Signal Corps officers on principles of selecting optimum radio frequencies, based on the records of noise measurement.

To pursue the problem of anomalous radar propagation, OFS sent a team consisting of Drs. P. A. Anderson, S. T. Stephenson, K. E. Fitzsimmons, and G. M. Grover, physicists working with Burrows at Washington State College, to the theater in July 1944. They were to encourage the establishment of meteorological stations as far forward as possible in order to secure data on weather which drifted down from Japanese-held territory.

When the Director of Scientific Developments in New Zealand learned that this mission was in prospect, he urged that low-level sounding equipment and a scientist familiar with it be brought to the Radio Development Laboratory in Wellington to assist in analysis of radar data.

After the team had established headquarters with the Australians at the Radiophysics Laboratory, Anderson went to Wellington to deliver the radiosonde equipment to the New Zealanders. He then conferred with the Australians about setting up in western Australia and the Dutch East Indies a program similar to this NDRC–OFS mission. Stephenson collected meteorological and oceanographic data in Australia as background for siting the weather stations that were later set up on Noemfoor and Woendi to assist this propagation study. Fitzsimmons and Grover borrowed ships from the Navy and made a series of land-based and ship-based soundings near Hollandia. Stephenson went to Saipan to assure that radar weather coverage of that area would be adequate.

On November 7 a conference of all interested groups was held in Hollandia. Since a sizable group of AAF meteorologists had arrived in the theater, it was decided that the Weather Central of the Far East Air Force (FEAF) should take over responsibility for accumulating data on anomalous radar propagation and the peculiarities of weather associated with it, disseminating information on this to all interested parties. Consequently the civilian team withdrew and returned to America in December.

When Dr. Compton proposed that a team of American radar men work with the Australians at the Radiophysics Laboratory (RPL) in Sydney, the Radiation Laboratory agreed to establish an Australian group (AGRL). This was headed by Dr. Samuel Seely and consisted of Dr. George G. Harvey, Richard W. Griffiths, Eugene A. Holmes, Gerald S. Heller, Robert S. Levine, and James E. Zimmerman. It was a decidedly youthful and energetic group. Five of its 7 members were under 30, and the youngest was only 21. Although the team was based at the RPL, operational control of its work was in the hands of General Akin at GHQ.

The AGRL began operations in July 1944. Because so many isolated combat bases had to be reached entirely by air, the greatest need at that time was for air-transportable radar. Two major development programs were undertaken by the group. One was the design and development of a search set to demonstrate the method of detecting low-flying planes preliminary to the introduction of the similar set, Little Abner, under development in the United States. The second was the building of 5 lightweight GCI sets that would have a range of 50 miles on fighter planes.

Some components of these sets were shipped from the mainland and some were supplied by the U.S. Army in Australia. Antennas, huts, and some parts were to be produced by Australian manufacturers on AGRL specifications. Experimental models of both sets were completed and tested and production designs were drawn up. There were unforeseen delays because of difficulties with RPL-designed antennas and because of the congestion of Australian industry, however; and before all the sets were finished, other standard ones for similar purposes were available from production schedules in the United States.

When GHQ moved to Manila in March 1945, the AGRL at Sydney was nearly 5000 miles away, a distance that made effective liaison impossible, and the original requirements for lightweight equipment were no longer essential. Consequently the AGRL was disbanded. Some of its members were assigned to field-service units nearer the front in the Philippines and the others returned to research programs at home.

Until May 1945 operational control of all radio and radar counter-measures in MacArthur's command was in the hands of a staff section, known as Section 22, in the Office of the Chief Signal Officer, General Akin. This unit included officers of the American and Australian Armies, Navies, and Air Forces, and of the New Zealand Army. At first its function was primarily the collection and dissemination of RCM intelligence. In the fall of 1943, however, RRL sent two experts to Australia to help establish a regular, systematic, countermeasures search program using Ferret aircraft. The following spring J. M. Moran replaced these emissaries and initiated the use of more active counter-measures — deception tactics and radar busting.

Under the sponsorship of Bowles's office, Drs. Guy Suits, Chief of Division 15, and Frank Lewis of the War Department visited the theater in May to survey the RCM situation. They supported General Akin's earlier suggestion that a group of about six civilians be added to Section 22, including analysts of RCM and equipment specialists.

In the fall RRL sent the first contingent of another exceedingly youthful team to SWPA under the leadership of 29-year-old physicist Dr. Robert G. Sard. His initial party included Arnold R. Harman and Melvin P. Klein. Alden F. Stucke arrived later in the fall, and Edward F. Vidro and Anthony J. Yakutis in January. These men were all in their early 20's; but the average age of the group dropped even lower in April 1945 when Peter J. Sutro, an able 24-year-old physicist, replaced Sard and Klein and took over direction of the RCM project. This reflected the fact that the fields of radio, radar, and counter-measures, more than any other technical phases of the war, were filled with boy wonders both in and out of uniform. Developments in these subjects were so rapid that men under 25 were often the only ones in the country who knew the details of a new piece of gear well enough to introduce and maintain it.

For several months the RCM group examined captured Japanese radar sets to determine how they could best be jammed. Then as GHQ moved from New Guinea to Leyte and finally to Manila, they became more concerned with operational matters, helped in the planning of operations, installed new jamming equipment, and studied the coverage of both our own and the enemy's radar. By mid-April an offensive RCM program was in full swing and jamming was standard procedure whenever an air mission was headed for targets where antiaircraft radars might be found.

To enumerate the individual activities of Sard's group would be tedious. Working with units of the 5th and 13th Air Forces, they installed direction-finding antennas on radar busters, introduced the use of "Rope" — an RCM device dispensed from planes which simulates a large group of aircraft, worked out techniques for jamming, instructed military personnel, repaired equipment, and studied the operating characteristics of Japanese radar defenses. Lack of equipment was a perpetual handicap. Often they improvised new gear for Liberators by salvaging material from damaged Navy planes. The effectiveness of their work is illustrated in the case of the 90th Bomb Group of the 5th Air Force. Its targets were cities in Formosa where the Japs were using radar for AA fire control. Yet from January to September only 4 of its ships suffered major damage, only 2 were lost to enemy action, and the Group averaged only 4 planes out of 24 per strike that came home with holes from Japanese flak.

When the European phase of the war terminated, considerable expansion of FEAF was expected and preparations were made for moving its major base of operations to Okinawa. MacArthur took over command of all Army forces throughout the Pacific and the Seventh Air Force was added to the Fifth and Thirteenth. Raids of the 20th Bomber Command had demonstrated that the radar defenses of Japan itself were considerably stronger than any encountered earlier in the Pacific campaign. It appeared, therefore, that the RCM effort would have to be intensified.

It had become clear that a small laboratory close to the Air Force base of operations was badly needed for short-term research and to provide quick answers to technical questions. Ordinarily the RCM shop of a bomb group had neither the apparatus nor the trained personnel to handle the numerous technical requirements that were constantly changing as the enemy changed his tactics and equipment.

Section 22 took steps to establish such a laboratory for RCM and late in July a detachment went to Okinawa with as much RCM equipment as was then available. By the time of the surrender most of the Fifth and Seventh Air Force units were on Okinawa and the Thirteenth was planning to move forward. Construction of laboratory buildings was to start. A great deal of new RCM equipment had arrived and the need for additional civilians had become steadily more pressing.

Less than five years ago the word "radar" was kept in the files marked "secret"; but today it is part of our language. Like so many wartime technical advances, this was a secret that had to be shared by multitudes, even when shells were still flying. For we had created a gigantic new industry to build the magic mechanical sentries that guarded our homes, our factories, our ships and planes and outposts. We are only beginning to appreciate how radar will revolutionize transportation in the years ahead. But the word has a different and special meaning to sailors who blew to perdition hostile warships they could see only as points of fluorescence on a translucent CIC screen; to bombardiers who dropped their pay loads through clouds that obscured the objectives they blasted; or to pilots who brought their battle-scarred bombers safely to base in a blanket of soup. Only they can ever appreciate fully what it meant to have with them in the field men trained in the wizardry of science to help them keep their electronic eyes sharply in focus and to cast paralyzing electrical motes into those of the enemy.

Rocket Barrage
Clearing the beaches for our island landings

Weapons for the Future

GORGON, a guided missile under development by the Navy since the end of World War II

CHAPTER XVII

FANTASIES, PHANTOMS, AND FACTS

ROCKETS, RAM-JETS, AND ROBOTS

Two YEARS ago, when the atom exploded into terrifying headlines, an astounded world was pitched headlong into the age of nuclear energy. The blinding flash in New Mexico that turned a steel tower into gas in a fraction of a second and fused the desert sand into an irradiated glass was a climactic symbol of the startling acceleration in scientific achievement produced by the actual necessities of total war.

As the curtain of secrecy surrounding this progress has been drawn aside a little wider every day, we have discovered that advances in nuclear physics and electronics during the past few years overshadowed evolution in many other fields. We know too that, even though the men of OSRD who were so much a part of this development have returned to their peacetime pursuits, the progress of science has not slowed down. The technical men are rapidly turning the inventions of war into comforts of peace, to enlarge, enrich, and lengthen our lives. Things that were prospects a few months ago are now practical, accomplished facts — pilotless planes that will take off and land at the bidding of radio signals; radar beams that bounce off the moon; rockets that will explore the air 100 miles overhead; jet-powered fighters that whip across the nation twice in a single day; robot-controlled missiles guided at long range with uncanny accuracy by radio, radar, or television, or that seek out and "home" on the heat, light, magnetism, or sound of their targets; six-motored bombers that may travel non-stop from Canada to Patagonia; sprays of gas, or germs, or poison that can bring writhing, tortured death to every living creature touched by them; and — probably — better atomic bombs.

We dream today of space ships and interplanetary journeys and disintegrating rays. And we talk glibly of hurtling through our own thin upper air to circle the earth a thousand miles an hour, keeping pace with its rotation, or even going faster; of potions that will retard the degenerative processes and permit our sons, maybe even some of us, to live twice as long; of driving ships and heating homes and lighting cities by unleashing the invisible power in a stagnant pond. Our grandfathers dreamed some of these things too, but to us the images are less fantastic than they were before the first V-2 hit England.

The development of an atomic explosive, revolutionary and awesome enough of itself, would not fire our imaginations half so much nor inspire such universal apprehension had we not at the same time come so close to building the push-button consoles that will launch and control the missiles of the future, or found the fuels and engines to drive these weapons at supersonic velocities halfway around the globe. It is the combination of nuclear energy, radar tracking, jet propulsion, and guided missiles that worries us. And we have just begun to glimpse the wonders that will come from continued intensive research in these fields.

Rockets, jet propulsion, and guided missiles — in that order — were only coming of age during the later months of the war. They proved so effective in combat operations, and the possibilities for improving them are so great that they must be regarded — along with atom bombs and biological warfare — as weapons of the future. In all such developments OSRD had a prominent role, and it was inevitable that specialists in these fields should be included in the roster of OFS. What they did in helping to introduce and to evaluate the latest devices in the field was seldom spectacular; yet their work produced the myriad little steps that together make the gigantic strides of science.

Though few in number, the field-service experts in rocket ordnance had a substantial influence on the greatly expanded use of this weapon in the Pacific. Had the laboratories been able to spare a larger group, many phases of our island-hopping offensive might not have been so costly. Fortunately from experience in other theaters the Services had learned the importance of special training for rocket crews and had sent officers and enlisted men to the Pacific who knew something about this new type of ammunition. As Fowler reported, the civilian expert had to be a counselor, a trouble-shooter, and a teacher, rather than a salesman.

After Fowler's survey of the rocket situation in SWPA, when the

OFS group at GHQ queried commanding officers to determine more specifically their need for professional aid, it appeared that at least 7 men would be required. The research and development program at home was moving so rapidly and the demands from all theaters for rocket weapons were so great that a critical shortage of top-level personnel trained in this new type of warfare was unavoidable. Consequently the requirement was revised to a request for 3 or 4 men who could circulate between the various units of Army and Navy in SWPA. But even this could not be met. OFS was only able to supply one man at a time to provide technical advice, assist in determining operational needs, aid in procurement, and participate in training programs for offensive operations.

In August 1944 Dr. Lorenzo A. Richards, physicist from the Division 3 program at California Institute of Technology, arrived in SWPA. For the next seven months he was concerned chiefly with the types of rockets used by the Navy. He supervised launcher installations on rocket gunboats (LCM's) and DUKW's for amphibious operations, helped to formulate rocket gunboat doctrine for the Seventh Fleet, and to plan rocket operations for the Leyte landings.

Richards was overseas 150 days, made 41 trips by plane, and covered some 30,000 miles. He showed rocket movies to 29 different groups of officers, distributed pamphlets, manuals, and up-to-date summaries of information, and obtained considerable data for the home laboratories on the performance of rockets in Service use.

By the time he left in February 1945 the theater was thoroughly rocket-conscious. He reported that the prelanding rocket barrages were so successful in clearing the beaches and driving the enemy to cover that the first wave in an amphibious assault was then the safest. In the five or ten minutes preceding the landings on Leyte, some 15,000 rounds of barrage rockets had been fired and the first wave was almost unopposed.

Since the Jap suicide planes were smashing many ships, on his return to California Richards took up with the rocket-development people the possibility of using barrage rockets as a defense against this type of attack.

In February Dr. Paul E. Lloyd, physicist from California Institute of Technology, replaced Richards as the rocket consultant of the OFS

Research Section and worked on Leyte, Luzon, and Samar. Lloyd commented that Richards had done such an excellent job of familiarizing many units in both Services with the potentialities of rockets that his chief function was to continue in Richards' footsteps, make sure that suggestions were being properly followed up, and acquaint the military with latest progress in the laboratories. He paid particular attention, however, to the use of rockets by PT boat squadrons, his specialty in the development program, and interested the Air Forces in rocket applications. He also investigated 20-cm. and 45-cm. Japanese rockets captured on Luzon, supervised firing trials of these, and trained units of the Sixth Army to shoot them back at the Japs.

In July Robert E. Sears, mechanical engineer from the California Institute of Technology laboratories, and Raymond V. Adams, Jr., physicist from the University of California, went out to replace Lloyd. Sears visited PT Base 17 at Samar where plans were in progress when the war ended to initiate a training program for practice fire. He conferred with gunnery officers of the Amphibious Forces, inspected all the rocket gunboats, and assisted in completely overhauling many of them. Sears reported that officers assigned to this type of ordnance were decidedly competent and the doctrines well established. Assigned to the Far East Air Force, Adams served as a specialist on airborne rockets, particularly those used in fighter planes. Surveying the use of these weapons by the 13th Air Force, he reported a favorable pilot reaction but said that the theater had too little knowledge of airborne rockets. He recommended that a training program should be instituted. Although his work was also cut short by the end of hostilities, he developed an outline for a peacetime rocket school that included a satisfactory course for instructors.

Eventually field-service specialists from Division 3 were also attached to the balanced team at Oahu. In May 1945 Dr. Frank T. McClure, physical chemist of the Allegany Ballistics Laboratory of this Division, joined the ORS. His primary assignment was to introduce the use of rockets to the 7th Air Force. This involved special training of men who had been accustomed simply to fly planes, dump bomb loads, and fire guns. Rockets were a new experience to them. The planes were each equipped with ten 5-inch and three or four 11-inch rockets. If these were used properly, they could be far more destructive in the hands of well-trained airmen than the normal bomb load because of their greater penetrating power and the greater accuracy with which they could be fired.

At the end of July Lewis H. Mahony, Jr., chemical engineer who had spent seventeen months in indoctrination with Division 3, arrived to assist McClure. It was planned that he would aid Army and Navy units with problems in the installation and maintenance of new equipment and draw up a prospectus for an extensive program to train pilots of the Seventh Fighter Wing in the proper handling and firing of rockets. Navy pilots already versed in this technique were to act as instructors. The equipment necessary to start the program was not available immediately. And before Mahony could really get his teeth into the assignment, news of the surrender brought cancellation of his orders.

When hostilities ceased, McClure was already working with the Air Force to develop procedures for firing rockets from airplanes by radar; but this had not yet been done in actual combat. There is no question, however, that in a few months it would have become standard operating procedure.

The Germans made tremendous strides in the field of jet propulsion. Ardent Nazis among their technical men wail because the High Command did not put the heat on the manufacture of jet fighters six months sooner. And our own bomber pilots will quickly agree that this could have altered the course of the air war. It would probably not have given the enemy more than temporary mastery of the skies, however, because the British and the Americans were also carrying on vigorous research in jet power and would soon have put large numbers of comparable craft into the struggle. Nevertheless, now that we are adding the German progress to our own, it seems certain that development of the jet engine has outdated all other methods of air locomotion almost as conclusively as the atomic blast has rendered obsolete all other types of explosive.

Consequently, the comprehensive survey of jet-propelled missiles instigated by Admiral King in December 1944 has continuing postwar implications. Its over-all purpose was to review the status of jet-propelled missiles, with particular emphasis on their future possibilities, and thus to aid the Navy in shaping requirements for these weapons and for research in fields related to their use. COMINCH created under supervision of CRD a Panel of civilian consultants and officers to look into many aspects of jet propulsion and guided missiles. OFS furnished Dr. Edwin R. Gilliland from the chemical engineering faculty of M.I.T. as Chief of the Panel, and supplied five of its regular members and one consultant: Neil P. Bailey, mechanical engineer from Rensselaer Polytechnic Institute; Alexis W. Lemmon, chemical engineer from the University of Delaware; Dr. Lloyd W. Morris, physicist from Louisiana State University who was then instructing in a pre-radar course at the Cruft Laboratory of Harvard; Dr. Theodore H. Troller, mechanical engineer from the University of Akron; Harold A. Wilson, mechanical engineer from Rensselaer; and Dr. C. C. Monrad, chemical engineer from Carnegie Institute of Technology, whose assumption of duties in an intelligence mission to investigate the Nazi synthetic rubber industry permitted him to participate in the work of the Panel in its initial stages only.[1]

For six months this group carried on extensive liaison with research programs of the Army, Navy, OSRD, and the British agencies, and studied information and equipment captured from the enemy. In so short a time it was impossible to make detailed analyses of the many ramifications of this subject. The study was confined, therefore, to a marshaling of data in convenient form to illustrate progress already made, trends in research, and possibilities for the future. Various aspects of the subject were assigned to Panel members for investigation and their individual reports were used as the basis for an over-all summary report. This pointed up the need for a great deal of research in the design and utilization of jet-propelled missiles and indicated some of the directions it should take.

Aerodynamic knowledge applicable to the design of these missiles was reviewed by Troller, Director of Aerodynamic Research of the Guggenheim Airship Institute. Morris and Krause summarized and evaluated the known techniques for guiding or controlling flight. Lemmon, at 23 the youngest member of the Panel, who had been working

---

[1] Other non-OFS members of the Panel were: Dr. Howard W. Emmons from Cruft Laboratory; Dr. Ernst H. Krause of the Naval Research Laboratory; Lieutenants John C. Quinn of Bureau of Ordnance and Edward M. Redding of Bureau of Aeronautics; Dr. Merit White of Division 2 and the Joint Target Group; and Glenn C. Williams of M.I.T.

on heat-transfer problems in cooling aircraft engine cylinders, devoted his attention to a study of possible fuels for jet propulsion, since an appreciable improvement in the utilization of the existing fuels, or the discovery of new and better ones, would increase the performance of all types of rocket motors.[2] Wilson and Bailey concentrated on intermittent jet engines; Williams and Lieutenant Quinn on ram-jet power plants; Lieutenant Redding on turbo-jet engines; and White on the damage power of jet-propelled weapons.

By carrying out the sort of periodic, critical review and inventory necessary when the march of science and technology is so rapid, the members of the Gilliland team contributed greatly to our advance toward the era of space ships and push-button warfare.

In Air Force Headquarters a similar study was initiated when a high-level Scientific Advisory Group was established under the direction of Dr. Theodore von Karman. The field of interest of this unit was, however, even broader, including as subdivisions guided missiles and jet power. The Group prepared a comprehensive report for the Commanding General, AAF, on research that should be encouraged or inaugurated in many fields. And obviously there was some degree of overlap in the interests of the Gilliland and the von Karman committees.

OFS also supplied a member of the von Karman panel. Dr. Nathan M. Newmark, structural and civil engineer from the University of Illinois and Consultant of Division 2, became a part-time participant in March 1945. He had returned only a short time earlier from a tour of duty as the senior member of the Weapons and Analysis Subsection of the ORS staff in Hawaii. Newmark traveled extensively until October gathering data on the state of knowledge of terminal ballistics that would be pertinent in aircraft armament and on the structure of planes and the materials of which they were made.

An early effort to provide a mechanism that would control the fall of a missile and thereby increase the accuracy of our tactical sorties was a bomb that could be guided toward its target by radio. The first suc-

---

[2] OFS had earlier been interested in the problem of fuel for B-17's over Germany when Dr. George W. Mackey, mathematician from Harvard, was loaned to the ORS of the 8th AF and made a statistical study of the effect on its fuel consumption of the position of a bomber in the flight formation.

cessful bomb of this type was developed by NDRC. A flare attached to its tail ignited after the bomb left the bomb bay and this enabled the bombardier to follow its trajectory downward. He applied the necessary radio control to a unit adjustable to several frequencies and located in the tail-fin assembly. If, for example, the target was a high-way bridge, the bombing run would be made roughly parallel to the road. The bombardier could then guide his egg to the right or left (that is, in azimuth) so that it would at least hit the highway. But he could not control its fall in range. It might land short of or beyond the bridge — and yet do desirable damage.

Since this system could exert control in azimuth only, it was known as Azon. One of the less-heralded of the secret weapons that came from the drawing boards of OSRD, it had limitations. Not only did it lack range control, but also its radio could be jammed. Nevertheless, even the control in azimuth represented a striking technical advance, and 1000-lb. Azons dropped smack on critical targets more than paid for the whole development effort. Moreover, work on Azon led eventually to a system for controlling both range and azimuth. This was the guided missile known as Razon and it promised even more spectacular results.

The first use of Azon in Mediterranean operations was disappointing to the enthusiastic scientists and development men, not because the equipment failed, but because the military men did not set up conditions that would have given definitive, conclusive results. Several Flying Fortresses were equipped with Azon and went to the Adriatic for operational trials. Abner J. Wollan, Technical Aide of Division 5 which had developed Azon, went along as an OFS consultant to as-sure proper tuning and utilization of the new weapon. Unfortunately, however, the military masterminds always insisted on sending the Azon bombers in the company of a group of regular heavy bombers. Con-sequently it was difficult to distinguish which bombs had done what damage. When Azon crews claimed a direct hit on a target, the crews of the other ships were unwilling to admit that they had not scored directly also.

A specific case was an attack on a viaduct in the Brenner Pass. Azon aircraft were the lead planes and sighted for range and deflection. Yet, since all bombs of the Group dropped simultaneously with the special

Azon bombs and landed within the target area, the Fifteenth Air Force refused to credit four direct hits on the viaduct claimed by the Azon crews.

Experimental trial runs in combat operations had thus failed to yield the positive information that might have led to an eager acceptance of this guided missile and large Azon procurement orders for the continuing tactical and strategic assaults in MTO and ETO. Wollan returned disappointed and certainly unpopular with young officers and men who would not admit that a radio system had improved on their boasted accuracy.

Introduction of Azon in the Burma-India theater was quite a different story; but it would surely not have been if OSRD had not sent a combat scientist to follow through the operational trials. Thomas J. O'Donnell of the Gulf Research and Refining Company, who had also been active in development of this guided missile and had introduced it to the Eighth and Ninth Air Forces in Europe, left Miami in December 1944 and arrived in CBI as a consultant to the 7th Bombardment Group which was to test Azon in operations. The Group had previously been assigned such experimental jobs. They considered them of the "long-hair" variety and had not followed them through beyond initial disappointing efforts.

An Azon maintenance team, consisting of an officer and 10 men, and 10 aircrews with Azon-equipped B-24 Liberators had been trained at the Fort Dix Special Weapons Training School and sent to the theater in August. No Azon missions had, however, yet been assigned when O'Donnell arrived. Only 3 Azon ships were on the field, 3 had been lost, and 4 were being used to haul gasoline to China. The maintenance team was intact but had no equipment except the sketchy minimum O'Donnell brought with him. His reception was cold and the prospects were discouraging.

Bridges on Japanese lines of communication were the main targets, particularly those along a rail line from Rangoon through Mandalay to Lashio and several short spur lines that supplied the North Burma front. Allied naval interference with the Japs' shipping forced them to route a major part of their supplies over the Burma-Thailand Railway, which was therefore of high strategic importance. Destruction of bridges would, of course, be the most effective way to cut communications. Bridges had been attacked by fighters and medium and heavy bombers at altitudes ranging from six or seven thousand feet down to three hundred feet. At these lower levels the results were effective but very dangerous for the heavy bombers.

The first test mission was flown 10 days after O'Donnell arrived. Eight bombs were carried in each of 3 Azon ships. The target was a three-span steel railway bridge on the line between Rangoon and Mandalay. Using 1 Azon and 1 standard bomb on each pass and coming in at 9400 feet, the planes made 3 passes at the bridge. The center span was totally demolished and another span severely damaged. The standard, unguided bombs all missed. The nine Azons had finally brought destruction to a bridge attacked at various times over a period of 2 years without previous damage.

Numerous Azon missions were then flown. On 7 of them a total of 154 Azons was dropped. Sixteen bridges were knocked out and full confirmation of the results obtained, either from photographs or from observation on reconnaissance near the target after the smoke had cleared. Thirty-five of the Azons were wasted, but an equal quantity either were direct hits or were close enough to damage the targets. These results do not include the bombs that fell over or short of the bridges but that nevertheless damaged roadbeds or trackage. It was calculated that, conservatively, 1 out of 5 of the Azons had produced a damaging hit. So this guided missile could be considered many times as effective against bridges as standard bombing; or, in other words, a single squadron equipped with this new device would be equivalent to two and one-half standard Groups with ordinary bombs.

And again one wonders how different the results might have been without the field-service specialist. Regarding O'Donnell, one of the officers associated with him wrote: "I would like to pass on a personal word of thanks for the services of Mr. O'Donnell. He is one in a million. As you probably know, my project was diverted several times and Mr. O'Donnell had to be diverted with it; but in each case he fitted in perfectly. He is a diplomat and an expediter the like of which I have never seen; and his personal courage cannot be overexaggerated. He felt the necessity to go on a number of extremely hazardous missions, and, as a result, solved some very important problems."

*   *   *

The word about exceptional results with Azon and the perfection of Razon that filtered out to the Pacific theaters through OFS and Air Force representatives stimulated great interest in guided missiles. Learning that Dr. Hugh H. Spencer, new Chief of Division 5, was headed for SWPA to introduce the equipment to the Far East Air Force, GHQ in Hawaii asked that he stop over to acquaint personnel in POA with these remarkable developments. The more lengthy tour had to be canceled because of his heavy commitments in research and development, but Spencer did manage to spend two weeks in January 1945 at Oahu. Loaded with reports and training films, he also took along Razon equipment that might be adapted to guide the aerial trajectory of a glide torpedo to be launched from aircraft.

Spencer reported that although commanders of bomber squadrons were impressed by the superior performance of these guided bombs, understandably our pilots were hesitant about using them because this would mean continuing their runs after releasing the bombs in order to guide them. The thought of staying on the bombing run any longer than was absolutely necessary, even at what would be considered a reasonably safe range, was not attractive. Spencer pointed out, however, that much of the bombing in that theater could be done above 23,000 feet and that at that altitude the pilots would be essentially safe from Japanese antiaircraft, especially because analysis had shown that they could take a reasonable degree of evasive action.

By midsummer the remarkable successes with Azon in Burma had excited the imagination of officers throughout the Pacific and General Kenney asked for Azon and Razon squadrons, maintenance crews, and OFS specialists to introduce these guided missiles to the Far East Air Force. Elaborate preparations to fill the requests were in progress when the war ended. There is little doubt that had the air offensives continued, guided missiles would eventually have replaced a large part of the bomb load on tactical operations. The logical next step would have been wide employment of guided projectiles like the V-1 [3] and the Baka bomb — first those that could be released and con-

---

[3] Larkin and Ertsgaard, OFS specialists on the VT-fuze, had a rough introduction to the efficacy of the jet-powered V-1. When they arrived in London and reported to OSRD headquarters, they learned that the hotel where they were to stay had been wrecked by a buzz-bomb the night before; and, although they were there on the last night of such raids, several of these disconcerting missiles landed within half a mile of their beds.

trolled from a mother ship, and finally, when rocket or jet propulsion and automatic control over long distances proved feasible, those that could be fired from our own shores.

A similarly spectacular guided missile that represented a step in this direction was developed under auspices of the Navy and used with telling effect by the fleet air arm in the Southwest Pacific. This was a device known as Bat, a projectile equipped with its own small radar transmitter and receiver. Since the controls for its flight were motivated by the image on a radar receiver, it would automatically home on a target.[4] Released from an airplane attacking a ship while the plane was well beyond range of the vessel's antiaircraft fire, the Bat could be brought in to its target for a kill — unless it was shot down or jammed before it hit the ship. Many a Japanese surface craft lies on the bottom of the Pacific because it moved into the path of this ingenious mechanism from Uncle Sam's arsenal.

Bat was another of those astonishing contrivances that came from the co-operative effort of science, industry, Government, and the military. It was developed by Division 5 of NDRC in collaboration with the Experimental Unit of Naval Ordnance, Bell Laboratories, and an M.I.T. group at the Bureau of Standards. And again OFS had a hand in helping to introduce it to the field units. Navy officers who accompanied Bat to SWPA were fully competent to cope with the routine technical problems. But the Navy wanted two experts who had played leading roles in the development of radar-homing missiles to go along and expedite changes in design that might grow out of the operational use of Bat. Consequently Dr. Perry Stout and Franklin C. McCoy of the M.I.T. Field Station in the Bureau of Standards became OFS consultants on the Bat project in the Pacific from March until May 1945.

As this was written, a group of pilotless Flying Fortresses, loaded only with many kinds of scientific instruments, took off from Eniwetok and flew into the mushrooming, radioactive cloud that rose over Bikini. Each was guided in the air by a crew member in another Fortress

---

[4] The same thing can now be accomplished with television systems. The missile can be guided unerringly to its target by remote control in the hands of the bombardier, who sees a replica of a television image created in the head of the bomb as it falls toward its target.

that served as a mother ship and remained at a safe distance. And the whole group was subject to control by a B-17 supermother that could take charge if the robot "Babe" or "Phantom Fortress" had somehow been blasted away from the influence of the mother plane by the turbulent vortex above the historic explosion. This performance represented the extent of our progress since the war in only one phase of the program to improve mechanisms for launching, guiding, and controlling the flight of an object from afar.

Remote-control take-offs and landings of B-17's were not achieved until February 1946; but the Germans learned that our Air Force could operate robot planes once they were in the air when the submarine pen at Helgoland was attacked by "Weary Willie." This was a guided missile on the grand scale — a battle-worn B-17, stripped of most of its gear and loaded to the doors with tons of high explosives; it was guided into the target by mechanisms perfected by OSRD. Here was the American equivalent of the kamikaze, but it lacked the fanatical pilot.

The fantasies of yesterday have become the frightening facts of today — or will be in the headlines tomorrow. Gigantic rockets that may span the Atlantic in less time than it takes us to drive to the airport are but one possibility foreshadowed by the piloted projectiles and propellerless planes that came out of this war. Science has created new challenges; and our greatest need is for statesmen to determine whether such rockets and robots are loaded to deliver penicillin — or plutonium.

CHAPTER XVIII

BRAIN TRUST IN HAWAII

THE BALANCED TEAM AT GHQ

IN JUNE, when POA became MIDPAC and MacArthur took over command of all Army forces converging on Nippon, things had changed for the men from the Research Section at Hawaii. Nimitz had gone forward to Guam and the 7th Air Force had joined FEAF on Okinawa. The centers for operational planning were then thousands of miles from Oahu and General Richardson's area became a rear echelon functioning merely as a major base for supplies, repair, and training. Many of the ships bringing Armies from Europe to help in the final drive on Japan were not even stopping at Honolulu since it lay far to the north of their routes, and the harbors up front were now ready to take them. When the war ended, most of the staff of the "balanced team" were already forward and others were scheduled to leave. Eventually only a small nucleus of the ORS would have stayed at Fort Shafter.

To those who remained in the Islands the war then seemed as remote as when they were back on the mainland. They grew restless and wanted to be closer to action.

General Richardson knew there would still be technical problems. He had come to depend on the broad knowledge and versatility of this panel of specialists. But he recognized that their greatest usefulness would be at or nearer the front, and he made no effort to hold them. This was consistent with his liberal thinking right from the start and with his generous and far-sighted policy in authorizing ORS men to work for the Air Forces and the Navy, although the Section was technically a creation of Army Ground Forces. During the previous months approximately half the manpower resources of ORS had been devoted to problems brought in by these other agencies. Indeed, there were times late in the war when as many as a third of the ORS group were detailed to the Air Forces alone and were serving at forward outposts. Moreover, by giving Marshall's men a clear staff position as a subsection of G-3, Richardson had made it easier for all branches of the Army to request their help.

The establishment of an Operational Research Section like this one had never before been attempted in Army organization and could not have been successful without the constant interest and strong backing of the General and his staff. In the early stages of ORS organization Marshall was in almost daily informal contact with Major General Clark L. Ruffner, Chief of Staff, Brigadier General W. S. Lawton, Deputy Chief of Staff, Colonel Ernest V. Holmes, Assistant Chief of Staff, G-3, and Colonel Herbert Sparrow, who also gave strong personal support to the civilian team. In handling the complex administrative relationship between ORS and the many agencies it served, Lieutenant Colonel Fred J. Sengstacke proved decidedly helpful. Obviously, Marshall's men could never have chalked up the record of accomplishments described in this book, if problems of liaison with the military in the theater had not been relatively minor ones. All branches of the Armed Forces in POA had benefited because these key officers and a score of others were sympathetic and co-operative.

Richardson's broad concept of purposes to be served by the OFS men is seen in the early announcement about ORS, made in June 1944: "This section will consist of a group of civilian personnel, mostly scientists, who will act in an advisory capacity on technical problems of all kinds." A large order to be filled by a handful of men. They would have to be first-rate scientists. And it was obviously intended that the balanced team should constitute essentially a technical brain trust. The statement was later amplified and areas of major emphasis marked out more concretely. But right to the end ORS was receiving an assortment of requests for help on problems beyond the experience of its members. These were discussed at the Sunday morning staff meetings each week and the group tried to find solutions by pooling their ideas, or by calling on NDRC through OFS at Washington.

The living and working conditions at Oahu had been ideal compared with those at many other headquarters. Daily collaboration between members of the "balanced team" brought to each problem the benefit of several points of view. The men could travel about in the theater without too much difficulty and communications with the main-

land were relatively easy. The scientists were in no immediate danger,
except when they went up front.

The office space provided for ORS in the headquarters building at
Fort Shafter had been adequate and comfortable. Telephone lines
and other means of communication were supplied and arrangements
made for access of the group to shops and laboratories of the Army and
Navy. The scientists could not have asked for much more in physical
facilities — except command cars and jeeps for their exclusive use. For
some months transportation had certainly been inadequate and their
work had suffered. Although the Army later provided cars with
drivers, this was wasteful of the time of the military personnel. Everyone would have been better off if the ORS men had been permitted
to use drive-yourself jeeps.[1]

When Marshall, Stephens, and Burchard first arrived in POA, they
were accompanied by Helge Holst, biologist from Lever Brothers, who
for some months was Technical Aide of the growing Section. In
November John K. Howard, insurance executive and administrator
who had been with ABL-15, became the Senior Executive Officer of
ORS. "Kay" Howard knew his way around in the Army. He had
been in charge of an Army training program at Harvard and had held
a commission as Colonel. From the moment he landed at Honolulu,
the affairs of ORS had gone more smoothly. Then in December Donald S. Pond, formerly with the Underwater Sound Laboratory at New
London, Connecticut, replaced Holst. Pond relieved the men of administrative details so effectively that they affectionately called him
"Pappy." The following summer when Marshall went to Manila and
Howard returned to Washington on temporary duty, Pond became
Acting Chief of the Section. Much of the credit for the success of Marshall's specialists belongs to these scientist-administrators.

In the fall of 1944 it became apparent that a number of agencies with
overlapping functions had been set up in the Middle Pacific, associated
with the Ground Forces, Air Forces, and Navy. By September there
were seven in addition to ORS and several of them were drawing on
OFS in Washington for personnel. ORS took the lead in establishing
regular meetings of representatives of five of the eight agencies until

---

[1] They could not help thinking enviously of some of their scientist colleagues in ETO
who were provided not only with jeeps but also with airplanes large enough to take these
handy vehicles with them when their OFS business required long journeys.

the Air Force and Navy headquarters moved forward in February 1945. Although formal liaison and co-operation between these groups was directed, policy considerations of the Air Forces and especially of the Navy dictated that normally their requests upon ORS would be made on an informal basis. This proved advantageous since it actually meant that scientific skills could be applied immediately to matters affecting operational planning because the help could be given without the time-consuming delays that would have been inevitable in normal channelizing of formal communications.

The bomb data summaries prepared by Newmark's Weapons and Analysis Subsection were invaluable to the airmen in their task of choosing the right missiles and fuze settings; and the work of Edlefsen and his radar men in siting the MEW on Saipan was a big factor in our ability to use that island promptly as a major base of air operations. These two early contributions of the balanced team established among Air Force leaders such confidence in ORS that thereafter they besieged the Section with requests for help. By May 1945 relations had become so cordial that Brigadier General Ankenbrandt, Director of Communications, announced a policy of asking for all technical assistance through ORS, and Marshall was invited to visit the forward headquarters of the Air Forces to discuss the basis for future assignments of his men to Air units.

Much of the work ORS men did for the Navy was informal and remains unreported. Nevertheless, as we have seen, material prepared by members of this group was written into Navy doctrine as operational procedure — the use of DUKW's on transports and cargo vessels, detection devices for underwater obstacles and mines, and the use of radar for precision navigation; and these OFS consultants were also responsible for Navy adoption of new devices and modifications to equipment.

Marshall became a member of the Joint Army-Navy Radar Countermeasures Discussion Group. Since some of his teammates had much previous experience with the types of jamming apparatus in use on vessels of the Pacific Fleets, at each of its meetings the Discussion Group scheduled at least one speaker from ORS to consider most recent developments in this rapidly changing field.

Close collaboration with the Subgroups of Morse's ORG at ComAirPac and ComSubPac was arranged easily since all three units were OFS projects. In the final few months of the war, ORS and ORG men were working together intensively to improve the performance of early-warning radar gear that was a critical item in defense against the suicide attacks.

The New Developments Division had played a significant part in the operations of both the ORS and the R/S. It brought together on a common ground the points of view of the military men and of the civilian scientists. Because the officers of NDD were able to help in synthesizing the opinions, solutions to problems were found quickly. NDD also sent officers to the theaters with information on most recent developments of new weapons and their applications. These emissaries always worked closely with the OFS field branches. Whenever possible, officers from the theater came back to Washington for temporary duty with NDD. Lieutenant Colonel Sengstacke spent six weeks on the mainland through such an arrangement. This sort of exchange helped materially to bring about a common basis of understanding between workers in the field and those in the home agencies who were endeavoring to meet their needs. In the rather complicated conditions imposed by war, the understanding that can come from such firsthand personal acquaintance with both sides of an activity is essential if a high rate of progress is to be maintained.

In Army parlance a "team" is a group of 20 or more men who have had at least 6 months of indoctrination for the jobs they are to perform. The balanced team at GHQ in the Central Pacific would surely not fit this description. Neither was it an operational research group in the true sense, but a scientific advisory staff who applied their imagination, ingenuity, technical knowledge, and, above all, their common sense to a multitude of daily problems. Its members were as much at home in greasy overalls as they were in officers' pinks at the conference table, and worked as well with the lad who bore no stripes on his sleeve as they did with the men who wore eagles.

In a book of this length, that must relate the story of so large and varied a program, it has only been possible to highlight the many solid achievements of the "brain trust in Hawaii." The credit these combat scientists reflected on the Office of Field Service is brought out succinctly in the enthusiastic letter General Richardson sent Dr. Marshall after the Section was deactivated:

"I therefore wish to take this opportunity to express my sincere appreciation of the services rendered to this Command by the Operational Research Section during the fifteen months of its existence. The technical assistance afforded to the various echelons of the Army and Navy in this area by the highly-qualified members of that Section could have been obtained from no other source. Furthermore, through the liaison established by the Operational Research Section and your Office of Field Service, the full power of the scientific agencies established in the United States has been brought to bear upon the problems confronting our forces in the field.

"Many of the individuals who have been connected with the Operational Research Section are no longer in this area, and it will be impossible for me to express to each one personally my appreciation of his efforts. I should therefore like very much to have you consider this letter an expression of my heartfelt thanks to all who have participated in the splendid contribution made by the Operational Research Section to the success which has crowned our operations in the Pacific."

CHAPTER XIX

ISLAND-HOPPING

FIELD OFFICE WITH MACARTHUR

IN EARLY September 1944, MacArthur's General Head-quarters was moving forward to Hollandia in Dutch New Guinea. Island-hopping had started in earnest.

The scientists had been assured their unit would participate in the move. But no schedule was set for their departure. The relocation of a huge headquarters is a big operation. Perhaps in a few days word would be flashed, authorizing them to pack up too. However, weeks went by and the R/S was part of a dwindling rear echelon. Communications were worse than ever. One might as well try to administer the field projects from San Francisco or New York.

Having completed his survey in Richardson's command, late in September Klopsteg, who had succeeded Harrison in July as Chief of the SWPA Research Section,[1] got approval to fly to Hollandia to confer with General Akin. Whereupon the welcome radiogram approving transfer of the scientists to Hollandia arrived at Brisbane.

The move to Hollandia brought administrative changes. Three Wac secretaries were assigned to the Section to replace the Australian civilian girls OFS had hired. It was several months before they had learned not to recoil at terms like "phenylmercuric acetate." The new group would have to have the same indoctrination and would have to learn the office procedures set up by Edward B. Hubbard, Technical Aide and Executive Officer, who had accompanied Harrison to the theater.

When R/S was established Hubbard had taken on the job of managing the office, processing and orienting the field men as they arrived, and handling their travel and fiscal affairs. Before he left the United States he had been given an intensive short course in Government fiscal procedures and policy so that he could serve as an authorized

---

[1] During his administration the Research *Section* was renamed the Research *Division*. The original title is, however, used throughout this chapter to avoid confusion.

disbursing agent for OSRD funds deposited in Australia. At that time it was thought that the Research Section would function much as did the London Office of OSRD. This idea was largely dispelled shortly after R/S was established when Harrison was told summarily that there would be no nonmilitary channel for handling purely administrative details. Now that the Section was to move forward it would be under even more rigid military control, and any remaining hope that it could operate as a semi-independent civilian unit was abandoned. The OSRD funds would no longer be needed to pay for office facilities and clerical help, and the field men would have to send their vouchers through to Washington for payment.

In July MacArthur had issued a directive that clarified the position of R/S and broadened its responsibilities. This specified that the Section would serve as a liaison office for Ground, Air, and Naval Forces with civilian research agencies in the United States, Australia, and elsewhere, and as a clearinghouse and channel for all work requiring the use of civilian scientific personnel in that theater. It stated further that all communications concerning OSRD activities would be co-ordinated with the Research Section. This was a comprehensive order. To carry it out would take a staff of experts in a variety of technical fields. Harrison had selected Dr. H. Kirk Stephenson, geophysicist and Technical Aide of Division 17, to assist in the liaison and technical administration of R/S, but his arrival in SWPA was delayed until midsummer. He had undertaken a high-priority study of the deadly nonmagnetic land mines that were creating heavy casualties to our troops in Italy and this had taken longer than OFS expected.

When Klopsteg talked with General Akin, he persuaded him that the Section should be expanded by adding four or five able men as Technical Aides to follow the needs of the theater in several scientific fields. This meant that, if these specialists could be procured from NDRC, R/S would become a panel of consultants more nearly comparable with the balanced team at Hawaii. This was approved and a theater request for the men was dispatched. Klopsteg also recommended that the Section be transferred from the Signal Office to become a subsection of G-3, as was Marshall's team, but this was not approved.

When arrangements for the Section to be attached to the Signal Corps were made, they had seemed excellent. General Akin was a decidedly able and scientifically trained officer who had demonstrated keen interest in the sort of help OSRD might provide, especially on problems of radar, RCM, and communications. Some branches of the command, notably FEAF, were reluctant, however, to call upon a group at GHQ responsible primarily to the Chief Signal Officer. They preferred to procure help more directly themselves and to have the experts exclusively under their own jurisdiction. Moreover, General Akin was exceedingly hard pressed with the duties of a key staff officer in a combat theater and was frequently away at the front. At such times the head of the OFS unit did not have direct access to him but had to consult junior officers who either were unwilling or did not have the power to act promptly. This latter difficulty was remedied when General Akin arranged to have Colonel Paul W. Albert, head of Section 22, as his contact with R/S after the move to Hollandia.

At the end of September, Stephenson, Hubbard, and the three Wacs flew to New Guinea. A fighter escort past Wewak re-emphasized the Army's desire that scientists should not fall into enemy hands. The secret documents were brought separately by an officer assigned to the Section who spent two days fuming at Nadzab where he was deplaned for higher-priority passengers. When the R/S staff walked into GHQ they found Klopsteg seated behind a small table at one end of the Quonset hut that became the new OFS office.

As we have seen, while R/S remained at Brisbane it had been difficult for the scientist-administrators to discuss urgent scientific matters with the actual operators in forward areas. But now the Sixth Army was within easy reach for the first time and the OFS men could talk more readily with the Alamo Scouts and other combat units. By the time the Section was functioning at Hollandia, however, plans for the Leyte invasion were already drawn and the scientists could only give incidental advice. It was too late to get additional experts from the mainland to tackle the technical problems of this next operation.

Heavy commitments at home forced Klopsteg to relinquish his position as Chief of R/S, and in October he returned to Washington to help OFS select a senior scientist as his successor and recruit the additional technical aides needed for SWPA. Hubbard went back with Klopsteg, and Kirk Stephenson, who had handled himself very capably and had won the confidence of officers throughout the command, remained as Acting Chief. For several months he tried heroically to keep in touch with the 30 or 40 OFS specialists who were working with field units in many parts of the theater and whose contacts with the home office had to be through the Section. The AGRL group was still back at Sydney and other projects were soon operating on Leyte. This meant that Stephenson single-handedly was attempting to co-ordinate activities some 4000 miles apart. In addition he had to jeep his way around the headquarters, conferring, informing, and planning on everything from vitamin problems to guided missiles. Twice this liaison activity was interrupted when he went to Australia for conferences on radar and on chemical warfare. During these absences the Section was, of course, completely without a civilian technical man. Stephenson was in the awkward position of trying to run a big and important program on only a shoestring of scientific manpower.

Great distance from home bases, wide dispersal of forces and of the scientists aiding them, long and slow lines of communications, periodic remoteness of GHQ from the operating fronts, small supply of weapons and transportation, disagreeable climate, uncomfortable working conditions, repeated shifting of headquarters — these were the difficulties under which MacArthur and the scientists sent to help him had to labor for many months. It is not surprising that it took more than a year of experimenting before the most effective way of setting up an OFS group in the command was evolved.

The senior replacement for Klopsteg and the additional technical aides for R/S were hard to locate. Until V-E Day scientific manpower became more and more scarce as the number of new weapons or new models of old weapons that came off the production lines increased, and as more units of the Services came to realize what help scientists could give them. As long as the Southwest Pacific Theater was considered less important than other areas, as was evident in the allocation of equipment, the technical men could justifiably feel that assignments in ETO or even at home should carry greater priority. Moreover, the difficulties in SWPA that handicapped the efforts of scientists in that theater had become widely known. The NDRC laboratories, accus-

tomed to the freedom permitted their men in ETO and essential to
progress in scientific matters, were understandably reluctant to release
key people to a program in which the returns would be doubtful and
the working relations with the military less satisfactory. As the weeks
passed and OFS was still unable to secure the men needed, it was
evident that major changes would have to be made in the organizational setup of R/S if OSRD was to bring to MacArthur the same caliber and concentration of scientific help that had been furnished to
Eisenhower.

In December Dr. Bowles went out to the Pacific to offer General
Kenney a group of Advisory Specialists on radar and RCM like those
that had proved so successful in the European campaigns and to discuss further participation of scientists in various phases of the Japanese
war. General Akin asked Stephenson to serve as a civilian aide to
Bowles and his party. By that time our units were established on Leyte,
and Bowles held the initial conferences with Generals Sutherland,
Krueger, Kenney, Akin, and Marquat on this island. He offered an
Advisory Specialist of first rank to serve as MacArthur's personal advisor on all scientific matters and pointed out to General Akin and
others the difficulties under which the Research Section and OFS had
been operating in their efforts to give the theater the quality and
quantity of scientific help needed. Bowles then went to Hollandia,
Brisbane, Sydney, and Melbourne for further conferences with other
units of the command and with the Australian scientists, and Kirk
went with him. After Bowles took off for Ceylon in January, Stephenson returned to Hollandia to catch up on his work as the sole scientist,
liaison man, and administrator at R/S headquarters. But GHQ had
moved again in the meantime and he found orders to proceed at once
to Taclobán, Leyte. His staff and files had already left. This time the
scientific unit had gone forward during the early part of the transfer.

Word was also waiting that R/S had been transferred[2] from the
Signal Office to become an entity in the USAFFE[3] Board (later known
as the Pacific Warfare Board). General Akin explained later that he
had requested this change because he felt that his duties as Chief

---

[2] And once again called the Research *Section*.
[3] U.S. Army Forces in the Far East.

Signal Officer and in several staff appointments would increase greatly as the Pacific war gained momentum. He thought he would be unable to devote sufficient time to the affairs of the Research Section as the scientific effort in the theater expanded.

Although, as Stephenson points out, "from the standpoint of both animal comfort and scientific achievement Leyte was the low point in the Research Section curve," the transfer was a fortunate change, even though it interposed one more link in the chain of command. The USAFFE Board consisted of a group of technical officers from all branches of the Army. Their function was to act as field observers on new equipment and techniques and they could move about the theater with great freedom. Colonel William Alexander, President of the Board, proved thoroughly co-operative and determined that R/S should operate in the same manner as it had previously. He and Stephenson planned to have each new civilian scientist from OFS accompanied to the field by one or two officers of the Board who had similar interests. They had the proper contacts, could save the R/S men a great deal of time, and would help make their activities more effective. In addition, the Board would serve as a "home" for OFS men arriving at R/S, should Stephenson not happen to be available.

In January and February, with the Philippines campaign in full swing, few new projects could be initiated. Stephenson felt that he could explain to the Washington office the many changes in the SWPA situation much better in person than by correspondence. He had been in the theater for almost a year and out of touch with so many aspects of the research program that he felt he could do a better job in SWPA after a refresher visit to the United States. With Alexander's approval, Stephenson wrote to OFS suggesting that he come home for a short time.

While awaiting Dr. Compton's reply, Stephenson went to Manila on a scientific intelligence mission. This was the first time he had been allowed to fly over and enter an area of active combat. It was symbolic of the much greater freedom of action that OFS scientists would enjoy under the jurisdiction of the USAFFE Board.

Then came orders to move R/S to Manila by boat during the first week in March. But Alexander asked Stephenson and Lloyd to fly to the Philippine capital to examine new Jap rockets that had been captured. When they found officers of the Board already at Manila, the OFS men moved into their office in the Trade and Commerce Building.

Compton approved Stephenson's proposal and suggested that Waterman go out to become more familiar with the situation in SWPA and take over temporarily the administration of the Research Section. Since the R/S was in a turmoil of moving, it was decided that Waterman should wait in Washington until Stephenson arrived in April, even though the Section would be unmanned for a short time.

By late April the tempo of the Pacific war had greatly accelerated. MacArthur was firmly established in Manila; the B-29's were mauling Japan; the Navy was whittling away at shipping close to the home islands; Germany seemed about to give up; and redeployment of equipment and troops to the Pacific would soon be under way at long last. It was obvious that OSRD would then be able to concentrate much more of its scientific manpower on the final knockout efforts. But these would have to be co-ordinated. Dr. Bush ordered that all OSRD field missions to the Pacific were thereafter to be sent out through OFS.[4] This made it essential that arrangements with the military in the theater would have to permit speed and freedom and flexibility. Lieutenant Colonel Henderson of NDD therefore accompanied Waterman to confer with the commanders about a broad program to increase OSRD aid in the whole Pacific area, to bring about an even more effective setup of civilian missions, and to improve the co-ordination of all OSRD efforts through OFS and its military liaison agencies. OFS was now beginning to exercise the full authority of its broad directive.

Late in June Waterman returned to the States with MacArthur's approval for an all-out scientific effort through the establishment of a Pacific Branch of OSRD (PBOSRD) with headquarters at Manila. Then a few days later Stephenson left to resume his duties as head of the Research Section until this Pacific Branch could become established.

[4] The problem of recruiting was therefore subordinate to the problem of handling a greatly increased volume of traffic through the still intricate mechanics of processing without a concurrent increase in staff.

He had found himself so woefully out of date that instead of spending one month brushing up as he had planned, he spent nearly three. But when he returned to Manila in June he was armed with a great deal of information about new devices that had not been available in SWPA — VT-fuzes, guided missiles, and infrared equipment.

In the Philippines he found that an Advisory Specialist Group (ASG) for FEAF had been set up, headed by David T. Griggs, Dr. Edwin G. Schneider, specialist in ground radar, and Dr. T. A. Murrell. The work of these radar experts from Bowles's office in introducing techniques of bombing through overcast in ETO and in adapting the SCR-584 as an antidote to the buzz-bombs had been exceptionally meritorious.[5] These men started a full radar program for General Kenney, and the theater began to ask for experts in many fields to give his airmen the latest word about equipment. Teletype conferences with Washington became a weekly procedure and the Research Section embarked on a schedule of "a new project a day." Big things were in the wind. Eventually there would be a large force of scientists at PB to deal with problems in many fields. But in the meantime, while the formal negotiations were proceeding at home, R/S and ASG were assigning men to combat units as rapidly as they could be secured from home. FEAF asked for radar and RCM men by the dozen. Bush's directive made it mandatory, however, that those procured from NDRC be processed through OFS and thereby through R/S in the theater. They would report to Stephenson for co-ordination and would then be loaned to work under the immediate supervision of the Air Force units to which they were assigned.

As soon as the war in Europe was practically over, RL began to send its men westward in larger numbers. Late in April G. M. Hare, expert on Loran, a long-range radar navigation system, arrived to assist FEAF in siting Loran installations and training operators.

In mid-July W. A. Hosier arrived as the civilian member of a team of officers with ETO experience who were to instruct crews of the 5th and 13th Air Forces in the use of another radar navigational system

---

[5] The ASG in Europe had played an enormous part in the strategic bombing of Germany, the campaign of the beaches, Patton's drive along the Loire, and the Battle of the Bulge. They evacuated equipment at the last moment; were fired upon; served as pinch-hit operators of gear in crucial spots; and covered themselves with glory that has been officially recognized in many a communication.

known as Shoran. FEAF planned to equip all B-24's and B-32's and part of each squadron of A-25's and A-26's for Shoran navigation. Even after the active campaign had ceased, this team continued to train FEAF personnel in Shoran mapping and computing procedures so that the system could be used in the aerial mapping of Japan.

Since early May C. M. Sorvaag had been in the theater as a specialist on Little Abner. Six sets out of the total of fifteen that were ordered arrived in SWPA and Sorvaag trained their crews. During the final weeks of the war he was working on a mobile mount of Little Abner for the 5th Air Force and teaching crews to use a longer-wave portable search set that could be used with the height finder in the assault phase of Operation Olympic, scheduled for November.

Late in July RL sent A. G. Bagg and R. T. McCoy to the Philippines to participate in the FEAF program of mobilizing early-warning radar for the forthcoming invasion.

J. B. Platt and R. L. MacCreary were sent out as specialists on the use of the SCR-584 for close-control bombing. By the middle of August one set of the special equipment needed for this had arrived and they had succeeded in training a single crew to use the plotting board; Olympic plans called for a total of six.

The Operations Analysis Section of FEAF wanted a general advisor on radar matters, and Talbot H. Waterman of RL served in this capacity from June until October. After V-J he went to Japan with an intelligence team from OAS.

When the war ended there were also three RL specialists in China, sent by OFS under arrangements made by Bowles's office. R. S. Powell had gone out in May to the 14th Air Force as a consultant on the AN/TPS-10 height-finding radar, and Dr. L. J. Chu and E. J. Faulkner arrived as consultants to General Wedemeyer on radar and other scientific matters only ten days before the surrender. They found a serious air-traffic control problem at Kunming, terminus of the air-supply routes to China. Using a long-range search set and the AN/TPS-10, they demonstrated that radar could alleviate some of the trouble.

In China many of the airfields are nestled in mountain ranges; personnel of high technical qualifications to operate control equipment are scarce; and there are few passable roads that can be used to establish aids to landing and navigation. The three Americans supplied detailed instructions for operating an efficient airport control system to provide the maximum flow of traffic with the least reduction in safety between and over the Chinese airfields. With the opening of seaports on the China coast, air traffic in the interior would drop considerably and the erection of a complete radar air-traffic system could not be justified. Nevertheless, Chu, Faulkner, and Powell recommended that additional radar installations be made to supplement the existing facilities at the chief air terminals — Canton, Shanghai, Peiping, and Kunming.

As the headquarters of the Pacific Air Forces moved to Guam and Okinawa and the 8th Air Force was transferred from Europe, a number of RL and RRL specialists were sent directly to these islands to assist the U.S. Army Strategic Air Forces (USASTAF) with radar and jamming equipment for the B-29's.

During the six weeks from Stephenson's return in June until "The Bomb" brought "The End," his life was a hectic round of conferences with theater officers and ASG men, teletype discussions with OFS at Washington, phone calls, and trips by jeep or plane. Then suddenly the work of R/S changed to the happy task of securing "tickets" home for all the men who had come out to help in delivering the final punches. By mid-September only a few stragglers were left, Moreland's scientific intelligence mission had gone to Japan, and the Research Section, Pacific Warfare Board, closed its files.

The men whose exploits constitute the history of the OFS field office with MacArthur, much of which has been told in other sections of this volume, were among the best of the combat scientists. Their stock in trade was pleasing personality, thorough knowledge of their specialties, willingness to work, and unlimited courage and persistence in the face of discouraging administrative situations or personal danger. They took rebuffs and even insults and stuck with their assignments because there was a terribly important job to be done.

The tale of the Research Section might have been a story of failure. But the civilians learned their way around in the maze of military attitudes and regulations; and the military men learned how to take advantage of the help the scientists could offer. Both lessons came the hard way and took time. One observer noted that the co-operation of

CHAPTER XX

MINIATURE IN MANILA

THE PACIFIC BRANCH, OSRD

ON THE day in June when Waterman walked quietly into the Washington office of OFS, still in his sun-faded khakis, there was a twinkle of pride in his eyes and the corners of his mouth turned up in a smile of well-earned satisfaction. In his briefcase was an outline of the most comprehensive single field project that had yet been proposed, a plan to set up in Manila a miniature of OSRD. MacArthur had assured him that the help of scientists was of more vital concern than ever to the top echelons. For weeks Waterman had conferred with the highest staff officers, evolving the details of a field organization that would win the fullest support from OSRD because it had the flexibility and freedom the scientists demanded. Then General Sutherland approved the pattern and guaranteed the strongest possible backing of the theater. The evolutionary process of finding the most effective way to make civilian scientific assistance of greatest benefit to the fighting forces had culminated in the request for a Pacific Branch of OSRD. When he had done the spadework, Waterman returned at once to secure the approval of Bush that would convert the paper plans into concrete realities.

Several months earlier, as events in Europe rushed toward a close and it appeared certain that the final crisis would occur in the Pacific, OSRD had felt it desirable to review at first hand the status of scientific efforts in that whole area. Further questions were in the air. MacArthur had assumed supreme command and there was doubt as to the role ORS in the Central Pacific might play in future operations. The conquest of the Philippines gave MacArthur for the first time a large base closer to the heart of the enemy. There was talk of creating a field electronics laboratory staffed with OSRD scientists; and it appeared possible that a setup like the field radar and countermeasures laboratories in ETO might be profitable. The probable collapse of the

European foe promised to release not only a full complement of materiel and military personnel with which to end the Pacific war, but also many battle-tried scientists.

Waterman had left on April 20, when the European war was almost over. A week after his arrival in SWPA, V-E Day was announced. The conjecture became a fact; redeployment was a reality.

At home this event led to conferences instigated by Burchard, Acting Deputy Chief of OFS, with General Borden and his staff, with Dr. Julius Stratton, acting head of Bowles's office, with Dr. Lee DuBridge, Director of the Radiation Laboratory, and with Dr. John G. Trump, who had just returned from assignment as Director of BBRL to head a new Field Service Division of RL that would bring concentration on field radar problems in the Pacific. With the backing of the highest military authority at home and using the experience of the OSRD laboratories in ETO as a guide, proposed plans for a field laboratory, approved by Compton and Bush, were drawn up by Burchard and forwarded to Manila.

In the theater Waterman found that OSRD help was needed on serious military problems — defense against suicide attacks, location of enemy mortar fire, radar aids to tactical and strategic air offensives, and the more effective employment of rocket barrages. It soon appeared that far more than the proposed laboratory was desirable and that the scientific needs of the theater could only be fully met by a fairly complete cross section of OSRD.

Before Waterman left the States there had been conferences with Bush, Compton, Carroll Wilson, General Borden, Bowles, Suits, Dr. F. E. Terman, Director of RRL, and Drs. DuBridge, Loomis, Rabi, and Ewing of RL. The idea of an electronics laboratory had been approved but only on condition that it would be in a position to serve all branches of Army and Navy in the theater. An entirely civilian laboratory, set up as independently of the military as possible, was favored. Yet those familiar with the theater were certain that the command would not permit an independent establishment, free from military control. It was also clear that Bush preferred to have such a laboratory represent OSRD as a whole rather than a single Division of NDRC.

Assuming that the theater wanted an expanded field organization, what were the alternatives? The first would be an organization set up under General Akin that all elements of the command would agree to use and support. Or it could be established instead under FEAF, which would be its chief customer. Or it could become a unit within the R/S. But this latter would not place it at a high enough level. The time had come for centralizing OSRD support in a single major activity at the topmost level and with freedom to operate such as had made BBRL, ABL-15, and the Liaison Office in London potent factors in ETO.

Waterman's conferences with MacArthur, Akin, Marquat, Krueger, and Kenney disclosed that the command felt the need for a highly qualified group of top-notch men to act as a consulting staff on pressing and bewildering problems that could not be solved by standard military methods. The consultants should be men of such standing in OSRD that immediate assistance in personnel, equipment, or information would be provided when they asked for it. But men of such stature would not be willing to go out unless liaison with the military would permit effective work, nor should OSRD permit them to do so.

Akin abandoned his suggestion for an electronics laboratory because of a lack of expressed interest on the part of branches other than his own. On the other hand, FEAF had learned what OSRD could do in radar, rockets, guided missiles, and proximity fuzes, and was apparently ready to support a laboratory and staff under any terms satisfactory to OSRD.

Burchard had secured agreement of Bush, General Borden, Bowles, DuBridge, and others that Waterman should negotiate further for a laboratory — to include in its staff and facilities all aspects of OSRD that would be of immediate concern in the Pacific war. This would not be created for long-term research and development, but to provide technical facilities close to the front where modifications and repair and short-term, applied research could be carried out. The staff, scientific equipment, and fiscal support were to be supplied by OSRD; the space, buildings, meals, power, and other utilities, security, and authority by the Armed Forces.

General Kenney, impressed by the eloquent efforts of Griggs and his other Advisory Specialists, expressed enthusiastic interest in such a laboratory and gladly accepted the suggestion that he present a proposal, endorsed by Waterman, to the Chief of Staff, that a Pacific Branch of OSRD be established. It would be dependent upon the theater for facilities and would have the greatest possible freedom for work that could be granted by the Commander in Chief. It would include a consulting staff of outstanding senior scientists, medical men, and engineers; a pool of scientific specialists closer to the operating units and already processed for assignments with the fighting forces; a headquarters administrative office; and laboratory facilities for emergency work.

It was immediately apparent that the theater would exercise operational control in the military sense. Such a unit would have to report directly to the command and follow the customary regulations of military control over personnel, equipment, and communications. Provided these conditions were satisfied, General Sutherland favored the plan and proceeded in statesmanlike fashion to formulate ways and means of putting it into operation.

It was agreed further that the Research Section should be continued as an entity to provide administrative assistance for OFS projects and to co-ordinate OSRD work in the theater at least until PB could get into full operation. Thereafter the Chief of the Research Section could hold a staff position in PBOSRD[1] and thus make more effective the work of the scientists in the Pacific Warfare Board.

Sutherland accepted the suggestion made earlier by Bowles that MacArthur have a senior advisory specialist as his own consultant on technical matters. Even though he would remain a civilian, he would be appointed Special Staff Officer on scientific and technical affairs and would report to the Chief of Staff independently of the Director of PBOSRD. Obviously the two would have to work in close co-operation. Since Dean Moreland, who had been Executive Officer of NDRC, was selected for this important post, such co-operation was assured.

*   *   *

[1] Just before these negotiations were completed in the middle of June, reorganization of the Pacific command was announced. The entire Army in the Pacific became AFPAC; Services of Supply in SWPA became WESPAC; POA became MIDPAC and USAFFE was absorbed into GHQ, AFPAC. FEAF and the Seventh Fleet remained attached to AFPAC. The USAFFE Board was renamed Pacific Warfare Board and attached administratively as a subsection to G-3, AFPAC. Since the new directive of PacWarBd included the Research Section, Stephenson's R/S was finally placed in the same relative position as Marshall's ORS under Richardson.

During the negotiations, Sutherland requested that Marshall visit the forward areas to discuss co-ordination between PBOSRD and ORS. He was also asked to stop at headquarters of USASTAF and of the Navy at Guam to consider relationships of ORS with those organizations. The Navy requested that the services of ORS be continued on the existing informal basis. En route to Washington to talk these matters over with Compton, Marshall was advised informally by the Air Forces Chief of Staff that the Air Forces would like to have an operating group similar to ORS. They recognized that any such unit would have to become a subsidiary branch of the PB and would probably draw personnel from that organization. The chief of the proposed ORS group would report officially to PBOSRD on technical matters. Nevertheless, the Air Force officers felt that independent channels for technical communications through AAF in Washington should be maintained, so that there would be no delay in routing them from the field via the main office of PB at Manila.

There were questions regarding the relationship of civilians under AFPAC with the Eighth Air Force. This unit was operating independently of the theater command. Yet it would be attacking Japan proper and would have many of the same RCM problems as FEAF. The Eighth would undoubtedly have its own civilian advisors and perhaps its own laboratory; but in any case an informal arrangement could be made to avoid duplication of effort and provide close liaison between the technical men of the Eighth and those of the PB, particularly because they would both be largely supplied by OSRD through OFS.

When consultants were detailed to forward areas to work as individual specialists with a subordinate echelon, the problem of getting information on technical details back quickly to the home laboratories had been acute. An ORS man working with air squadrons on Saipan found, for example, that a report he wrote in December had not yet been cleared through the series of local commands for transmission to Oahu by the latter part of February. After forwarding from Saipan, it would still have had to go through Air Force headquarters at POA, then through ORS and G-3 POA, and finally through NDD and OFS before it could be sent to the Radiation Laboratory. Obviously such a situation was intolerable and RL, accustomed to direct communications with its men in ETO through its British Branch, was understandably reluctant to place its ablest technical people in such an awkward position. Something would have to be done to shorten the channels if the Pacific command wanted full support from RL.

When the final proposal was drafted, the Pacific Branch was to be an operating unit, occupying a place in the command similar to General Krueger's Sixth Army or General Kenney's FEAF. In this way it would be available to serve directly any element of the command. Its Director was to report to the Commander in Chief, AFPAC, who would exercise operational control on policy, priority of theater needs, movement of personnel and equipment, and general behavior. It was to be staffed and financed by OSRD, though necessarily dependent upon the army for accommodations, food, and other necessities. It was permitted to have direct communication with OSRD at home on technical and internal administrative matters by radio or by letter, just as Army Technical Services overseas have with their offices in the War Department, and teletype conferences were to be standard procedure, with the Director of PB in charge in the theater and OFS in charge in the Pentagon.

All in all, here was a plan that seemed at once to solve all the difficulties OFS had experienced in the Southwest Pacific, and Bush agreed that OSRD would give it full support.

Since it was agreed that the Director of PBOSRD should look to a single office in Washington for administrative assistance in procurement of personnel, handling of communications, and requests for information, Bush asked that OFS assume primary responsibility for attention to the needs of the new unit. This large undertaking presented a serious problem to OFS with its limited staff, for it was contemplated that some 200 or more scientists would be sent out to the activities at Manila within a few months. OSRD approved a proposal that OFS finance and run the Pacific Branch by means of a contract with the National Academy of Sciences. The Director of PB would remain an appointee of the Director OSRD and report directly to him on matters of policy; his technical aides and secretarial staff would be Government employees, but the rest of the staff would be supervised and administered under the Academy contract. This would have provided a speedier mechanism both for employing and for processing non-OSRD personnel, and the convenient location of the Academy in Washington would mean that co-ordination with OFS could be accomplished easily.

As a signal to the rest of the organization that OSRD really meant business, the Director of PBOSRD would have to be a man of outstanding scientific stature. Dr. Compton agreed to accept this position and resigned as Chief of OFS. As Director of PB he would have the responsibility of supervising the entire OSRD program in the Pacific. This would include ORS at Hawaii, the Research Section at Manila, and any unit that might be established under USASTAF.

It was clear that OSRD units should no longer hesitate to release their most competent personnel for aid in delivering the final blows at Japan. The Army had approved a plan that held strong promise of good working relations between the scientists and the military and that would give the technical men direct access to the topmost levels of the Pacific command. Through Conant and Richards, Bush therefore requested all Divisions of NDRC and CMR to back the powerful team of Compton and Moreland to the fullest extent possible. This was the third and most potent medicine that finally removed the manpower headaches of OFS.[2]

OFS set about to implement the plans for PB at once and the organization began to crystallize quickly. As his technical aide, Compton was to have John L. Danforth of Division 14. The project activities would be supervised by a Project Chief and Klopsteg was chosen for this assignment. He was to have a staff of leading men from representative NDRC activities, each with a group of appropriate size to handle projects in his respective field. Administrative details would be handled by J. K. Howard, who was to come forward from ORS to cover such matters as accounting, personnel administration, transportation, and maintenance. His assistant in the theater was to be Ephron Catlin, Jr., who would supervise fiscal procedures for the PB. The Divisions that would be primarily concerned with problems of

[2] The first was the sudden release of technical men from ETO for work in the Pacific after V-E; the second was Bush's directive that all OSRD personnel for Army or Navy in the Japanese war must be procured through OFS.

the theater gave Compton recommendations of key personnel who would be available on call for the special staff of senior consultants. These men were then alerted by OFS, began their processing, and stood by for theater requests. The Radiation Laboratory made elaborate plans to contribute specialists in radar. As we have seen, a substantial number of RL men were already in the theater; more than a score were preparing for departure; and it was contemplated that most of the returning BBRL staff would eventually be shipped to the Pacific. Divisions 3 and 15 presented comprehensive plans for projects on rockets and countermeasures. Division 3 expected to contribute at least five members to the original staff and McClure was to come forward from Hawaii as initial head of the rocket group, which was to be increased to ten or twelve by November. The RCM program was to be in charge of Dr. Gregg Stephenson of RRL. Since the need for radar countermeasures is more seriously felt by a strategic air force than by a tactical one, it was expected that Division 15 would contribute more heavily to the group at USASTAF than to the main laboratory at Manila. The Committee on Medical Research selected Dr. William S. Tillett of the New York University Medical School to be its senior advisory consultant on medical matters at PB. The Tropical Deterioration Committee chose mycologist Dr. Leland Shanor to represent its comprehensive interests and planned to have facilities for field tests and a small laboratory.

FEAF was much interested in the proximity fuze developed by Division 4 for bombs and rockets. Dr. Fred S. Atchison was to leave in mid-August as the senior representative of Division 4. FEAF had also laid plans for extensive use of the guided missiles, Azon and Razon. Three men from Division 5 were to depart in mid-August — W. H. Nichols to the Thirteenth Air Force, Abner J. Wollan to Okinawa with the Fifth, and the Division Chief, H. H. Spencer, to tour headquarters of the various Air Forces in the Pacific and Asiatic Commands.

In the Pacific Branch, OSRD, assimilated ranks were to be arranged according to a schedule worked out by the Chief of PB, the Chief of OFS, and NDD so that the top administrators under Compton would be Brigadier Generals, the Directors of the research units would be

Colonels, and their subordinates would be ranked downward regardless
of their salaries.

An agreement was reached between Mrs. Ruth Shipley, Head of the
Passport Division of the State Department, and Colonel Sweeney in
the Office of the Joint Chiefs of Staff charged with issuance of military
permits, whereby the PBOSRD would be recognized as a single high-
priority project by both agencies. OFS would put a special stamp on the
processing papers of men going out to staff this activity and the State
Department would instruct its personnel to give prompt and efficient
handling to such documents. The Joint Chiefs would issue the military
permit when they received a request bearing this identifying symbol,
recognizing that the dispatch of a quota of personnel had already been
approved in advance by the theater command. The customary exchange of cables between the Washington office and the theater to establish permission to enter that area for each individual in this quota
would be unnecessary. Cancellation of the PB directive shortly after
V-J Day obviated the necessity for utilizing this simplified arrangement; but it is estimated that it would have saved a week to ten days in
the average time required for processing.

Priorities for the shipment of supplies, apparatus, and personnel
were to be issued by PB itself under a blanket authorization. By eliminating another customary exchange of radios, this would likewise
have expedited the whole processing procedure.

In order to take full advantage of the authority for direct communications on technical and internal administrative matters and yet
insure supervision by OFS and NDD without interposing delay,
arrangements were made to establish two subcenters of OFS — one at
Compton's office in Cambridge, and the other at the California Institute of Technology. Such communications would be channeled
through these offices to the appropriate Divisions without first going
to Washington. Official correspondence containing requests for equipment or personnel would, however, still have to be routed through
NDD to OFS in Washington as usual.

The stage was now set for implementing the ambitious PBOSRD
program. Suddenly the Pacific command had recognized and remedied
all the difficulties that had been interfering with full scientific aid.

There were many factors in this, of course, but not the least of them was the patient persistence and quiet diplomacy of Alan T. Waterman, who had been Bush's representative in the complicated negotiations.

Bearing the assimilated ranks of Major General, Compton and Moreland left for the Philippines on the third of August. Word of their trip had gone ahead by teletype and they were met at the airfields en route and accorded the military courtesies appropriate to this high rank and the importance of their missions. They arrived at Manila on August fifth and Compton laid the details of the plan for PB on General Sutherland's desk before the first A-bomb was dropped. The program was formally approved immediately after this event, but prior to the surrender. The Pacific Branch, OSRD, was a reality.

On the 13th of August the theater agreed to provide 20,000 square feet of building space for laboratory, shop, and offices; a 150-KW power supply; water at a minimum of 5000 gallons per day; approval for shipping approximately 300 tons of equipment from OSRD; quarters and mess for approximately 200 scientists and technicians; 24-hour guard service; permission for OFS to send out 15 to 30 experienced secretaries and stenographers; adequate transportation facilities, including individually assigned jeeps and trucks; and access to the general motor pool during emergencies.

Although Compton had arrived in the theater only a few days before the capitulation of Japan, it would be a mistake to conclude that the Pacific Branch was merely an ideal paper organization. There were already in the theater about 60 first-line men from various NDRC Divisions. They were to be transferred to PB and would constitute Compton's initial staff. The central OFS office was preparing some 70 more, and formal theater requests for a large contingent of them were received in Washington in the midst of the victory celebration.

From the day OFS was established, it had been obvious that field service would be needed as long as there were American forces anywhere in the field. Even after hostilities, there would be medical problems, the gathering of intelligence, and a need for scientific help in planning certain phases of occupation and control of the enemy's technological facilities. Bush had made it very plain that OSRD was to be strictly a war agency, to go out of existence at the close of the war; but he expected that OFS would be one of the last scientific units to turn over its records to the archives.

In the months before the Allies broke over the Rhine, no one knew whether German surrender would precede, come concurrently with, or even follow a Japanese defeat. It was impossible to foresee the course of OFS. Since both enemies appeared to be definitely on the run, the only sound policy was to continue meeting military calls for scientific aid as fully and as quickly as possible and to "play by ear" the directions of emphasis in the field-service effort. It was evident, however, that the volume of OFS activity would increase right up to the end of the war, regardless of retrenchment in laboratory research.

Some of those who knew of the plan to use atomic weapons against Japan believed this would bring an early end to the struggle, yet there could be no diminution of the strenuous effort to set the PBOSRD into full operation. For security reasons alone it would have been ill-advised for OFS to rely on the power of this terrible weapon and slow down. Consequently, even after the first of the paralyzing blows had been delivered, OFS was in high gear, getting men ready for departure and conducting conferences on administrative details of PB, details that only a few days later became academic.

Immediately after V-J, Bush formulated a demobilization policy for OFS. The field men overseas were to be recalled as soon as their missions could be completed. No new missions were to depart without specific individual approval of the Director, and this would be given only for problems in which OSRD could properly maintain a continuing responsibility. None of this liquidation was to be accomplished with such haste that values of the scientific work would be destroyed, the amicable relations of OSRD with the Services jeopardized, or the individual workers left in awkward positions with regard to employment; but a spirit of positive action for demobilization was to prevail.

Despite its speed, the reconversion was entirely orderly and not a single employee of OFS was out of a job for more than a few days. Scientific and specialized personnel continued to be at a premium for some months after the war — and there is sound opinion that this condition will remain for a number of years.

During the next several months while a small administrative staff remained on duty there were repeated calls on OFS to loan scientific manpower to the Army and Navy. OFS made it clear to the Services, however, that it could merely give scientific counsel and aid in locating qualified personnel who would undertake the assignments as War or Navy Department employees.

When there was no longer an urgency of combat needs to motivate speed in handling paper work, to justify making exceptions and waiving regulations, the whole business of procuring and processing civilians became more difficult. All the offices involved were subject to the same ills of rapid turnover and relaxed effort — normal reactions from the intense days of the war. Scientists who were brought to Washington to deal directly with the Army or Navy during this postwar period began to appreciate that, although the delays they experienced in the hands of OFS had been irksome and had seemed protracted at the time, OFS and its major liaison offices in the Services had operated with remarkable speed. Officers who depended on OFS to get things done in a hurry bemoaned the policy that OSRD should go out of existence so rapidly when, in some senses, the war was not yet over. There is little doubt that if the basic purpose of OSRD had been extended to cover scientific aid to the military during what is technically peacetime, OFS would still be taking on an impressive list of projects.

The story of OFS is largely a story of organization and of personnel, the tale of an experiment in developing an alliance of the military man and the civilian scientist or engineer. Unlike much of the history of OSRD, it is not an account of the magic of creating ingenious weapons and wonder drugs. It is, rather, a record of trial and error in an effort to get the right man into the right spot to help the Army and Navy use such things correctly. In that sense, when we have examined the administrative progress of OFS, we have seen the real history that was made.

We are still too close to the war to evaluate the contributions of individual combat scientists to our victories. That should be done by impartial observers in the true perspective that comes with distance. We can point with a glow to the spectacular achievement of a single man or a certain day. But too much of what was done by the field-service pioneers of this war does not appear in the factual records of their technical reports. It is intangible, imponderable, known only imperfectly even to those whose lives and homes they helped to save. The most important fact is, of course, that we won the war. And in every major engagement civilian scientists, armed only with technical knowledge, fought side by side with professional soldiers and draftees for the first time in history. Lessons that came out of the experiment can guide us, if ever again the scientists of this land have to turn their creative genius to ghastly destruction in combat.

CHAPTER XXI

LESSONS FOR TOMORROW

THE MESSAGE OF EXPERIENCE

PESSIMISTS who maintain that another war is inevitable warn that it will be an affair of push buttons, to be settled in a few hours or in a single night. They foresee mass attacks by ocean-spanning, pilotless, radio-controlled missiles with atomic warheads. These fantastic weapons would travel much faster than sound and would come down out of the stratosphere without warning to devastate all the major centers of a nation in a single, pulverizing blow. Few would question that eventually such attacks are possible. If they could be mounted in a year or two, it would be idle and academic to talk of things one should or should not do about setting up and operating another Office of Field Service in a future OSRD. But these horrifying prospects are a result of extrapolation, of projecting in imagination far beyond the awesome realities of modern total war. It may be only years or it may be a century before a battle of push buttons is feasible. No one knows better than does a scientist or an engineer that the rate of scientific and technological advance toward such terrifying objectives cannot be predicted with accuracy.

Nevertheless, in the meantime we need no reminders of man's ineffectuality in maintaining the social and political equilibrium essential to a lasting peace. The speed at which the chaos of World War II came on us is fair warning that long before any nation or any combine of nations can organize and control such inanimate mass assaults, there may be occasion to settle issues by recourse to whatever less effective but yet ruinous weapons and devices may be available at the time. The jet fighter, the V-2, the guided missile, and the nuclear explosive were but tokens of the frightfulness that can come to the world when the full genius of science is marshaled for destruction. Our ardent hope that the United Nations organization can avert such a calamity must still be tempered with the practical wisdom of preparedness lest it fail. There is, of course, no necessity for regarding another war as inevitable. But who would question longer that a vigorous and sustained application of science and technology to military matters is our first real line of defense?

The need for a permanent Government agency as a successor to OSRD to keep science mobilized for defense and for co-ordinated effort on many matters pertaining to the nation's health and welfare was widely discussed for some months after V-J Day. In his report to the President, Bush presented a plan to establish a National Science Foundation[1] that met an enthusiastic press. Soon the scientists and engineers of the country were flocking to testify at public hearings on proposed legislation that would translate into law an almost universal sentiment favoring the creation of such an agency. For a time it looked as though an over-all federal scientific body might soon come into existence. The recommendations of Bush, Compton, Conant, and hundreds of the foremost scientists were daily front-page items. Then contention over price and wage controls, international credits, and internal reconversion crowded this important subject into the background. Perhaps it is too much to hope that before this manuscript, reduced to printed pages, has reached the thinking citizens of this land, the scientists' proposals will again be headlined. It seems reasonably certain, however, that eventually the Congress will establish some sort of national science authority and lay down the fundamental policies to guide its operation.

In public discussions of this issue little attention was given specifically to field-service aspects of the vast program of applied research for national defense that was to be one of the Foundation's major functions. Undoubtedly, however, provisions of the legislation will be broad enough to include them as soon as the need is recognized and a constructive pattern suggested. In other words, we may very well have to set up another OFS type of program, this time as a functional part of a national science agency from the outset — and in the near future.

* * *

[1] See *"Science the Endless Frontier, A Report to the President,"* by Vannevar Bush, July 1945; Government Printing Office.

As originally proposed the agency was to be called the National *Research* Foundation; but testimony in the hearings brought out the suggestion that the more general term "Science" in the name would be in keeping with the broad objectives contemplated.

Field service is not a thing to be switched on only when there is war. The OFS experience demonstrates that it can be an integral and necessary part of the applications of science to defense as well. Moreover, if there is a future war, it will come too quickly. There will be no time to recruit and indoctrinate field-service men; they will be needed at once. Meanwhile the special skills of civilian scientists should be applied in many directions just as they were during hostilities. The truth of this has already been recognized by the Services. The Navy has taken over the Operations Research Group [2] as a permanent part of its organization, the Operations Analysis Division of the Air Forces is continuing, and the Army Ground Forces are negotiating to set up a similar activity. Thus, continuity of at least some field-service work is assured. But the need for field consultation is evident in so many aspects of preparedness that supplementing such Service activities through a civilian agency, as was done by OFS, can be justified readily.

How then should this be accomplished? What relationship should the field-service branch or subdivision have to the rest of the agency? What sort of work should engage its men (and women) during peacetime? How can the civilian effort be integrated with the national-defense activities of our military and naval Departments? In case of war, how can the field men render more effective aid?

Long before the shooting stopped, the combat scientists of OFS in the field and the senior central staff at home were trying to think such matters through. In the letters and reports of those who led teams of specialists and worked out techniques essential to smooth operation within the frameworks of military organization are many paragraphs about improving the military-civilian partnership. In the lessons learned by OFS that resulted ultimately in creation of the Pacific Branch of OSRD there are also guideposts for the future. This project was hailed by the military arms and the civilians alike as the type of administrative field organization that held greatest promise for bringing technical manpower to bear most immediately on the use of new devices and tactics in the urgency of day-to-day combat. The personal letters, formal reports, and verbal comments of numerous individual field men were likewise full of constructive suggestions.

In all of this contemplation, field service was not considered as part

[2] Now known as Operations *Evaluation* Group.

of a *permanent* national agency, of course, because no such thing was yet assured. The thoughts of these men are nonetheless pertinent and worth our attention now. Not all of them agree on many points. But out of their varied ideas we can synthesize a pattern for another OFS, if one is ever created in the future. As its major ingredients we may use the suggestions that would gain strongest approval among the experienced field consultants and the administrators. Such a review of the things OFS discovered during this war that would improve its operation or augment its effectiveness to meet similar future needs may not be futile writing merely for the archives.

If a merger of Army and Navy is effected; if universal military training becomes a law; if the Services extend their present plans to encourage the development of scientists within their own ranks; or if the basic programs of the National Science Foundation as proposed by Bush are modified in any substantial way, the answers given to our questions here, and to many evident collateral ones, would surely be revised. But, assuming for the moment that none of these changes is instituted, how would the field-service men of the present wish to set up a field-service program for the immediate future?

To distinguish the proposed field-service branch of the Foundation from its imperfect prototype, the OFS, we may refer to it as the "Field Service Division (FSD)." It would, of course, be associated chiefly with the military defense portion of the Foundation's comprehensive work. But the title suggests that it should be a major subdivision, reporting directly to the head of the Foundation. It would function as the channel for all of the organization's operations that could be properly construed as "field service," defining this in the same broad terms as those used in the basic directive of the Office of Field Service in OSRD. All phases of assistance to Army, Navy, and Air Force in order to make the most effective use of the weapons, devices, medical discoveries, and scientific information that are developed by the Foundation or by other scientific agencies would thus be included in the definition.

The experts of FSD would be in the field periodically, both at home and at bases overseas. They would aid in the installation, field testing, and maintenance of new devices, would analyze their performance under simulated or actual combat conditions, and would help to determine the force requirements. They would design practice maneuvers and tests that could yield maximum information for scientific analysis, and they would sit in as counselors to tactical and strategic planning. They would provide direct liaison between the home laboratories and the field units and give on-the-spot counsel on scientific and technological matters as they arise.

The home office of FSD could establish *ad hoc* missions for the study of special problems and it would operate any necessary laboratories or advance offices in theaters of war. It would function not only on direct request of the military and naval Departments, or other national-defense agencies, but would institute projects on its own initiative and have authority to place them in the field upon due approval from the commanders involved.

Among the activities of the Foundation this Division would have a priority because basically its business would be improvement in the use of items already developed and in use or coming off production lines, rather than design and perfection of new ones. All other units in the organization would be instructed that in peacetime, and more particularly in time of war, work of the Field Service Division could only be carried out effectively if field-service matters were handled with the greatest possible speed. There would thus be no loss of time in acquainting the rest of the parent organization with the purposes and necessary methods of operation of this Division.[3]

During a war no special pleading would be necessary to secure field-service personnel from units of the Foundation engaged in research and development. Requests of FSD would carry the force of directives from the top. There would be little question of the release of personnel because it would be acknowledged that field assignments, still arranged on the basis of temporary loans to the Armed Forces, should generally take precedence over other activities of the Foundation. This postulate stems from a conviction that, given appropriate auspices within the military organization so that the work can be of maximum effectiveness, there is no service of more immediate utility in combat operations than the presence in the theater of a man who really knows the equipment

---

[3] In its early days OFS spent considerable time doing this because it had come into existence when other OSRD people were already engrossed in dealing with many apparently urgent items for the multiple research Divisions of NDRC and CMR, and the relative priority of OFS had not been established.

his organization has created. And in another war the pace of military operations in the field will doubtless be so rapid that delay in getting the right man on the job may be disastrous. In fact, it is not inconceivable that once the conflict starts, the great majority of the nation's scientists will be needed in the field immediately. Progress of research and development, even on what were considered "crash" programs this time, was far too slow to warrant keeping our best brains at work in the laboratory on things that might not be ready within the few weeks or months the next war lasts.

One of the first tasks of the Field Service Division would be to procure a pool of competent personnel, including some on permanent appointment and others to be available on call. They would all be given indoctrination and training, a group of them for each type of new device in the research program. Some scientists would be brought into the Foundation only temporarily to acquire over-all familiarity with its research activities in their particular fields. Returning to civilian employment, they would thereafter maintain liaison with this work through progress reports and occasional visits to the laboratories for short periods of special study. In this manner FSD would develop a small group of full-time "shock troops" of field-service personnel who could assume key positions or be sent first to active areas in time of war, and could call upon a larger "reserve" of similarly, though less intensively trained people to fill out the teams they might need to create.

As was the case with OFS, representatives of the Field Service Division should have security clearance for access to the work of all parts of the Foundation. They should cross divisional and project security lines, always conscious that this privilege obligates them to observe special discretion in handling information they acquire. As a result, the individual specialist whose field might be electronics would never be sent to a forward area without a fair understanding of at least some devices developed by his coworkers in other specialties. He might not have intimate technical familiarity with them; but he would have a general understanding of their purpose and their effectiveness. His personal acquaintance with the research people would give him ready access to sources of more detailed information if that were needed to answer fortuitous questions.

Every individual affiliated for even part of his or her time with the Field Service Division should be provided with appropriate identification cards and credentials, authorizing visits to military installations and naval establishments or vessels and access to classified information or devices. The authorizations could, of course, be graduated and specific, according to the responsibilities of the individual and his subject fields; but extension of their coverage in an emergency would not be as difficult as securing them in the first place.

The permanent field-service men and many of the part-time consultants would be kept in a state of constant readiness for service overseas. Their immunizations would be renewed periodically by Army or Navy medical dispensaries. They would be provided with passports that could be validated on short notice, and with military credentials that would require only the insertion of a date or an official seal to ratify them. The men would secure appropriate uniforms and insignia, to be worn at once the moment war broke out, or even during periods of service at military bases in peacetime.

In other words, FSD would create and maintain a reserve body of scientists, trained, indoctrinated, and processed for duty overseas on a moment's notice. These would be the Minute Men of the Field Service Division and they would be backed by an army of their colleagues, also ready to act quickly in making the very best use of whatever weapons we have.

The FSD would establish extensive contacts with the military and naval organizations and with all other agencies through which it would be expected to operate in a war emergency. This would involve the forming of close personal relationships with key individuals, so that rapid action could be obtained merely on the basis of telephoned requests.

The administrative central staff, responsible for processing field personnel, would have a thorough, up-to-the-minute knowledge of regulations and procedures. These should be studied constantly in an effort to reduce paper work and eliminate duplication. Travel and fiscal matters within the Foundation, procurement of passports and credentials, creation of military appointments, shipment of equipment, and maintenance of records to guard the accountability status of the organization would all be reduced to the simplest possible systems.

In order to eliminate needless effort in processing civilians for military attachment and service overseas, the FSD would work out with the Services a combined procedure, using standardized forms, accepted by all the agencies concerned, as the official documents to initiate action, and requiring only initials or endorsements before they could be forwarded to set up the next step in the action sequence.[4]

The fiscal affairs of the Field Service Division should be administered by persons closely familiar with the duties of the individuals involved and the consequent necessity for speed in putting the papers through the mill. They would also be willing, as occasion required, to act in advance of the paper work and on informal approvals. In order to assure such efficiency, it seems essential that the FSD have its own business office. The staff for this could be small, since their only responsibility would be the proper handling of travel and fiscal matters for the field service personnel. Thus they could not be swamped with routines deriving from other less critical phases of the Foundation's activities.

Experience of the OFS demonstrated that employment of technical personnel through Civil Service, or even under direct Government personal-services contract, is not the swift and efficient way to get things done. The Government employee is too encumbered with procedural mechanisms designed "to protect the public interest." Matters relating to his employment, travel authorization, and fiscal arrangements must go through too many hands and must appear in too many documents to assure expeditious handling. Complicated formalities are a serious deterrent to the speed in recruiting, employing, and processing that should characterize a field-service organization.

Government regulations also prohibit the use of funds for innumer-

---

[4] A single, combined OSRD-Army processing form had been designed by OFS in collaboration with other units of OSRD and with the Army and was ready for introduction in the summer of 1945. Termination of the war made its issuance unnecessary; but it would have saved untold hours and headaches in dispatching personnel from an OSRD contractor's laboratory through the Office of Field Service, the New Developments Division, and the Adjutant General's Office to the war theater. One piece of paper would have accomplished the whole job — recommended the individual, secured his appointment, credentials, and travel arrangements, and set up authority for his official military orders. There is great need for similar application of the work-simplification technique to many aspects of Government administration. Condensation, rearrangement, and revision can be effected, and the result would be enormous savings of the public funds and the nervous energy of public servants.

able special purposes without detailed explanation and accounting, infinitely aggravating to the individual and his sponsors and enormously costly to the public. These special purposes constitute things that are vital to efficient and smooth operation of field groups. They include the maintenance of more or less permanent hotel accommodations at especially busy centers, for the members of a group who have frequent business there on unpredictable schedules and who should not lose valuable research or consulting time frantically seeking a place to stay; the provision of a petty cash account to cover emergency use of taxicabs, temporary advances of funds, and the similar thousand and one items that come up in the ordinary operation of a swiftly moving organization that handles transient personnel. Such things are accepted routines in the conduct of private business and, although they are admittedly open to abuse, accounting on them is usually extremely simple.

Unless there are drastic modifications in the Government procedures and policies indicated above, it is the considered opinion of the OFS central staff that a field-service operation in the future should be conducted in the greater flexibility and freedom permitted under a Government contract with a corporation or university, as was the Operations Research Group under the Columbia University contract in its early history, and as would have been the far-flung technical activities of the Pacific Branch, OSRD, under a contract with the National Academy of Sciences. By way of illustration, through use of this Academy contract, OFS was able to procure the services of a specialist from his previous employment, place him formally on the pay roll and in the personnel records of the employer, provide him with a travel authorization and an advance of funds, secure a priority for his travel, issue the necessary credentials and instructions, and dispatch him to an important mission, all within the space of six hours. Yet nothing that was done was illegal, and many of the steps were virtually accomplished through telephone calls. The same operations, had he been required to accept employment with the Government, would have taken many times as long, even if important and busy people of the OFS staff could have spared the time to carry the necessary papers personally through the devious channels to the many different offices involved.

*   *   *

The Field Service Division should have branch offices either within or in close proximity to the offices of its major liaison channels in the War Department and Navy Department — or, in case a single Department of National Defense is created, in the appropriate branches of that organization. One or more alert executives would be stationed in each of these offices. Their major function would be to expedite Service handling of FSD matters. Each Service channel would likewise detail a mature officer to duty with the central staff of FSD. He would also be essentially a liaison man and expediter, keeping abreast of major administrative plans and policy formulation within FSD, and so familiar with day-by-day progress of projects sponsored by his branch of the Service that his word would help to secure prompt official approval from higher authority.

In the foregoing discussion we have been concerned primarily with the peacetime activities of the Field Service Division. In case there should be war, however, some OFS men recommend strongly that any mission to a combat theater should be accompanied by a mature officer who would serve continuously with the project in the field as its liaison representative. His function would be to provide personal introductions of the scientists, keep a weather eye on provisions for their transportation, billeting, and other items affecting their comfort or their facilities for work, clear their official communications through the military channels, and guide them in the more delicate aspects of military etiquette. His rank should be high enough so that he can get them into the right places, straighten out administrative snarls quickly, and lend an atmosphere of authority to the party. To such duty the Service could assign officers not fit for combat or command functions through minor physical disabilities, but sufficiently alert and healthy to move about freely under hardships. Many officers would probably welcome such duty and be far more effective in it than they would if stationed instead among the "chairborne" troops.

Whether or not it is desirable to follow this recommendation will depend in large measure on the degree of understanding which develops in the military mind about the Foundation and its potential contribution to field problems. If, as it is hoped, a national science agency has operated for some years before another war, the great majority of Service personnel will be much better acquainted with it than were battalions, squadrons, and headquarters staffs with the alphabetical OSRD.

Others have suggested that Army, Navy, and Air Force should each develop a separate Special Staff Section that is primarily responsible for scientific liaison, writing this into permanent Tables of Organization so that every officer becomes aware of machinery for using civilian specialists.[5] This Section should educate its respective Service on applications of science to military problems and should serve as the channel and clearinghouse for scientific and technical information and for requests from that Service for help from the Foundation. It should process and indoctrinate civilian experts and provide administration for them in the field. It could assist an FSD in selecting personnel for field activities and in instructing them thoroughly in military organization and etiquette, in communications and administrative procedures.

Representatives of this Special Staff Section would be attached to all field commands. When civilians arrived in a theater, these officers would insure that proper credentials, introductions, billeting, communications facilities, transportation, and privileges were provided. In short, the military men would handle all the administrative details so that the scientists could devote full attention to scientific work.

To discharge most effectively the functions outlined, the officers of this Section should have had at least basic training in science or engineering. They could be individuals who were not temperamentally suited to furthering science in research, but who might aid its applications immeasurably through their understanding of science and scientists, by exercise of their administrative talents, and by their personal effectiveness in human relations.

In any case, the military commanders in combat theaters should accord FSD the same freedom that was provided for the British Branch of the Radiation Laboratory and for the Pacific Branch of OSRD to establish its own priorities in shipment of personnel and equipment within a blanket allocation, and for a field man to send communications

---

[5] Recent reorganization in the War and Navy Departments has already partly accomplished what is proposed here. The Office of Naval Research and the Research and Development Division of the Army now have sufficiently comprehensive authority to serve as the major co-ordinating units for both Services and to implement their liaison with civilian science in the manner outlined above.

on purely technical matters directly to a scientific colleague elsewhere. Information copies of these technical communications would go concurrently to the military sponsor in the theater, the military channel in the United States, and the central office of FSD. And the field scientists should have the same freedom to use radio, radiotelephone, teletype, or other means of speedy communication as do the technical branches of the Services themselves.

Since periodic refresher visits to home laboratories can be arranged for personnel of overseas teams, both military men and OFS consultants have recommended that assignments be established on a more permanent basis than the maximum six-month loan which characterized OFS basic policy. A scientist can scarcely be accepted enthusiastically in a theater if he is manifestly a transient visitor who may come to counsel the military for only a brief interval, leaving them to carry on for an unknown period without benefit of his special knowledge, or to spend weeks in exhausting repetition just bringing a successor up to date on the local situation so he can go to work.

Some advocate strongly that in time of war a scientist sent out for field duty with the military, either in this country or abroad, should be given a temporary true Reserve Officer status, commensurate in rank with his stature in civilian life or the importance of the duties he is to perform. His uniform should then carry special insignia indicating that, although he carries true rank for purposes of administration and housekeeping, he belongs in a category of people whose work demands greater freedom of action in communications and the use of channels. It would be understood that he is subject to the authority of the theater commander in the planning and prosecution of his work, but that he could not be detailed to combat duty except as this might be demanded by the nature of his technical activities. Neither could he be given functions of administration or command. In all other respects he would enjoy the same privileges as regular officers of equivalent rank and would acquire the benefits accorded veterans.

There is some doubt that such a plan would be endorsed by the military and naval departments; and there are disadvantages which would militate against its wholehearted acceptance even by the civilians.

It is, however, one suggestion for placing the scientist in a less awk-ward position than he held in this war. It is, moreover, a plan that was used to great advantage by the British. Their scientists were given true Reserve commissions which they held only while on field duty and relinquished when they returned to laboratory or office work at home. They wore special insignia which indicated that they would not com-mand battleships or lead infantry charges but that in all other respects they merited the respect and treatment given officers of their particu-lar rank. This system has so many obvious advantages over the Ameri-can plan of assimilated ranks and anomalous uniforms that it deserves serious study.

The scientists of OFS have also given much thought to the function-ing of a National Science Foundation since it became a subject for pub-lic discussion, and some of their suggestions are worth recording here. If these are adopted, the results would necessarily affect some operations of a Field Service Division, and certain recommendations on preceding pages might be altered.

Some men have advised that during peacetime the National Science Foundation should make a concerted effort to draw into its activities on at least a part-time basis every man and woman trained in science or engineering. In effect these people would constitute a "Scientific Re-serve Corps" of individuals already somewhat familiar with military protocol and with the application of their technical specialties to mili-tary problems. More than paper records of their personal qualifications would then be available to placement officers in the Foundation. Ar-rangements could be made whereby they were subject to periodic call to duty with the Army and Navy, in the same way that officers in the regular Reserve Corps are, but under close surveillance of the Foundation.

In plans that have already been considered publicly, an individual who accepts Government subsidy to underwrite his technological edu-cation through a scholarship or fellowship is automatically thereby under special obligation for service to the Government in time of na-tional emergency. It would not be amiss to encourage the view that, because of the critical importance of science in national defense, all people trained in technical fields have a similar patriotic obligation, irrespective of financial support which they may or may not have secured from the public treasury.

The National Selective Service Act was designed for universal application to men within certain age groups, with too little regard for their activity in the public interest. During the war adjustments in its application to special groups were arrived at only after expensive deliberations; and in the meantime men were lost to essential work through misunderstanding, delay, confusion, and social pressure. One hopes that the importance of scientists and technologists to activities other than combat has now been made sufficiently evident so that a future draft law will provide either that they be exempted from ordinary military service as a group or, better, that they be drafted for assignment as civilians to the National Science Foundation. This organization could properly be given the responsibility for placing them where they would individually be most serviceable to the nation. This would eliminate much of the wasteful pulling and hauling so prevalent during the war. It was always a struggle to prevent blind application of Selective Service from putting behind a rifle the vigorous youngsters who, admittedly physically fit for front-line action, were nevertheless the only men in the land thoroughly familiar with some of the newest and most effective technical weapons. Senior administrative officials on both sides could more profitably have used the energy expended in this struggle in action of greater import to prosecution of the war.

It seems logical that one important function of the National Science Foundation should be to maintain a complete roster of the country's scientific and technological manpower. It would eventually include every man and woman who had reached the senior year in college or technical school concentrating in a field of science or engineering. The records would be kept up to date with changes of address and the additional training or experience of everyone listed.

Existence of such a roster would be widely advertised, and the obligation of everyone included in it to supply current information should be considered comparable with his obligation to file an income tax return. Professional societies in the various scientific and engineering fields could aid materially in developing the lists and keeping them complete.

This science roster should, of course, contain information on the roles played during World War II by every scientist, engineer, or other specialist drawn into war work. The individual personal records would carry pertinent information not only on education, professional concentration, and prewar experience, but also on the nature of the individual's position in the war and of the specific work he did. They would carry data on security clearance, military service, and any other facts that might be useful in placing these specialists quickly and most advantageously in the service of the nation. A system of coding this information for entry on I B M punch cards would make it possible to prepare statistical summaries and to locate individuals quickly.

Security investigations of all persons listed would be conducted and checked periodically so that at any time the great majority would be cleared for handling the nation's military secrets. This would be essential to their participation in research projects for national defense and would obviate delay in mobilizing them for war service.

The Science Foundation should also seek to procure a single security clearance procedure for scientists and technical men, recognized as valid by the Army, Navy, State Department, and all other Government agencies concerned, so that once an individual's clearance was established, duplicate investigations would be wholly unnecessary if it became desirable to shift him from one agency to another.

The recommendations enumerated here are comprehensive but abbreviated. They could be expanded in detail from OFS experience. In some respects they are overlapping and interdependent. Organizational changes in the Services and modifications in Government procedures might influence them considerably. They are certain to meet with differences of opinion among our military men, our legislators, and the general public — even among the scientists themselves. But, doing so, they may provoke discussion and become a working basis to guide our planning. Then there will be hope that the successful experiments in mobilizing science for this war will not be forgotten and that the lessons learned by the combat scientists will profit those who have to do this job again.

If Congress does enact the legislation necessary to establish a National Science Foundation, there will be continuity in the application of science to military problems. In itself this will greatly alter the relations between civilian scientific agencies and the men who use the new devices they create. In another war the situation will then be vastly different from what it was this time, because the scientists and the military men will have been working together closely in the meantime.

Fortunately such co-operation is continuing at the present time. While Congress has been absorbed in other issues, the Army and Navy have launched far-reaching programs of both basic and applied research, and are calling for assistance on the men who made OSRD. Co-ordination between these programs is assured through the newly established Joint Research and Development Board.

It is now about two years since the words "uranium," "plutonium," and "nuclear fission" came out of the lexicons of physics to join the vernacular of many lands, and many months since Dr. Bush urged that Government take the lead in keeping strong our first lines of defense in science and technology. Volumes have been written on our needs, both for an international policy to control this new force that threatens the peace and safety of mankind, and also for the creation of a National Science Foundation to consolidate the gains we won at so great cost. Yet in meeting either of these desperate challenges we seem to be only slightly farther ahead than we were when the tragedies of Hiroshima and of Nagasaki first made them clear. Somehow the wages paid to those who tighten bolts in an assembly line, the credits we may lavish on our brave allies, or the age at which a man should step into the Army have overshadowed issues that involve survival.

How soon can drift be turned into direction?

On this may hang the future of the world.

PART TWO

The Story of
NALOC and DOLOC

by

JOHN E. BURCHARD

Amphibious Operations

DUKW's and LVT's landing on a small beach at Tinian

Constant Peril

A near miss on DUKW's ferrying supplies at Anzio

Keep Your Head Down!

Infantry approaching enemy-held side of the Rhine at Oberwesel

CHAPTER XXII

FINDING THE BEACHES

THE PROBLEM OF AMPHIBIOUS NAVIGATION

IN 1943 Operation Torch had been successfully carried out — the Americans were ashore at Casablanca and other key points; the offensive campaign against the Nazi had finally begun. This created a general public satisfaction; but the Army and the Navy, who knew that they would face other and far more difficult situations before the war was won, were not so satisfied. Critiques of the operation had revealed several flaws: flaws big enough to have resulted in defeat at the hands of a better entrenched and more determined enemy.

One matter of great concern was how to get our landing craft ashore at the right place and the right time. Even granting the break that on D-Day the normal heavy surf off Casablanca had miraculously subsided to the lowest in forty-eight years, we had done none too well there. At times we had missed the intended beaches by as much as five miles. Against a well-co-ordinated enemy, this would have been fatal. A battalion would need to land where it was supposed to be, and a battalion beach was 400 yards long.

The reasons for the failure were not far to seek. At the outset, the Navy had seemed to show much less interest in the landing part of the amphibious operation than had the Army. They had let the training of amphibious brigades go to the Corps of Engineers. The question of exactly at what point on the littoral the Navy gave up control and the Army took it over, though settled at high level, was interpreted diversely in theaters. These first amphibious landings were made by the Army. The Higgins boats were operated by Army personnel under operational control of the Navy. The skippers were apple-cheeked boys from the Kansas plains with no tradition of seamanship or navigation to guide them in what would have been a difficult operation even with such a tradition behind them.[1] The boats were troop carriers intended to

---

[1] Navy small-boat pilots, in fact, had the same genesis as Army pilots. Few came from Marblehead or Salem.

beach, limited in gear to the simplest rudiments, such as a compass. Even if the boats could be individually equipped with more complicated gear, there would not be enough skilled personnel to operate them. What was needed was a lead boat running at the head of a wave of landing craft, guiding them near to the shore and then sending them to the beach on their own.

Under the operating procedure that existed at that time, even this would not be simple. A group of transports would rendezvous some ten miles off the intended target. They could not be expected to have a better initial navigational fix than the best then available to a single comparable ship, which could not rely on radio or radar (since surprise was one of the requirements of the planning at that time). Such a fix might be accurate within 1000 yards if everything were favorable, and already the possible error was greater than that permissible at the beachhead. The transports would then steam slowly back and forth, always changing their position so as not to be sitting ducks for enemy artillery, aircraft, or torpedoes as at Safi and Fedhala. Over their sides they would lower the Higgins boats, the boats would then circle near the mother ship and be called to the side a few at a time. Down rope ladders would stream the infantry. The filled boats would then rejoin the circle until all the boats were loaded with troops and weapons. From the uncertain position of the circle, the boats would then set forth, in a V or abreast, for a ten-mile trip to a destination marked clearly enough on the chart.

Between the unreliable starting point and the finite intended point of arrival were two to ten miles of water, with tide, currents, and wind all tending to alter a compass course. These diverting forces could be predicted only with the most general accuracy for a given time on a given day. The speed of the boats was such that the trip would take about one and one-half hours, during which time the forces could change. There would be no navigational aids such as channel buoys; indeed, the landings would usually be on isolated beaches where even the charting might not have been done with the care lavished on the chart of a harbor. Moreover, there would be no visual aids on shore, for part of the doctrine was that the operation would involve surprise and that the landings would be made just after dawn. The navigation, therefore, had to be done in zero-zero visibility. Under these circumstances, even the best small-boat sailors, operating on a coast with which they had thorough personal familiarity, would have to be very lucky.

The Navy had begun to study the problem. A small boat of some twenty-five tons, with powerful engines and a cabin which would accommodate a considerable amount of apparatus, had been designed, and hulls were on the ways. This boat was named the Landing Craft Control (LCC), and it was expected to be manned with skilled navigators and to head waves of craft from the offshore rendezvous to the beach, but not to beach itself. Some gear had been proposed for the boat, but there was reason to doubt that it was adequate to the task. What was needed was the application of as much imagination as possible and from as many sources. It was a project made to order for the men of NDRC.

On April 3, 1943, the Commander in Chief, U.S. Fleet, through Admiral Purnell, requested the Co-ordinator of Research and Development to establish a project with NDRC on Navigational Aids for Landing Craft approaching hostile beaches. The project was accepted. It was a new sort of venture for NDRC; it cut across the knowledge of several divisions; an *ad hoc* committee was clearly indicated; and on April 28 Dr. Conant appointed such a committee and named it Committee NALOC.[2] It was made up of Palmer Cosslett Putnam of DUKW and Weasel fame; Dr. Lauriston C. Marshall, radar expert, then at the Radiation Laboratory; Dr. A. F. Murray, radio and television expert and Technical Aide in Division 13; and Professor John E. Burchard, then Chief of Division 2. Burchard was Chairman. The persons selected were told that the project might last six weeks and should be given top priority. It actually lasted formally for seventeen months, and members of the committee continued to work with the project in the Pacific until nearly the end of the war. From it came a solution of the problem which would put the boats within fifty yards of a predetermined position on the beach and within a minute of the scheduled time of arrival. This solution was used with varying success in the operations in both oceans from Kwajalein on, with increasing impact in the late Pacific operations at Palau, Iwo Jima, Okinawa, and Lingayen Gulf. From it came a method of inshore navigation which should

[2] Meaning: Navigational Aids to Landing Operations. The "C" does not stand for Committee but was appended later when it was found necessary in order that the word NALO could be used in Navy dispatches without confusing the code.

have extensive peacetime application. When found, the solution was very simple. Between the day when the committee was formed and the day it turned in its final report, it became necessary not only to make a selection from among many methods and to refine the one actually selected, to redesign the boat which housed the apparatus, and finally to abandon the original vessel for a more seaworthy one, but also to question and change the whole standard operating procedure for this part of the amphibious operation, to demonstrate the method to the topside in both oceans, to sell and resell, to expedite the procurement of equipment and the training of personnel, and to press and press against time and inertia.

For these purposes the committee was admirably selected. Putnam was energetic, foresighted, unconquerable — a man who never allowed a negative decision to be made from lower than the top, and not always then. Marshall was a fertile-minded, forceful, well-indoctrinated exponent of the most imaginative ways to use radar; Murray was a solid investigator of all the detail of what might be available and a sound critic of every type of proposal; Burchard was an active co-ordinator. Putnam, moreover, was an amateur yachtsman of skill who knew his way around in the small-boat world. To his skill was soon added that of an invaluable member, Olin J. Stephens, II, distinguished yacht designer and small-boat sailor, skilled navigator, member of the afterguard of Vanderbilt's *Ranger,* winning navigator on his own of many cross-ocean yacht races.

Two days after its formation the committee met with Dr. Bush, who set forth the urgency and importance of the problem, pointed out that it was a new type of venture for OSRD, the kind of operational venture for which OSRD was well equipped. If it were brought off, the effect would not only be important in itself but could lead to other similar co-operations.

For about two weeks the committee spent its time in establishing contacts and in orientation.[3] Meetings were held with Captain I. N. Kiland, formerly Commodore of Transports at Guadalcanal and then Chief of the Readiness Section of COMINCH, and his subordinate,

---

[3] Putnam had prepared between the day of the appointment of the committee and the meeting with Bush, 48 hours later, an admirable brief of what then appeared available.

Lieutenant Commander G. K. Carmichael, who was to be COMINCH liaison; with Lieutenant Commander W. R. Royall, who had been named as liaison for Commander Amphibious Forces Atlantic (ComPhibLant); [4] and with Lieutenant Commander H. Gordon Dyke, liaison for the Co-ordinator of Research and Development. Individuals visited the Division Chiefs of NDRC to see what they might have to offer which could be applied; the Joint Communications Board; Marine and Navy intelligence to determine the amount of oceanographic and coastal data available; and the Naval Research Laboratory to look at sonic buoys and other devices which might be applied.

From this investigation it became apparent that the directive needed to be clarified and sharpened. A memorandum was prepared and discussed with COMINCH. Could the Committee challenge the operating doctrine? It could. Could the Committee consider as well the related problem of navigation of the transports to the rendezvous? It should. Must the operation be possible in zero-zero visibility? Yes. Was surprise a dominating factor and must radio and radar silence be maintained? Yes. What accuracy was actually desired? Plus or minus 100 yards on the beach, and one minute of time. Ultimately some of these questions had to be reopened, notably that of surprise, but for the moment this was the framework within which NALOC had to work. For the time being, too, its operations were of more importance to the Atlantic than to the Pacific war, and the work would, therefore, be done in co-operation with Amphibious Forces Atlantic, based at Norfolk under Rear Admiral Alan G. Kirk, and not with their opposite numbers on the Pacific coast.

The possibilities before the Committee were legion, even though many were far-fetched. A narrative of this length cannot list them all and tell why NALOC finally discarded them, but a clearer picture of the entire project will be obtained if a few widely diverse ones are mentioned.

Sextant and compass were too slow and not accurate enough. The Navy had expressly asked NALOC to look into a British proposal of taut wires. Under this scheme two wires attached to anchors, or to vessels, or to shore, were paid out and held taut from the stern, and a

---

[4] Royall was one of the most helpful of all Navy men. He took a personal interest in the project and followed it closely. It was a loss when he was detached.

measuring device provided their length. The length of the two wires at any given moment would evidently define two possible positions, and the boat could be at either. Given a bearing from one of the anchors, or a known distance from a starting point, a position could be determined. This was too clumsy and too unreliable.

The marine odograph, an NDRC development, was also surveyed. The land odograph, mounted, for example, in a jeep, provided a continuous trace of where the jeep had gone. Mounted in a boat the odograph would also provide a trace of the course, but this would not be a true course unless there were no wind, no tide, and no current. Consequently, the odograph trace had to be corrected for these factors. This left the navigator just about where he was before he had the odograph. This apparatus was standard gear for the LCC when NALOC was organized, and the Committee spent many hours afloat trying to make the odograph work for its purposes but finally recommended that it had no value save as a crude piece of checking and stand-by equipment. Long after NALOC recommended that it be removed altogether, it remained a vestigial piece of apparatus, with no bearing on the job.

Could beacons be established ashore? Could parachutists be dropped to plant the beacons in prearranged positions, or could the beacons be dropped as spiked bombs which would stick when they hit the land? The beacons would in either case send forth directed and coded short-wave signals to a receiver on the navigational craft. These were clearly in the dream world. The accuracy of position would be dubious. They risked compromise of the operation. Worst of all, the clever enemy might find them, change their position, and bring about disaster. They, too, were discarded.

Perhaps underwater beacons might be helpful. The Navy had a fairly well developed buoy which could be laid through the torpedo tube of a submarine and anchored on the bottom. It could be set to begin a coded underwater signal at any predetermined time after launching, send this signal for a predetermined time, and then destroy itself. How good would the signals be? It was found that they were often hard to pick up. How accurately would the position of the buoys be known? It was found that without shoreward-seeking radar the submarine fix would not be good enough; with it there was some possibility of compromising the operation. Would the enemy pick up the buoys with its sweeps or on its own sound listening gear? These were unknowns. NALOC spent many days afloat evaluating this device from submarines, destroyers, and other surface craft. In its early standard operating procedure it included the buoys as a method of establishing the transport line, but by the time the buoys had developed far enough the method of navigation had become so simple that all this was not needed; all the questions surrounding the device had not been satisfactorily answered and the complexity was too great.

Indeed, all devices requiring anchoring to the bottom were under suspicion as an over-all technique. For the European coast they might suffice, but the waters of the Pacific generally deepen sharply from the shore and anchoring would probably be impossible.

Through this same strainer went underwater sound-ranging devices such as Asdic, Radio Loop Direction Finders, the technique of buoys which would rise and give off coded radio signals at predetermined times, and the rapidly improving Loran, which was, of course, an admirable device for long-range navigation and for locating the transport area but not suitable for the close inshore work in which split-second fixes were almost mandatory and continuous fixes were desirable.

What, then, could be done by soundings? There were several well-developed fathometers which recorded depth beneath the hull continuously by sending down a signal which would be reflected from the bottom. The time between the start of the signal and its return gave a very close approximation to the depth, regardless of temperature, salinity, and other variables in the water through which the signal passed.

Given a well-charted bottom, a skilled navigator can do a close job if he knows constantly the depth beneath his hull. He can set his course generally to cross a bar or other point of sharply differentiated depth or height and of varying width. With a reasonable record of his ship's heading and his water speed, he can estimate on the chart the place at which he crossed the bar. By zigzagging two or three times he can calculate the set and drift prevailing. He can then put these into his calculations and determine a compass course which, taking account of the set and drift, will bring him from the point where he is, which he knows with reasonable accuracy, to the point he wants to reach. But the navigator must be skilled, and the bottom truthfully charted. Men like Stephens and Putnam could navigate well by this method under favorable conditions. Could the shotgun-trained navigators from the Great Plains? Moreover, how good would the charts be? Bottoms shift and are not plotted regularly, especially in war. Nor are they plotted at close intervals in areas where close-in navigation is in peacetime unlikely. Would all the beaches even have the characteristics which would make such navigation possible? To have all these circumstances favorable was too unlikely. The fathometer remained until the end an important piece of equipment as a rough check and to serve warning when the waters grew too shoal, but it was always a second-string member of the team.

Finally, there was radar, and this was the only solution which really gave promise. The doctrine of radar silence was indeed troublesome, for if search could be made forward, there were many more chances of success. NALOC was from the outset unable to perceive the wisdom of the idea that amphibious operations would be conducted, like Indian fighting, by stealth. The enemy spies would observe the mounting of an operation in the UK; their search radar would pick up the fleet and the transports and probably even the small landing craft; there would surely be a considerable preassault bombardment from the sea and from the air. All these things obviously added up to the fact that radar ought to be used freely, but it was not until later that our fighting forces learned that we gained more by the free use of radar than the enemy did by intercepting any of our signals. In the final clean-cut solution of NALOC, the radar was beamed shoreward and became much more reliable and simple thereby; but for the moment these were the rules, and NALOC had to work within them.

More troublesome to the Committee was the possibility of countermeasures by the enemy, jamming our radar so that spurious or confusing signals would come. This was of major importance, because if enemy jamming were effective, the whole solution would break down. Here compartmentation for security laid its heavy hand on the work of the Committee. At that time nothing was held more closely secret than the matter of radar countermeasures. The Committee was not allowed either by the Navy or by OSRD to become fully informed on the risk. By grapevine and by intuition it was able to learn enough to have some confidence that by using 10-centimeter radar equipment for the time being and 3-centimeter equipment when available, the risk of enemy jamming would be reduced to the sort which one has always to run in combat operations.[5]

This was as far as NALOC could go on paper and by discussion. Indeed, some of the decisions which have been so lightly sketched above could not be confirmed or even approximated until subject to test, often months later. In any event, nothing more could be done around the conference tables in Washington. It was time to go to sea.

On May 13 Putnam, therefore, went to Norfolk with Commander Royall. Acting as the advance agent, he made further contact with Admiral Kirk and Lieutenant Commander Roger L. Putnam. LCC hulls would not be available for some months; a boat was needed. Admiral Kirk turned over to the Committee a converted yacht, the *YHB-9*, at that time assigned to his personal use and berthed at Willoughby Spit, Norfolk. Within twenty-four hours after Putnam's arrival, the *YHB-9* had been made ready for the Committee and arrangements put in train for the installation of an SO radar in her after saloon. By the 17th of May the first crude trial run had been made, and at that time Marshall and Burchard also arrived at Norfolk for what was to be a forty-day tour of duty, interrupted only by necessary trips to other stations. With him Marshall brought additional crews from the Radiation Laboratory and the equipment necessary to set up the corner reflectors, which were to be a key part of the apparatus in the first stage of the development.

In so brief an account as this, one cannot deal with every minor change in the design of reflectors, the radar sets, or indeed with all the personnel who made important contributions.[6] Only the most marked stages of the development can therefore be described.

Among those who joined the team at this time to make superior contributions to the whole venture was Edward E. Miller, brilliant and imaginative young member of the Marshall team at Radiation Laboratory. He was present during the whole Norfolk stage, and made important suggestions for using equipment which later became a key element in the whole procedure. He subsequently went to Europe where he acquitted himself with distinction. Frank M. Pease, California

---

[5] The same compartmentation made it very hard for the Committee ever to come to grips with the true potentialities of infrared, which again could be suspected, however, as not important.

[6] Including R. E. Meagher, J. P. Nash, J. M. Wolf, S. F. West, and G. Mann.

radio engineer, another member of Marshall's group, also joined at this time. Skilled in ferreting out "bugs" and eliminating them, able to train young naval officers to a high degree of competence, affable and exceptionally skilled at getting along with all Naval personnel from the bridge to the forecastle, he was the solid core of daily work on the project from the day he joined it to the end of the war, participating in every demonstration, moving with the project from base to base, accompanying Marshall finally to Oahu, and there steadily bringing the project to its full fruition. Had the Committee issued awards to its loyal supporters, he would assuredly have been one of the Abou ben Adhems of its list.

With these people working day and night, progress was fast. The requirement of radar silence had been relaxed after discussion to permit the use of radar, provided it was directional and beamed always away from the shore. This led to the use of the corner reflector as the first approximation to a solution. The corner reflector is a pyramid-shaped device about two feet on an edge, mounted on a mast, and rotated when this is desirable. It will intercept a radar signal and return it with considerable intensity. Moreover, it can be so arranged that the signal will be coded and identifiable. If, then, two LCM's or stake boats bearing corner reflectors were anchored a mile or more apart and to seaward of the navigational vessel, she could transmit a radar signal and receive its reflection and know which reflection she was receiving. The bearing and range of each of the LCM's or stake boats would then be known. If their position was known, the position of the navigational craft could be determined. For example, if a circle was constructed around each stake boat, using the range as a radius, the intersection of the two circles would determine the position.[7] Or, if the bearings from each of the stake boats were plotted, the intersection of the two lines would give the position. The line of bearing of one intersecting the range circle of the other would also give the position, though there could sometimes be doubt here as between the two possible intersections.[8] The exact combination of these methods that was chosen

---

[7] There would, of course, be two such intersections, but one would be off shore from the stake boats and thus could be discarded by common sense.

[8] Because the chord represented by the bearing might intersect the circle made by the range radius at two closely spaced points; and common sense could not then tell which was right.

would be the one likely to be the most accurate under the circumstances. Leaving aside for the moment the problem of determining the location of the stake boats, the Committee established them by sextant and other standard navigational methods near the Norfolk shore, and by May 18 had conducted highly promising runs.

Even as early as this NALOC was not satisfied with the stake boat technique. Anchoring would sometimes be impossible. Positioning would at best be uncertain, though calculations showed that errors in stake boat positions, cut in from the transports, would probably not result in too great errors at the beach. Constant trouble might be had with the machinery for rotating the reflectors. Two additional craft not available for troop carrying would have to be aboard the transport; or alternatively, combat vessels such as SC's, PC's, or destroyers would have to be taken from combat for this purpose. The stake boats might be sunk. More plotting would be needed in the navigator's cabin than was desirable, and the fixes would then lag behind the position of the boat by the time of plotting. As early as May 20, Miller arrived with the Virtual PPI[9] Reflectoscope (VPR) which ultimately became the heart of the solution, and with remote plotting equipment which was ultimately abandoned as too complicated for the job in hand. The VPR was immediately installed, and promising runs were made on the same day. In order not to confuse the story, however, the explanation of this development will be deferred to the point in the tale where it became clear that it would be the basis of the standard operating procedure (SOP).

While these early radar runs were being made and in the intervals while equipment was being installed and mended, Putnam and Burchard went out in other boats to test sound buoys and recording fathometers. As a result of these investigations and conferences with Lieutenant George H. Hoague, Jr.,[10] it was concluded that the cabin of the YHB-9 should be mocked up into a full replica of the cabin of the forthcoming LCC and should include all the other navigational apparatus, including the recording fathometer, the QBG gear for pick-

[9] PPI (Plan Position Indicator) is a cathode presentation giving the information picked up by radar in plan form.
[10] Hoague was another one of the daily faithful officers with lots of ideas. His early departure for the United Kingdom was a great loss, especially as he did not work on navigational problems when he got there.

ing up underwater-sound signals, and the marine odograph, which was still very much in the picture. This involved ship cabin design, and by May 27 Olin Stephens had been brought into the picture as consultant to the Committee for this purpose. He remained to become a member of the Committee and to participate not only in cabin design but much more significantly in the whole development of navigational SOP. Runs were continued during construction and many had been recorded and much progress made by the time the mock-up was completed on June 3, three weeks to the day after Putnam had first gone to Norfolk.

Meanwhile, another complication had developed. Before NALOC came on the scene, Admiral Kirk had indicated to the Navy Department that he would no longer require the *YHB-9*. The Assistant Secretary of the Navy, Mr. Forrestal, had been marked down for the boat, and the order had gone out that she should be refitted and delivered to Washington almost at once. This required special negotiation at the highest levels, as a result of which the *YHB-9* was allowed to remain in the hands of the Committee until July 1, by which time the Navy hoped it would have found another vessel for NALOC.

The *YHB-9* was a semideluxe houseboat type of cruiser, with a high center of gravity, prone to roll, with too much draft to permit close approaches to the shore, unsafe to take outside Chesapeake Bay, and not even safe in all weather within that shelter. With her many cabins she had been ideal for the early stages, as she could house the Committee and its coworkers on board in Norfolk, where the housing situation was acute. But she would not be useful in the later work. During the three weeks available in the first mock-up, the Committee made the stake boat technique as watertight as it was ever to be, established an SOP for this method of navigation, and culminated its endeavors on June 25 with a full-fledged demonstration to Commodore Lee P. Johnson of ComPhibLant and his staff. With Putnam as expositor and Lieutenant Hoague as navigator, the boat was successfully taken over a ten-mile dog-leg course, part of which was jinking at the discretion of the skipper on the bridge in simulation of evasive action due to air attack. All this was done while Hoague remained below and navigated blind. He split the marker buoys nicely. So far as ComPhibLant was concerned, the project was a success. On June 26 the colors were struck, the gear removed, and the Committee prepared to move on New London and Fisher's Island, which was to be its next base.

At this time Lieutenant Hoague, who had been invaluable and who was one of the few officers really familiar with the details of the project, was ordered to the ETO. This was a foretaste of what would happen with almost every experienced officer on the project, and culminated when both Carmichael in COMINCH and Royall in ComPhibLant also went to other duty. The shifting of personnel at critical moments was a thing OSRD learned to cope with but never to accept. Any project in which it occurred lost time inevitably, because indoctrination and selling always had to be done over. And experience had shown that no matter how persuasive the civilian sponsors, every project marched faster when one or more officers thoroughly familiar with and enthusiastic about it remained with it from beginning to end.

By July 8 the Navy had found a second boat and dispatched it from Norfolk to New London. This was the *YP-440,* a battered dragger which had been used on antisubmarine patrol off Cuba and had finally run aground and been slightly beaten up. Homely as she was, she was also seaworthy. Her shaft was out of alignment; she would make but nine knots; she rolled heavily and had much too deep a draft (12–14 feet). Her deck house was small and would accommodate very few people in addition to the gear, and this was a liability both for experiment and for training, for which she was also soon destined. Moreover, she was still rated as a combat vessel, and carried Y-guns and depth charges.[11] Nonetheless, she served, and served well, and was the boat on which the final method of navigation was brought, if not to perfection, at least into full being.

This was the method of VPR. Under this method the stake boats were to be abandoned and, by a major change of procedure, the radar was to be beamed at the beach to be hit. A map was made from existing charts, in the first instance on ozalid paper, and at a scale corresponding to the PPI scale. The map was mounted on a table, and by thumbscrews could be moved in any direction in a horizontal plane. It was then reflected by a beamsplitter so as to appear to be on the face of

---

[11] Which the skipper was still anxious to use, since he could never forget his days of submarine hunting. One day off Cape Cod he was with difficulty diverted from joining a general chase which turned out to have been instigated by signals obtained from a school of whales.

the PPI tube, giving the observer a simultaneous view both of the outline of the coast as reflected from the map and of the radar map of the coast as portrayed on the PPI. By moving the table with the thumbscrews, the two presentations could be brought into juxtaposition. When they were thus arranged, the center of the PPI tube indicated the position of the radar antenna, and therefore of the boat carrying it.

To assist the navigator in stating his position quickly, the navigator's chart and the VPR map were both provided with corresponding grids. The radar operator could call off the position co-ordinates from the grid and the navigator could plot them at once on his chart.[12] By use of a clock and a tachometer, the navigator could keep track of time and speed, as well as position.

Meanwhile, however, Commodore Johnson, having bought the idea, was concerned that Naval personnel know how to use it. No LCC's were yet available, and a good deal of the time of the Committee was spent at this juncture in pushing against the procurement people in the Bureau of Ships — on the craft itself, where slowness rather than opposition was the cause, on the radar components, where the opposition was unconcealed, and even on the navigational idea, which was liked better by COMINCH and the operating branches of the Navy than it was by the design and procurement branches. In the absence of any LCC, an arrangement was made whereby the facilities of a small Naval station at Woods Hole, Massachusetts, would be placed at the disposal of NALOC and a training program set up with the assistance of Radiation Laboratory personnel.[13] Accordingly, after a few days of shakedown at New London, the *YP-440* left Fisher's Island on July 26 and navigated to Woods Hole in thick fog at full speed entirely by NALOC methods. After some days of runs out of Woods Hole, a final cruise was made around Cape Cod to Provincetown, and the *YP-440* returned to Woods Hole on August 3, where it went into the training program.

On August 7 week end NALOC was visited by Commander

---

[12] This sounds simple. The process was, but the selection of proper grid was not. One was a polar grid with bearings indicated by polar angles, and the range in time or distance by circles concentric to the target point. Another was a straight rectangular grid with the zero lines passing through the target point. Finally, navigation was sometimes made without a grid, relying on the distance from latitude and longitude lines or from points on a predetermined course marked both on chart and on VPR map.

[13] Notably P. S. Clymer and H. H. Wheaton in charge.

Phillips, fresh from duty as navigator of the task force in Operation Husky (Sicily). His experiences were invaluable in further planning. On the next day, with Commander Royall aboard as well, a run was made to the south shore of Martha's Vineyard around Gay Head to dissipate the impression that a long, flat, rather anonymous beach without appreciable indentations would impede the successful operation of the method. The following week end Admiral Kirk, back from the Sicilian campaign and making ready for the next and more important Operation, Overlord (the Normandy invasion), was given a successful demonstration and approved the method for ComPhibLant. The following week, similar success attended a demonstration for Admiral Furer and Dr. R. C. Tolman, Vice-Chairman of NDRC. On September 4 a further and equally successful demonstration was held for an Army group headed by Major General Roger B. Colton, Office of the Chief Signal Officer, USA. The only fly in this ointment was that, after the radar had been shut off in Woods Hole harbor, and just before docking in the darkness, the Navy steersman put the boat aground, and the Army officers had to remain on board until an Army boat came along and took them ashore!

Two other principal questions were engaging the Committee at this time. The VPR method required for most efficient use that the radar be provided with a true bearing device (already developed for other sets) so that the zero point on the PPI presentation would always be at the top. This could be accomplished by the use of a gyrocompass or a magnesyn and was ultimately worked out satisfactorily. To dispose of the problem in so few words is to minimize the actual difficulties. Overcoming these became the role of M. D. McFarlane, also a radio engineer from California and a member of the Radiation Laboratory staff. From this small beginning, he became a key person to NALOC. He it was who carried on when Putnam was detached in September for a job in the South Pacific and Marshall in the same month to become head of the British Branch Radiation Laboratory.[14] With Stephens and Burchard, he carried on through the arduous work of introducing the method to the Pacific and to the development of the final and im-

---

[14] Putnam was released from the Committee but was kept informed; Marshall was retained as liaison in the British Isles. To succeed him as the active Radiation Laboratory Committee member, R. G. Herb was appointed.

portant refinement, probably his idea, of the navigational microfilm projector, which will be described shortly. With Pease, he was an Abou ben Adhem.

For the moment, though, what seemed more serious was the question, "Where are the LCC's?" Stephens spent countless hours at the shipyards and in the Bureau of Ships trying to eke these boats off the ways and into the water. Again there were countless difficulties and objections, which cannot be listed here. Finally, the first boat was ready for speed trials, attended by Stephens and Marshall, on September 8. It would be delivered to the Brooklyn Navy Yard September 15 for radar installation. This installation would be completed September 22. Two further LCC's would be delivered October 1, and about one a week thereafter. This was, of course, optimistic. On October 11 the Committee was finally invited to a trial run of the first equipped LCC, and this had to be put off to October 12, when it finally took place.

Meanwhile, the early speed trials had jelled the opinion of NALOC that the LCC would not really serve the purpose for which she was intended, though the proposed navigational method would. She was too heavy, would test the davits of any transport, and could be lowered only from the larger ones; she would occupy deck space which could be used to advantage by cargo and troop carriers; she needed an hour or so in the water before going into operation to let her gyro settle down; she would be very rough in any sea, and her crew might be sick and unable to do a proper job. What was really needed was a boat which would go with the task force under her own power, which was big enough to accommodate stand-by navigators, which could be seen, which could be ready to operate at once. Such a boat was the PC; and the subtraction of a few PC's from the combat side of a Task Force would not be serious. All this was conveyed to COMINCH in mid-September 1943. A few days later COMINCH replied that PC's were not desired for this purpose at that time, but that the Committee should prepare a plan of cabin and gear and an SOP, together with a list of conversion equipment, so that conversions could be made rapidly later, should these be desired. It was more than a year after that before applications were made in any substantial degree to PC's or LCI's; and this was done only after Marshall had gone to the Pacific and fought the indoctrination battle all over again. In the meantime, and in various operations, all the defects of the LCC became apparent and were so reported in battle reports. Despite individual feats of brilliance, the LCC was in disrepute, and with it the navigational method. Only Herculean effort by Marshall and Pease finally restored the method at the war's end to the high place it deserved.

In this same month of September, it was possible to turn the attention of NALOC to refinements of mapping. The Miller maps required hand redrawing from existing charts, usually with a pantograph. Symbols of importance had to be laid on by hand. Grids had to be drawn at two scales. The maps had to be printed; and papers shrank and misbehaved to add to draftsman's errors. Since charts were required only for small areas, since these areas would be known only to the planners of an operation, and since there would be little time available, these maps would have to be made in theaters. All this led to an extensive study of the symbols for the maps, the best width of line, the best color of map to be easily read with the yellow, green, or brown presentation of the PPI, and the best methods for controlling or compensating for shrinkage in printing. In this D. B. McLaughlin, astronomer, member of Radiation Laboratory staff, took a leading part. At the same time contact was made with the Chief Hydrographer, Rear Admiral G. S. Bryan, and Mr. Guillermo Medina, Principal Engineer of the Hydrographic Office. These conferences, which included McFarlane, McLaughlin, Stephens, and Burchard, led (on the suggestion of McFarlane and with the enthusiastic co-operation of the Hydrographic Office and the Eastman Kodak Company) to the final development, that of the Navigational Microfilm Projector (NMP). This device, which was to replace the VPR, would project a microfilm photograph of a chart onto a screen which the beamsplitter placed in the plane of the PPI tube. The projector and screen would be moved as was the VPR table and the method of fixes would be the same; courses could be plotted on the screen. Filters could be used to sharpen the color contrast of projected and radar chart on the PPI tube. Several changes of scale would be possible. Moreover, charts could be photographed rapidly and accurately. If air maps happened to be the only or the best ones available, they could be duplicated at once. All this processing could be done even while the Task Force was at sea. This was a most promising suggestion. It took a good deal of working out,

But the working out occurred, thanks to McFarlane's persistence. Finally, it had been tested, and with other methods was displayed on an LCC to the staff of CINCLANT, headed by Admiral Kilpatrick, Chief of Staff, at Norfolk on November 21. That this demonstration was successful was evidenced by the immediate and affirmative response which he gave to Burchard's suggestion that a PC boat be put at the disposal of NALOC for further trials in the Caribbean in January of 1944.

These trials were aimed at the Pacific. One of the difficulties that might be encountered was coral reefs, which might not give such good radar echoes as could be expected from the Atlantic coast of Europe. The nearest test coral was in the Caribbean. With the demonstration to CINCLANT, NALOC lifted its sights from the European war and transferred its interest to the Pacific.

Naïve as it may now seem, NALOC thought its job was essentially done. The work had been regarded by those who instigated it as so important that the Navy would surely follow it up. NALOC had realized early the necessity for strong follow-up in the beginning, but also believed that if the Caribbean cruise should be successful, the role of spearhead, ram, and goad could be laid aside. The LCC's were coming off the ways in quantity; several classes had passed through NALOC training; there was plenty of radar gear; Lieutenant R. E. Edson, USNR, of ComPhibLant, an intelligent officer close to the project, had training well in hand at Norfolk. The method had been seen and approved by the Amphibious Readiness Officer of COMINCH; by the Chief of Staff of the Atlantic Fleet; by the head of Amphibious Training Atlantic; by the Commander Task Force for Overlord; by the Co-ordinator of Research and Development; and by the Director of the Supply Service, Office of the Chief Signal Officer, USA, Major General Colton. COMINCH had asked for, and received from the Committee, a report intended for top-brass reading, a manual for operators and for training, and a draft of SOP. These it was going to distribute to all the Fleets. It looked to a group of civilians as though their job were done. How far this was from the fact, though little which remained to be done was technical, will be read in the sequel.

For the European war, the die was cast. The amphibious action would take place in less than six months. The decision of the Navy not to put the gear on PC's left the success or failure of the navigation in Normandy to the LCC's. Admiral Moon had taken some of these to the Mediterranean with him, where they did well. In May the LCC's were suspect on the basis of their sea qualities, and few were committed to the Normandy show. Those which were, behaved well. They were relegated to service as guide boats and wave boats, and the basic navigation was done by PC's without the gear. Two of the LCC's broke down en route from England. One of the other pair was crippled in action. The second one not only took over the task of leading the other wave as well as its own to the beach but did it well; finally, when its companion PC was shot out of the water, it did the rest of the navigational control for the beach. Nonetheless, the LCC had a black eye and the battle reports did not conceal it. But all this was in the blind future in November 1943.

Meanwhile, NALOC was beginning to be felt on the West coast. Some LCC's were being delivered to the Commander, Amphibious Forces, Pacific (ComPhibsPac), at San Diego from West Coast yards, and Pease was dispatched to tune them up and give some instruction. There he remained until January, when he returned for the Caribbean cruise.

On January 4, 1944, *PC-576*, under the command of Lieutenant (jg) W. F. Colton, departed from Norfolk training base. After a tempestuous trip around Cape Hatteras, she put in at Fort Pierce, Florida, and then embarked on a cruise of some ten days in the Caribbean with Burchard, Stephens, McFarlane, McLaughlin, and Pease aboard.[15] Her general route carried her to Nassau, around Eleuthera, down to Guantánamo, thence to the south shore of Jamaica, to Portland Bight near Kingston, and back to Cuba at Cienfuegos. During part of her trip, Medina of the Hydrographic Office was also aboard. She had both 10-centimeter and 3-centimeter radar, VPR and NMP, two fathometers, VPR maps, and microfilm charts made both from maps and from air cover. She navigated equally well, whether scanning coral reefs or the mountains of east Cuba and Jamaica; she found her way by radar through the tortuous channels of Santiago Harbor, and made a quick and accurate test hydrographic survey of Portland Bight. Everything

---

[15] Also on the cruise, manning the short-wave set, were C. M. Sorvaag and G. B. Scheckels.

went well, and the comprehensive report then made brought to an end
the truly technical work of the Committee, though, as events disclosed,
the whole method was as yet unknown to the Pacific Fleet, where it
appeared most likely to be of importance.

This situation developed when Captain C. C. Voegeli, in charge of
the Amphibious Training Base in San Diego, asked the Committee to
supply some maps. As a result, McFarlane was dispatched to the West
Coast. On the basis of representations made by him, Burchard asked
for and obtained permission from COMINCH for a NALOC group
to go to San Diego to demonstrate the method to a group of officers,
help establish training, and set up the newer devices such as the NMP.
This led to the same pattern of events as had taken place on the East
Coast. The Training Command felt the need of a larger boat and, in
April and without the concurrence of the forward echelons, put an
LCI at the disposal of the Committee for installation of gear. Successful
demonstrations were held for Rear Admiral R. O. Davis and Commodore Herbert B. Knowles, who was to command transports in the
forthcoming operation at Saipan. Marshall, now returned from Eng-
land, and McFarlane participated in the final invasion exercises off
San Diego before the fleet put off for Pearl Harbor and points west.
Again everything seemed on the rails.

But it was not. In May when Marshall and Burchard departed for
Pearl Harbor, to set up the Operational Research Section, they were
both technically accredited to the Army, but were permitted also to
work for and with the Navy. Here was the golden opportunity to see
what NALOC could do for the Pacific war. What they found was like
a dash of cold water. Many LCC's had reached the base at Oahu, perhaps 100. There they were, tied up in rows with nobody wanting
them. Nobody knew how to use them. The officers who had been
trained to operate them had been detached for other duty. They were
looked upon as scout boats. They were even in risk of being cannibal-
ized of their gear for other purposes. Pacific SOP involved establishing
a line of departure marked off by PC's with no special navigating
gear.[16] NALOC had to start over again, except that the technique was
now known.

[16] Where PC's or DD's were used as primary control vessels, and LCC's as secondary
controls, the latter used NALOC navigational equipment and frequently guided the
larger ships by radio to their assigned positions.

There were three alleviating factors. In charge of training at Pearl Harbor was Commodore Wallace B. Phillips, who had been at Norfolk in the early days and knew the NALOC personnel. Coming was Lieutenant J. P. McKenna, dispatched by COMINCH to follow up the making of maps. He was a NALOC enthusiast. The Fleet Radar Center was up and coming, and was interested in the method, and Marshall was always active at that Center.

These were the thin straws from which the bricks had to be built again. A hurry call was sent off for Pease, who was dispatched and remained at Oahu for months. Roderick Stephens of Marshall's Army team was quickly indoctrinated and made part of the demonstrating group. When Burchard left to return to the mainland, he could be confident that the demonstration would succeed and that things could begin to move in the Pacific; he could be sure that Marshall would keep them moving.

But when he did return, the amphibious part of the European war was over, the research and development for NALOC was done. Whatever else might occur rested with Marshall and the Navy in Pearl. The Committee could serve no further useful purpose. Accordingly, after reporting to COMINCH on the state of things in Pearl Harbor, Marshall suggested that the Committee be discharged. This was concurred in by the Army and Navy by the end of September; a final meeting was held on October 9 at the Radiation Laboratory; the final report was delivered to the Chairman, NDRC, on the last day of October 1944.

But NALOC's job was not done with the termination of the Committee. In Hawaii, Marshall struggled on until December 1944, retraining, rebuilding morale, overcoming the prejudice against the method aroused by the bad performance of the LCC as a boat (not its navigating gear) at Guam and Tinian. The trials and demonstrations were a success and led Admiral R. K. Turner to address COMINCH and CincPac on August 30, 1944, affirming his belief that the "results of tests indicate that VPR–NMP used in conjunction with SO-13 Radar as a navigational aid on control vessels will expedite the location of proper landing beaches and of landing boat control." He went on to recommend installation of the equipment on PC's and SC's, and of Recordak (for processing microfilm) on AGC's. He added that tests were proceeding on the use of the device in fire-support craft and in APD's that were used as base craft for combat demolition teams. Their mission was to clear the beaches of obstacles.

These trials were a success and resulted in urgent fleet orders to BuShips for several hundred equipments. Due to its lack of enthusiasm for the method, BuShips was quite unable to meet the demand, and for a few weeks the gap was bridged in Oahu by Pease, who made equipments by hand out of parts procured by Marshall from the Radiation Laboratory through Army channels. Moreover, Pease personally installed more than fifty first equipments on various vessels of the Pacific Fleet. But now with CincPac sold, the civilian mission was accomplished.

By the end of the year orders had gone to Washington for equipments for 1500 ships, for the bombardment vessels of the battle fleets, for the LCI(g)'s, the PC's, and the SC's of the amphibious forces, for the APD's of the demolition teams, for the minelayers and sweepers. That this was justified was clear from the chorus of favorable comment from skippers and commodores alike, from control craft, support craft, and demolition craft after the operations at Iwo Jima and Okinawa, where the method was deployed unreservedly and in force for the first time.

In the year and a half of its existence, NALOC had developed and refined a new method of inshore navigation based on radar, with the widest possible applications, a method which made navigation possible for persons who had little if any navigating skill when they began, even though some familiarity with pilotage was, of course, indispensable. The bare principles of this method were based upon keeping a navigator visually informed at all times of the position of his vessel with respect to a shore line, navigational aids, and other vessels. This was accomplished by having before him an image of a chart (on which course and position might be marked) in register with a radar pattern on a Plan Position Indicator. Since the vessel's position was at the center of the radar pattern, it was clearly visible and could be marked on the chart. As the vessel moved a plot could be made showing the course and distance made good. A trained navigator or operator was familiar with the radar echoes from various types of objects and could maintain the match between chart and radar to a high degree of accuracy.

In POA operations, a PC or similar vessel was used as a primary control at 5000 to 6000 yards off shore, LCC's with navigational equipment convoyed landing craft from the transport area to the primary control vessel and then escorted the first wave to a point just short of the beach itself, correcting during this run for any errors of placement of the primary control vessel due to its lack of navigational gear. NALOC had trained many young men to be navigators by the method; it had provided standard operating procedure for amphibious navigation, and manuals of radar recognition which went far beyond the scope of this particular problem; it had seen its methods used with success in all the operations from Palau to the Philippines.

All this had required some ingenuity and applied development, but relatively little research. The long hours of its technical people had been spent more in prodding and in soothing than in designing. It had always enjoyed co-operation from the top ranks of operating officers, but ill-concealed opposition of those in the procurement and design bureaus, especially the Bureau of Ships. It had had to fight and overcome that opposition often almost by *force majeure*. It had had to struggle with bad communications and poor circulation of information and resell the project three times, after it had been approved at echelons which would ordinarily have been expected to make the job go.

This was, of course, no unique experience for OSRD. NALOC was a happy job in which there was less obstruction and indifference than in many other projects. That so much expediting work had to be done was but another evidence that the civilian mind is needed in wartime. No officer save of the highest rank, regardless of his enthusiasm for the project, could ever successfully have put his head on the chopping block as often as the personnel of NALOC had to do. Had any civilian's head been chopped off in the process, the result would still not have been fatal to the project. Unless human nature changes a great deal, the *per aspera ad astra* aspects of NALOC will doubtless continue to exist in all military research and development. In the *aspera* stage the resilience and independence of the civilian is essential.

CHAPTER XXIII

CLEARING THE BEACHES

THE REMOVAL OF OBSTACLES TO LANDING

BLOODY TARAWA had a sobering effect on amphibious planners. Here for the first time there was confirmation of the feeling that a determined enemy with some engineering skill and force could make the landing on a hostile beach a costly, perhaps an impossible accomplishment. One of the tools at the disposal of the enemy would be obstacles that would retard or arrest altogether the progress of amphibious craft to the beachhead. They would then be easy prey to the enemy guns, not all of which would have been put out of action by even the most intensive sea and air bombardment.

By the middle of 1943, even before Tarawa, it was clear that the big assault on *Festung Europa* would be delivered somewhere on the west coast, between Bordeaux or Biarritz at the south and the Hook of Holland at the north. Reconnaissance was beginning to bring in evidence of the way in which the Germans were preparing defenses. These were spotty but were increasing in quantity all the time. They were of several types. In the water, various kinds of obstacles would be so spaced that a landing craft could not go between them. They might be concrete masses, blocks with sharpened, iron stakes projecting seaward, calculated to impale the light hulls of the Higgins boats, or protruding steel rails jetted end-on into the sand. Between them or hung on them there might be lightly triggered mines. On the beach just above the high-tide mark there would be land mines to blow up vehicles and personnel, and various tank obstacles and traps such as concrete "dragon's teeth." At the exits from the beach there might be concrete walls many feet thick and so high that a tank could not go over them. Such walls in masonry had proved decisive in the ill-starred Dieppe raid.

The total amount of these obstacles visible from reconnaissance was not then (nor did it ever actually become) such as to constitute a solid line of defense along the littoral. But they could be expected at every spot that was in other ways an attractive place to land. Moreover, experiments already conducted at Fort Pierce, Florida, by Naval Combat Demolition Units and Seabees had shown that American engineers, armed with water jets, could place steel rails at a frightening speed. There was no reason to suppose that the German engineer would be less competent or efficient or have less satisfactory equipment.

Study of the general problem had been going on for many months; in America, first at Solomons Island in Chesapeake Bay and subsequently at Fort Pierce. Here two officers, one from the Army and one from the Navy, had sweated away with insufficient personnel, insufficient materiel, insufficient pressure and support from above, and insufficient idea men. Enormous credit is due Captain A. G. Hoel, Corps of Engineers, and Lieutenant Commander Draper L. Kauffman[1] of the Naval Combat Demolition Research Unit for their personal energy and ingenuity; but they needed much more help.

In England the problem was also receiving attention. At Appledore on Barnstaple Bay in Devon, Combined Operations Headquarters was testing out every idea which came to anyone's mind. Conventional approaches were clearly not working out. The only sure way to demolish or remove the obstacles was to send brave men ashore, in the teeth of enemy fire and up to their necks in surf, armed with light charges which they would wrap around the individual obstacles and then detonate. Though this would work, and though much could be done to make things easier for these demolition teams, it was rightly felt that casualties would be very high, probably too high.

Much the same thing was true on the beach. Location and removal of land mines was difficult enough in the long nights and over the

[1] Commander Kauffman had a spectacular career. Although he came from a long line of naval officers and was a graduate of the Naval Academy, he was rejected for a commission because of his eyes. He worked with the Merchant Marine until the war broke out in Europe, when he went to France as an ambulance driver. Captured by the Nazis, he later got away and made his way before the mast from Lisbon to London where the Royal Navy was glad to have him as a bomb-disposal officer. When the Japanese attacked Pearl Harbor, he was commissioned in the American Navy and flown from England to Pearl Harbor, where he led the bomb disposal. This was ticklish because Japanese bombs had not previously been diagnosed. For this performance he received the Navy Cross. He was distinctly a man of action. Although he worked very energetically at Fort Pierce during his stay there, he was anxious to get into the field and to lead combat demolition troops. This hope was ultimately realized when he was sent to the Pacific. In charge of a group at the Saipan operations, he won a second Navy Cross for distinguished performance in the water and on the beaches.

limitless sands of Tunisia. It approached the impossible as a manual operation when this was part of a scheme of assault from the water, where the speed of locomotion was necessarily so much less and the limits of the action area so much more sharply defined. The beach-exit walls could also be breached by hand. American engineers, some twenty to thirty to a team, carrying a pack of tetrytol in each hand, could be discharged from the ramp of a landing craft, worm their way across the beach, build up a wall of tetrytol of suitable proportions, detonate it and create a tank breach, all in a very few minutes. During these minutes they were none the less defenseless. It was a question, not of bravery, but of intensity of enemy small arms and automatic fire, as to whether any or enough of them would ever reach the wall. The British were working on a similar scheme, using a special form of shaped charge called the "General Wade." A sort of Trojan horse called an "engineer tank" provided somewhat more support for the men.

What was clearly needed was a way to remove the obstacles with less hand effort, by more remote weapons. The most obvious ones, long-distance naval barrage and bombing from aircraft, showed little promise of reaching the necessary intensity because of the close pattern of fire that would be required.

Some idea of the desperation felt by the workers can be gained by examining some of the suggestions which were duly tried out and reported, especially by Combined Operations Headquarters. There was, for example, the "Matador Sweep." [2] This was a simple idea. A herd of cows would be discharged from the ramps of landing craft, perhaps a mile out. Naturally they would try to swim ashore. Offering a low silhouette in the water, they would probably not engage the interest of enemy gunners and, when they got into either the offshore or the land mines, would set them off. Then there was the "Great Panjandrum." This was a sort of juggernaut with a body, which was an explosive charge. Its wheels were like pinwheels, with rockets arranged tangentially and armed to go off in sequence, thus providing a sort of jet propulsion. The vehicle would be driven to a concrete wall and would then detonate. At the trials the two wheels got to firing out

[2] The use of code names was common; and sometimes it appeared that names were chosen in advance of ideas. Among the colorful ones that appeared in DOLOC work were: Reddy Fox, Hot Dog, Hellion, Porcupine, Bucket Boat, and Woofus.

of synchronism. Then the Great Panjandrum adopted an erratic course and scattered the brass, who showed more proficiency in running than was to be expected from such elderly gentlemen, and this device was then stricken from the list.

Of somewhat more promise for part of the job was the British "Scorpion," a tank with flails to detonate the mines. It had been used with some success in Africa, but was not an easy thing to get ashore in the first wave. The same thing applied to our partially developed tank rocket launcher, which carried a box of some twenty 7.2-inch demolition rockets atop the turret of a Sherman tank. These would be launched sequentially at a concrete wall; and since the effect of each rocket was more than cumulative, a good tank breach might be made after twelve to fourteen rounds. Again there was a question of how to get this brute within range of the wall. The British had something similar in the "Flying Dustbin," which was a large hunk of explosive to be launched at the wall through a spring gun called a "Petard."

For removal of obstacles in the water we had a tube of explosive, about sixteen inches in diameter and fifty feet long known as the "Reddy Fox." It was to be towed into place among the obstacles and detonated. Static trials had shown fair clearance of obstacles, though several Foxes in parallel would be needed to make a breach wide enough to permit landing craft to pass and especially to retract from the beach. But no one knew how the Fox was to be carried to the line of departure or snaked in among the obstacles after it was launched. There was also interest in drone boats, LCVP's carrying many pounds of explosive, remotely steered by radio to a position among the obstacles, sunk and detonated. The diameter of clearance for a single boat was only eighty feet, which was on the small side. Moreover, there was doubt as to the controls; would they be positive enough? [3] Merely to enumerate countless other proposals would run this text to unseemly length.

What was needed was a good deal more steam, for here was a critical problem; not only was more manpower in the experimental work

---

[3] This doubt proved reasonable at subsequent trials off Kwajalein. The boats got out of control, gallivanted through the fleet, and had to be disposed of by manually operated craft. In the Mediterranean the Germans actually succeeded in wresting control from us and then insulted us by saying over the radio, "Dey vos your darlings yesterday; dey are ours today."

needed, but more people should be thinking about the problem in the hope that some one might find the Midas key. Under these circumstances, and with the success of the earlier NALOC Committee in mind, in August 1943 COMINCH asked the Co-ordinator of Research and Development to set up with NDRC a project for the Demolition of Obstacles to Landing Operations (DOLOC),[4] and suggested that this take a form somewhat similar to the NALOC group. The work of the DOLOC Committee began at an orientation meeting with the Navy on September 22 and effectively ended five months later, although the Committee remained in existence for another nine months after that to cover minor matters.

This is not a success story, but history cannot be made up exclusively of successes. In the long view, DOLOC never succeeded in finding a pat solution to its very difficult problem. Its efforts had a "too little and too late" taste. It is hard to say whether, under other conditions, the problem could ever have been solved. All we can say is that it was not. The Committee did dream up two or three approaches of its own, none of which finally proved to have promise; it restored confidence in the capacity of bombers or fighter-bombers to contribute notably to the total job; and it assisted in refining details of many devices, none of which finally played a significant part in the all-important Operation Overlord, the Normandy invasion. But it did focus the attention of the High Command very sharply on the actual situation. Looked at on the basis of sheer accomplishment, DOLOC was a failure; what it did on the way to that failure is still worth the eye of history.

It is hard to see how a committee better fitted by experience to make a contribution might have been appointed from NDRC ranks. It was made up of Dr. George Kistiakowsky, Chief of Division 8, an energetic and resourceful chemist with wide practical experience in explosives; Dr. Walker Bleakney, Deputy Chief of Division 2, who knew more than any other man in that Division what could be done to walls and mines by bombs and what aircraft might be expected to accomplish, and who had the support of a team at Princeton that had successfully engaged in the study of such matters; Dr. Thomas Lauritsen, one of the liveliest and most imaginative of the rockets group at the California

---

[4] As in the case of NALOC, the "C" does not stand for Committee.

Institute of Technology, who had already been working on the rocket tank; Herbert E. Bragg, Technical Aide of Division 17, who had been one of the spearheads in the study of land-mine detection and removal, and who was also familiar with the many varied devices of his Division that might be applied to this job; and Roger Warner, by then the Principal Technical Aide of Division 12, with long experience and success with the DUKW, the Alligator, and the Weasel both in America and in the field in combined amphibious operations. Chairman of the Committee was Burchard, then Chief of Division 2 and Chairman of NALOC, who had devoted the preceding several months almost exclusively to amphibious doctrine.

At the first meeting in September Admiral Furer presided. It was Captain Kiland of COMINCH who stated the general problem and who at the same time emphasized its importance, and then Commander Kauffman outlined all those matters on which it was believed that the group at Fort Pierce needed help. The more significant ones are worth rehearsing here and now:

1. Anything to accomplish demolition from a distance, and avoid enfilading fire.

2. Methods of placing charges by stealth, say a week ahead, and then detonating them simultaneously; and study of concussion detonators.

3. Substitutes for safety fuzes that would work under water, would be foolproof, and would not kink.

4. Methods for locating obstacles several feet below the surface, both in reconnaissance and during the actual demolition operation. To do this on a black night was almost impossible.

5. Development of a quiet, low-silhouette transportation unit to bring demolition crews and materiel from the fleet to the obstacle area.

6. Development of gadgets to increase the safety and range of underwater swimmers, including a small, easily read, waterproof compass to assist the swimmer in navigation.

7. Development of a container for at least 100 lbs. of explosives, having slight negative buoyancy and towed easily by a swimmer.

8. Methods of marking channels with buoys that could be placed before firing the charge, would remain after firing, would be visible to our side at night but not to the enemy, and would be practicable in heavy surf.

9. Further development of drone boats, containing many tons of high explosive, to be radio-controlled and detonated at the beach.

10. Development of a charge or other cable-cutting device for cables that were not under tension.

Then Major Fuller of the Corps of Engineers [5] related in much the same terms the corresponding problems on the beach, where the additional difficulty of working in the water did not exist.

This was evidently an armful. The Committee retired to get its breath, have lunch, and meet in camera to see what NDRC had that might be applied at once. At the afternoon meeting they discussed what immediately applicable commodity each had on his current NDRC shelf. There was really very little. No life-saving gimmick stared the Committee in the face. It was clear that further indoctrination was necessary.

Before this indoctrination took place, there was one matter, unimportant in itself but broadly symbolic, which deserves mention. Like us, the British had been conducting experiments in the breaching of concrete beach-exit walls. Their test walls were not like ours, and it was even true that neither all their walls nor all of ours were alike. Under the circumstances, it was natural for British scientists to propose to their American opposite numbers that both sides adopt standards so that performances could really be compared.

This suggestion was naturally appealing to the scientist. He cannot properly be happy in work that does not allow a reproducible or a comparable experiment. Though the Committee did not agree exactly with standards the British proposed, it did concur in the principle and proposed to forward it. The standardization was never achieved, however, partly because of the short space of time during which experiments had to be conducted.

This has an important significance for many of the DOLOC operations. DOLOC frequently found itself baffled by the rough and ready type of experimenting which seemed to be the fashion in this work. It is certain enough, for example, that final trials of a device to be used in a seaway will have to be conducted in the seaway. On the other hand, every such experiment is necessarily full-scale and requires the coordination of much more than the experimental equipment — of boats and men and all sorts of gear. Even then many difficulties arise from entirely extraneous causes, and each delays the day of the answer. In work such as that of DOLOC, it is clear that some of the testing has

---

[5] The Corps of Engineers had been busily engaged on the beaches at Fort Pierce even before the Navy Combat Demolition Research Unit got into action.

to be of a very empirical sort; but scientists would believe that towing-tanks, for example, could save a considerable amount of seaway experiment.

Consider the case of the land mine. The great problem in land-mine clearance was that experimenters were always having to work with a mine that was out of date. If the Nazis came up with a new model of the Teller mine, at first only a few would be captured and studied by the theater. Then they would be sent home most reluctantly and in short supply. By the time a good supply was available, the weapon to be overcome would be a different one.

Confronted with this problem in the abstract, a scientist would choose to develop a machine that could represent a mine and that could be set to any given sensitivity. When a new mine appeared, its sensitivity could be measured and the machine set to that quantity. From such knowledge and the knowledge of impulse produced by a proposed clearance device, it would be possible to make correlations that would give a close approximation to the area in any sort of mine-field that one could expect to clear with that device. Such procedures, slower at the beginning, accelerate at the end and will produce more dependable and faster results than *ad hoc* experiments. On the other hand, they are not as photogenic as standing off a beach all day and firing rockets with different fuzings and heads at a group of American test mines.

Stations like Fort Pierce have too many visitors who will not be impressed by a schedule that calls for firing one round and then spending half the morning moseying around an area of sand getting measurements, and the afternoon in calculation and discussion before firing another round. Under all these circumstances, one of the clear necessities was for DOLOC to impose upon the testing routine as much order and direction as was possible, to struggle to limit to not more than one the change in variables from experiment to experiment, and otherwise to bring the scientific method into play.

In defense of the military experimenters, it has to be said that in general they were not drawn from the experimental stations of the Army and Navy, where such procedures were understood; but they were practical men with a great deal of energy. It is also true that not all the problems were subject to this sort of analysis. Moreover, the military felt the heavy hand of the pressure of time, too little time. They could not be confident that this more leisurely initial approach would get to the answer in time. This same pressure was felt by DOLOC. For the most part it had to pursue the same methods as the Fort Pierce group. Several DOLOC representatives did, however, spend a considerable amount of time in tightening up experimental methods at Fort Pierce.

The further orientation was given the Committee during a three-day visit to Fort Pierce early in October. Most of the devices then in hand were demonstrated. DOLOC operated drone boats, followed combat demolition crews into the surf, and observed the first firing of the "Porcupine," an LCM mounted with sixteen 7.2-inch demolition rocket launchers outboard on each side.[6] They saw the tank launcher fire a string of rockets at a concrete wall, had cigarettes taken from their mouths at dusk by naval combat demolition people who had come ashore undetected, by stealth, and had a colorful and informative time. Navy commandos swarmed across ditches on ropes, and some of the younger committee members essayed a portion of the Navy commando-training course.

Most important were a number of tent conferences which established certain basic points. One was that the fifty-foot gaps which the demolition people had been intending to blow would not be nearly wide enough for a landing operation. Landing craft need not only to beach but also to retract, and there is steady traffic to a beach. DOLOC at this time also questioned the decision reached at Fort Pierce that bombing operations would not be of any assistance, and reopened the whole question.

Back in Washington, the Committee discussed what could be done. For the water phase, it was most important to find a means for wholesale, remotely controlled demolition. Whatever aids might be given to underwater swimmers and however brave they might be, the casualties would be too great if the enemy defended stoutly. Hence, little time would be spent on minor improvements for the

---

[6] Although every precaution was taken at the beach with the traditional barrier flags, something went wrong. Just as Commander Roger Putnam, USNR, in charge of the LCM, rippled his firing switches, to their horror the observers saw Captain Hoel, Army Engineer officer in charge, rolling down the target beach in his jeep. Captain Hoel escaped unscathed, but Army-Navy relations were strained for a day or two.

demolition crews. Instead, the emphasis would be placed on large-scale attack on underwater obstacles. For this, there were few alternatives. The knowledge DOLOC had then about bombing inaccuracy and the effects of relatively small charges under water made it pretty certain that aerial bombardment would not be very effective in this phase. This would have to be confirmed by test; but for the moment bombing could be set aside as unpromising. The same thing applied to rockets and naval bombardment. The drone or Apex Boat and the Reddy Fox would remain as possibilities.

Something could be done to improve the radio controls of the boat, and Dr. A. F. Murray of Division 13 would be asked to put some time on that. But it was more important still to find out what the boat could accomplish if it carried a really large charge. Generally speaking, it was known that the radii for various effects of an explosion would vary with the cube root of the weight of the charge, if the explosive remained unchanged. Would this be so for an explosion near the beach where the depth of water over the charge would not be in scale?

The Reddy Fox had been brought far enough to show that it could be towed without breaking up. When detonated statically it would effect a reasonable clearance. Two or three Foxes in parallel might be an answer. But no one had made any really plausible suggestions as to how the Reddy Fox might be placed tactically, and there were also doubts as to how this elongated snake could be carried in the holds of transports whose hatches and bulkheads were not of adequate dimensions. Clearly this needed a good deal of looking into. Warner was asked to look into it. Were there other ways of placing similar charges? Could torpedoes be used? This would be worth studying. Warner and Bragg undertook this investigation.

Could liquid explosive be pumped from an offshore barge into an empty tube which could be towed into position more easily empty than full? This was clearly on the edge of fantasy, but the situation was desperate enough so that it had to be considered. Could we get a liquid explosive, safe enough and sufficiently noncorrosive for the purpose? This was a problem for Kistiakowsky. Could we develop a tube to receive the explosive? This was a job for Warner. The total project was duly named "Hot Dog."

There were collateral problems. Could DOLOC help on delay fuzes and concussion detonators? This was assigned to Bragg. What was our actual potentiality at underwater reconnaissance in advance of the time when the task force moved in? This was of great importance. Bragg was asked to look into it.

Useful things might also be done for the land phase. The tank dozer looked very promising but needed no help from NDRC. The tank rocket launcher also looked good and was already well in hand under Lauritsen. He could have the advice of Kistiakowsky and Division 8 on such matters as fuzing and explosive heads. The principal problem which needed concentrated attention was that of the minefield on the beach. A thorough investigation of what might be accomplished by bombing was proposed and assigned to Bleakney.

It was also desirable that the Committee have full-time representation at Fort Pierce, both to try to bring the experimental program into better scientific focus and to keep DOLOC advised of daily developments. To this end Dr. Richard A. Beth of Division 2 and Dr. Eugene H. Eyster of Division 8 were sent to Fort Pierce in November 1943, where they remained until after the famous demonstration of mid-February 1944. On and off, they were joined by Roderick Stephens, truly an artist in the handling of small boats, who worked on the problem of getting the Reddy Fox into position. From January 13 on, they were further assisted by Stewart Coey, who was a senior engineer of the Research Corporation, and was loaned through OFS for the purpose.

By December 1, things had progressed far enough so that it was reasonable for the Committee to repair again to Fort Pierce, and December 2 marks the second landmark in the history of DOLOC. In the office of the Commanding Officer of the base, Captain Clarence Gulbransen, USN, General Henry, Chief of NDD, met with members of the Committee and of the Joint Army-Navy Board. He stated that the removal of underwater and beach obstacles was of highest priority, equaled only by the removal of land mines, and emphasized that development of techniques and materiel that would not leave the United States by February 15, 1944, would be of no use to General Devers.[7] General Henry added that research on methods that might be promis-

---

[7] At that time it was expected that General Devers would play a leading role in the invasion of the Continent.

ing for later fulfillment should not be discontinued but should be given second priority.

Six weeks to go! And nothing of real promise very far along! Stock had to be taken. No matter how much fire the Army and Navy might put under the project, no matter how many men they might assign, or how much they could expedite the procurement of materiel, this was less than a little time. Although much progress had been made both with the explosive and with the hose, Hot Dog was certainly out of consideration for such a short run. Only the Reddy Fox, the Apex Boat, the bombing of minefields, and the rocket boats remained as possibilities that would interest DOLOC. Even the torpedo projects, which had generally been named "Hellion," could not be expected to come through to such a deadline.

But Warner and Burchard both had reason to doubt that the High Command really appreciated how little promise there was in the Fort Pierce devices, for the reports were usually oversanguine. It was important to bring this home. To this end, with the wholehearted assistance of Captain Gulbransen and Commander Kauffman, a full-dress demonstration for top brass was arranged for the 11th and 12th of February, three days before General Henry's deadline. High representatives of the top command in Washington and representatives from all the major theaters would come to this demonstration. There they would see with their own eyes exactly where we stood. Joint Chiefs of Staff would make a record motion picture. There would be a critique after the demonstrations. In the meantime, everything it was possible to do would be done to develop the least unpromising of these devices.

The Reddy Fox was a sort of water-borne Bangalore torpedo, 8″ in diameter, 50 to 100′ long, carrying 25 to 30 lbs. per running foot of 80% vibrogel. It was equipped with flotation and a means for discharging this so that the tube would sink before being detonated. Tubes had been made of paper, which would not stand flexing in the water, of plywood, which was promising, and of steel. Clearance of obstacles with this contrivance was only fair. Methods of carrying in the charge were troublesome. Up to this time swimmers, rubber boats, and scooter-bugs pushing from the rear had been considered. In a meeting of

DOLOC with Beth and Eyster on the eve of their departure for Fort Pierce, it was agreed that they should determine within the degree of accuracy necessary for operational work what actual width of channel would be cleared by this device. They would find out whether or not, when several Reddy Fox charges were placed in parallel, the detonation of one could take place without destroying the others. And they would try to discover how to get the Reddy Fox into proper position.

By November 29 Warner and Stephens could report that booms had been constructed on LCM's for handling Reddy Fox. On December 15 Stephens and Lieutenant Ramsing towed one 50-ft. steel, inert Reddy Fox with the latest rigging. In a two-foot chop everything went well. The Fox was launched toward an overturned LCM and slid up on the LCM bottom with no difficulty. The next day two Reddy Foxes were towed with the LCM gear in seas up to seven feet and wind at twenty miles, testing all parts of the rigging and the Reddy Fox. A forty-five-minute, full-speed run in rough water disclosed no weaknesses. The boat could be turned hard over either way and the Fox ran without regard to the direction of the sea.

On December 24 Captain Hoel and Eyster laid out a program for testing the effect of detonating the Reddy Fox placed in rail and scully obstacles. Handling tests continued with inert Foxes, and the sensitivity of live Foxes in the water to various .50-caliber bullets, including incendiary ones, was determined.

On December 29 another approach to Reddy Fox launching was essayed. A 100-ft. inert charge was assembled on ways in the hold of an LCT and was launched through the lowered ramp by a stern line. The LCT was not well handled and the charge suffered severe distortions during launching, but was unharmed. The next day the stern-line technique came into serious question, however, and this fiasco was a good example of the sort of thing that grew premature gray hairs on the heads of the experimenters. First the firing line for the sinking charge became fouled in the reel. Then when the charge was finally sunk, the crew delayed in cutting the stern line free, so that the charge was pulled 100 ft. out to sea before it was freed. These were human errors, of course; but quite as likely to occur in combat as on the Florida strand. The day did show that it was hard for the coxswain to see obstacles over the ramp of an LCM and hard to push a 50-ft.

length fully into a belt of obstacles by the stern-line method and still stay clear of the obstacles.

On the same day Lieutenant Colonel J. E. Walsh, Corps of Engineers, returned from the European theater. Without naming the date or the place, he sketched general plans for the invasion and reported that the British did not like the Reddy Fox. They believed it would crater the sea floor and thought that a point charge such as the Apex Boat would be more effective than a line charge such as the Fox. American planners in ETO also wanted concentration on the drone boat and the Porcupine.

At the end of December Burchard and Warner conferred with Captain W. M. Moses, head of the Research Division in the Bureau of Ordnance, and with Captain C. L. Tyler and Commander J. H. Sides. All the devices were discussed and BuOrd pointed out that it would be unreasonable to try to tow the Fox across the British Channel, as had been suggested by the Corps of Engineers. Moreover, Foxes could not be attached to LCM's before the LCM's were taken off the transports. This meant that the Foxes would have to be provided in sections short enough to be loaded in the magazines and light enough to be handled on a landing craft at night in a pitching sea. This would reduce their length to approximately eight to ten feet and their weight to 300 or 400 lbs. There would then have to be a link between the sections that was good enough to permit subsequent handling and detonation. Warner and Burchard concurred with this, though they wondered what it did to the Reddy Fox project.

On December 31 at Fort Pierce there was a first trial of a 50-ft. loaded Fox to be launched from an LCM into a band of rails. The charge for sinking the Fox was improperly primed and failed to fire, and the Fox washed ashore. It was then placed by hand among scullies, was sunk, and then fired from the shore. It produced an elongated crater 32 feet in maximum width. The lips on the side washed away in about ten minutes. But the charge failed to clear a gap across the obstacle belt.

At this point the reader may begin to wonder why, in conditions of urgency, more than one trial did not take place in a day. There were not enough Reddy Foxes; there were not enough boats; there were not enough crews. It took nearly two hours for an LCM to get from harbor to trial beach and as long to get back. Such limitations were serious for a high-priority project.

On January 4, after further tests had produced erratic results, work was brought to a halt when the rudders of the one LCM available for these trials failed. One dropped off and the other froze in its bearings. The next day the Committee, meeting at Fort Pierce, agreed that as it stood the Fox was certainly not ready to be recommended to the fighting forces and that much more progress would have to be made before it could be. On January 6 the LCM was ready again, but in a heavy sea just outside the jetty the towing boom buckled and the tests had to be deferred again for repairs. These were completed by the next day, and once more the attempt to place 100-ft. lengths in an underwater rail belt failed when the bows of the charges remained connected by a line that fouled on a rail.

Part of the story of Reddy Fox has been bared in some of its gruesome details for the reader to draw such conclusions as he will. Similar difficulties, though specialized according to the problem, engaged those who, in parallel with the Fox experimenters, were driving day after day on the sand and in the water, repairing motors, acting as their own mechanics, plotting and planning always in this grim race against time.[8]

The Apex Boat was a radio-controlled drone, usually an LCVP or smaller. Loaded with such explosive as it could carry, it was directed into the obstacles and detonated. Records show that from the outset the Committee had no particular enthusiasm for this device. Nevertheless it represented perhaps the only "quick and dirty" method that might be available in time. At an early meeting DOLOC had faced the danger of a set rudder and a jammed radio. Either of these might cause the dangerous drone to career among the vessels of a Task Force. DOLOC wondered whether brave coxswains equipped with escape boats of

---

[8] Experience in this project seems, at least to the writer, to confirm the impression that in an appropriate setup the Director of OSRD would have been empowered to requisition and obtain adequate material for projects he was asked to assist. DOLOC was said to have the highest priority. Nonetheless the number of craft the Navy seemed able to supply from Norfolk was never adequate. Moreover, the boats furnished were in such condition as to require a good deal of time of the personnel to keep them in operation. This naturally cut down the availability of both personnel and boats for experimental purposes.

high speed might not be much more satisfactory. There were other major questions. What radius of clearance might be expected from various charges? Was it necessary to sink the boat before detonating and thereby create an additional complication and hazard? Would the detonation cause a crater in the bottom that might constitute with its seaward lip almost as much of a hazard to oncoming amphibious craft as the original obstacles?

On October 4 the Committee asked for static detonations of larger charges. On December 6, 8000 lbs. of TNT were detonated under water statically. Obstacles in a circle 80 feet in diameter were cleared. This confirmed the previous rough equation that the radius of cleared circle in feet would equal approximately twice the cube root of the charge-weight expressed in pounds. A few days later one of the two drone boats available at Fort Pierce was removed for other duty. On the 20th of December a 1000-lb. charge behaved in scale with the 8000-lb. one, clearing a circle of 40-ft. diameter.

Since the 80-ft. circle for the 8000-lb. charge scarcely seemed large enough, DOLOC continued to press for a larger charge, say 64,000 lbs., about the maximum an LCM could carry. The people at Fort Pierce were reluctant to shoot off such a big charge because they feared damage or annoyance to the townspeople some eight miles away from the proving ground. On the assertion of the explosives experts that this would not be the case and under vigorous insistence from Burchard, strongly supported by Commander Brunauer, BuOrd, Captain Gulbransen decided that the matter was so important he ought to take the chance. On the 3rd of February, about a week before the demonstration, a 64,000-lb. charge was fired — with no damage to the townspeople. Again the scale law was confirmed; the diameter of demolition was almost exactly 160 ft.

Until this big charge had been fired, there had been no serious crater lips in the water. Those that had appeared momentarily were washed away by the surf in a matter of minutes. The lips for the big shot were substantially larger, but were dissipated in less than half an hour. As a result of this trial, Burchard could write Dr. H. P. Robertson, DOLOC representative in England, that it did look as though the explosive-laden boat, directed manually and carrying the maximum possible load of TNT, tetrytol, or C-2, might be the only practical solution, though neither he nor Warner liked it any too well. The big demonstration would test this theory at high level.

At the first meeting in Fort Pierce DOLOC found that the group there had about given up use of the airplane for demolition on the shore. Since this seemed based on entirely insufficient information, the Committee urged that bombing be restored to the agenda, and many more trials were then made under the general supervision of Bleakney.

Early in November he reported that the British were opposed to bombing the beaches because they thought the craters would offer impediments. Yet a few days later our own Pacific-experienced forces, who had actually made landings on beaches, were found to favor the craters as God-given foxholes. Nonetheless, it would be important that the craters should not be big enough to engulf tanks or amphibians. The basic problem resolved itself into several questions: On the Continental beaches, what radius of clearance for mine or wire could probably be achieved with various weights of bombs and various types of fuzing? Knowing the accuracy and the pattern of the bombing, what force would we need in order to give a high probability of clearing one or more lanes made up of overlapping circles-of-clearance effected by the individual bombs? What sort of craters would be expected?

On the 10th of November a flight of bombers, flying a javelin-down formation and carrying 100-lb. bombs with instantaneous nose fuzes, attacked a test field at Fort Pierce. No lane was cleared, but each 100-lb. bomb that struck the field did clear a circle of about 15-ft. radius with very small craters. Since the mines used were USA practice mines, in no real way comparable to the German Tellers, much more information was needed about the actual clearance possibilities. Bleakney made several trips to the Aberdeen Proving Ground and other experimental stations to ferret this out through static trials and otherwise. Meanwhile, it was obvious that probability calculations would have to be made and the problem was assigned to Henry Scheffé, mathematician at the Princeton University Station. Two weeks later he reported that his first rough calculations were not altogether promising but suggestive enough so that more power should be put on the problem. He urged that Dr. J. Neyman, distinguished mathematician from the University of California, be asked to work on it. Arrangements were made with the Applied Mathematics Panel to loan Neyman and his team, and they studied the problem with energy, enthusiasm, and interesting results for months.

Working at Fort Pierce, Vero Beach, Orlando, and Eglin Field, Bleakney then laid out a program to determine the radius for 100-, 250-, and 500-lb. bombs; to secure and amplify existing data on dispersion and deflection of a single train of bombs and on the dispersion of a group of trains about the aiming point; and to discover the most promising formations, which were likely to be quite different from those hitherto flown in Europe. After he talked to experienced bomber officers from ETO it was concluded that a B-26 would be the best plane to use and that the lowest possible altitude men could be asked to fly on this mission was 12,000 feet. This altitude was therefore adopted as standard, since the accuracy would certainly decrease at the higher altitudes.

Meanwhile, Neyman's exhaustive analysis of dispersion data provided by the Air Forces showed that they were not sufficient, and he asked for more to be obtained by dropping inert bombs. Since the ground at Eglin was torn up from much bombing, the Command felt that strikes of the inerts could not be measured there with any confidence. It was decided to fly missions over the Gulf and photograph the strikes as they hit the water, and Bleakney went along on these missions. As was so often the case in these marriages between the civilian scientist and the military operator, the conditions of the experiment, carefully planned as they had been by the civilians, were not met. B-17's were used instead of B-26's. Instead of an average crew, the best available group of B-17 pilots, experienced in flying formation together, was mustered for the trials. Only the last pass was made at the scheduled 12,000 feet, all the others at 7,000 feet. The data were of some help, however, and Neyman tried to bring his calculations to a conclusion.

On January 26, twelve days before the demonstration, a full-scale trial was held at Fort Pierce on a specially prepared field that had taken a month to build. Burchard, Bleakney, Kistiakowsky, and Warner were thrilled as the formation of eighteen planes swept over in perfect alignment. From the sea it appeared that the bombing had been remarkably accurate and had split the target both in range and in azimuth. One could not have asked for better results — until the observers stepped on the beach. Here, it was evident that again the marriage had not been too happy. The bombers had not limited themselves to 100-lb. bombs as specified. At least one dud proved that they had carried some 250-pounders as well. Not equipped with instantaneous nose fuzes but with a delay, the bombs penetrated the beach before detonating. The result was a materially reduced radius of clearance per bomb. The yawning craters many feet deep would have defeated any landing.

The Air Force was contrite and ready to fly another mission at once. Unfortunately, there was no target left and insufficient time to clear, bulldoze out, and replant mines before the demonstration. There was scant comfort in the conclusion that, with the clearance per bomb expected from instantaneously fuzed bombs, the pattern achieved would probably have produced more than satisfactory clearance of paths. All that could be done was to hope, and use every means to implement that hope, that on the day of the demonstration the flight formation, the bombs, the accuracy, and the fuzing would all be right.

These three efforts have been described in some detail in order to illustrate the methodology of this type of research and the inherent difficulties even when time does not press. They consume here a space far disproportionate to the total time spent on them by DOLOC and to the other activities that are not recounted. The tale of the latter is sacrificed to better comprehension of the over-all job. If told, it would have included equally arduous, confusing, and discouraging efforts with naval bombardment, detonators, radio fuzes, projected grapnels, torpedoes, rocket boats, rocket tanks, and the rapidly cooling Hot Dog project.

The eventful days of the demonstration were fair, and preparations for the reception, care, and entertainment of the visitors were superb. In praising Captain Gulbransen and his base, Vice-Admiral Sharp, Commander Service Forces Atlantic, could honestly say that he had never seen a better run affair. Every scheduled test was carried out and not much behind schedule. The high officers moved smoothly from car to LCT where a special platform afforded a comfortable point of vantage to watch the work from the sea, to amphibious vehicles, to the shore, and back again to the sea.

The representation was high level. For the Army it included John J. McCloy, Assistant Secretary of War, General Henry, Major General A. K. Waldron for the Ground Forces, Major General G. M. Barnes of Ordnance, Brigadier General E. L. Eubank, AAF, Brigadier General Hugh Casey for General MacArthur, and Lieutenant Colonel Finley for General Richardson. The Navy was correspondingly represented by Admirals Sharp and Kilpatrick, Rear Admiral W. S. Delaney, head of the Readiness Division of COMINCH, and Captain Moses. NDRC's top echelon was represented by its Executive Officer, Dean Moreland. The total number of observers was close to a hundred, each provided with wet-weather gear, binoculars, an iron hat, and emergency rations (which were never needed). Each was given ready transportation, good shelter, good food. At the end there was a critique. It was quite a party.

What came out of it, at least from the point of view of DOLOC, can probably best be learned by excerpts from a letter Burchard wrote to Robertson two weeks later, describing and commenting on the results of the demonstration. This letter antedated any of the formal reports of DOLOC. Since it was informal, it is possibly also more informative. It explains that the views were personal and the comments limited to what was on the books at the moment. It did not discuss what might be done in time to make any of the items better. Taking up the methods in the chronological order in which they would be used in an attack, Burchard wrote:

"Long-range preliminary attack [9]

"Naval gunfire was not demonstrated . . . recent events [10] suggest that the total effect of heavy naval barrage may have been underestimated.

"Aerial Bombing. Two missions were flown . . . both at the altitude and in the formation shown in the program. The first, of B-17's, was practically perfect. It laid its bombs straight across the middle of the target. They were fuzed correctly, that is, with instantaneous nose and

---

[9] Only part of the material under these headings is quoted. The letter was a long and detailed document.

[10] The bombardments in the Marshalls, notably at Kwajalein.

tail. A splendid wire gap was cleared from beach to road, i.e., through all the wire, but no damage was done in the water which could be considered significant. No way of knowing just what would have happened to honest-to-God mines because all we ever have are the infernal M1B1's [11] which don't mean anything so far as I am concerned. The second mission flew to the north of the target and missed altogether. It was ragged anyway and made up of B-17's and B-24's. . . .

.   .   .   .

"On the whole, it looks to us as though a great deal could be accomplished by this pre-landing bombing. It cannot take place very long before H hour because repairs are so easy. It would probably be desirable to fly a great many formations. Though clear paths or almost clear paths are certain to be found somewhere on the beaches following such bombing, it may be a problem to locate them for the infantry.

.   .   .   .

"*Short-range pre-landing demolition, Underwater obstacles, Hand-placed charges* . . . Navy demolition people, approaching under conditions simulating night sneak attack . . . were able to stand while placing charges and generally did an expeditious job. Nothing has occurred to change our previous view that these are not practical on an assault of any consequence, or once the enemy has been alerted.[12]

"*Reddy Fox.* Towed by LCVP, a splendid job was done of floating a single Fox against Japanese wood scaffolding. I have never seen a better job. The sea was flat, there was no wind, the visibility was perfect, and the Ensign doing the job was the only one on the Base I have ever seen really able to do it . . . inspection made me think that most of the vertical timbers were not removed but broken about at waterline and would still have been obstacle.

.   .   .   .

"Reddy Fox is a good enough gimmick. Nobody yet has said how it will be carried to the transport area, put over side and otherwise got on to the line of departure. . . . Believe that there is considerable

---

[11] Code number for the USA practice mine.

[12] The Committee was, of course, wrong in this. In the final analysis it was brave men with hand charges who, racing against the tide, cleared the Omaha and Utah beaches. Not large in total number, the casualties were extremely heavy in terms of the number of men engaged, but nonetheless the mission was accomplished.

promise in clusters of Foxes self-powered but this is nonexistent now and in my opinion Fox will serve no useful purpose this spring. . . . Entirely disagree with 7th Interim Report Engineer Board that it is easy to place them normal to the beach through obstacles.

"*Bucket Boat, Apex Boat.*

. . . . . .

"Demonstration was practically a complete mess, partly due to too many safety precautions. Ensign drove the LCM to proper position and started scuttling charge. Something went wrong with preliminary charge and he was hurt and out on his feet. Stand-by officer went overside and pulled him out of boat and in confusion both left engine running. By the time detonation had occurred engine had driven LCM *through three rows of rails* and practically onto beach. Charge was about 25 tons of TNT. . . . Crater was a honey with seaward lip which did not recede at least for many hours and which sheltered a swimming pool of awesome proportions. Even if the rails had been taken out, landing craft would have touched on outer lip and anyone trying to get ashore would have had to be a good swimmer. . . .

"Somewhat shaken now on what to say about Bucket Boat.[13] . . . Gap is large enough to be significant. But not so sure about seaward lips . . . coxswains might get the charge where it should be, knowing that the Flying Mattress[14] is good gear to escape on. Not sure that landing craft could not push lip in anyway by backing off a couple of times, for profile is steep. . . .

. . . . . .

"There will be no tidal waves and no one on the beach is going to die of fright — and very few from fragments.

. . . . . .

"*Land Obstacles, Rocket Craft.* Porcupine is not in my opinion very useful. Doesn't carry enough rockets and will certainly be hard to put

---

[13] Code name for an Apex Boat without the radio drone controls. Bleakney did not agree with Burchard. He felt that the only failure in the Bucket Boat demonstration had been the placing and that the very calm sea, which would be most unusual, accounted for the slow reduction of the seaward lip.

[14] An electric, outboard-motor-powered rubber raft.

overside.[15] Haven't any good dope on Woofus.[16] Offhand it looks to me like a pretty wasteful use of landing craft. . . .

"But both these craft touch down in perhaps 5 ft. of water and on a 1–80 beach[17] this means 400 ft. out. With a rocket range of 300 yards, you can see that this stuff won't reach very far in.

"In view of vulnerability of boat, small range, uncertainty as to accuracy, and limited clearance, fail to see how this will do anything bombs won't do as well or better and easier and faster. The beach is pretty lively during the few seconds when the thing is going off but again I don't believe that an enemy under cover is going to fall dead from fright. . . .

. . . .

"*Demolition after landing in assault, Hand-placed charges.* Went extremely well as they always do. Placing time is almost always understated. This particular job took at least three minutes by my watch. Do think the sappers should have more protection and would like to see a Trojan Horse for them. Since it doesn't now exist, what's the matter with having them go up between two tanks which will at least cut down the loss from small-arms fire? If the tank gets immobilized there will be at least less distance to go under fire.

. . . .

"*Tank Rocket Launcher.* This gadget is much better than it looked at the demonstration. It can get off the LCT easily. It can jettison easily. It aims well. They were firing a brand new one and the circuits had not been checked and they tried to fire remotely as well and altogether this made for an interminable time between rounds.

. . . .

"Against Element C[18] the launcher behaved better than the evidence suggests. As you break some of the main members of the Element it gets easier and easier to shoot through without hitting. I had the clear impression, though, that a tank could have pushed aside the debris after many fewer rounds than were actually fired.

---

[15] Because of the rocket launchers on both sides.

[16] Woofus was an LCM, distinguished from the Porcupine by the fact that the rocket launchers were inboard rather than outboard. This, of course, used up the cargo- and troop-carrying space of the landing craft and made it into an attack boat pure and simple.

[17] The usual slope of the beaches in Holland, Flanders, and Normandy.

[18] A high fence made of heavy structural steel sections. This was a popular obstacle on the Continent.

"*Tank Dozer*. This is a honey, gets off craft easily, jettisons easily, and does more than seems possible. Can clear underwater obstacles until it loses traction in deep water and will do most anything on land except butt down a thick wall. Don't quite see how it can be effective in assault phase because, though it works fast, it is in the same place quite a while and I would like to have the job of shooting at it from a fixed and fortified position.

"The Dozer is so photogenic that I am sure it will see full service and, if used wisely, will give full service."

Shorn of its informal language and much elaborated, this was, in effect, also the tenor of the 2nd report of Committee DOLOC, which was dated February 15 and which was rendered to the Chairman, NDRC, on March 15. The conclusion is worth repeating, though it annoyed some people at the time:

"There is, as yet, no good solution to the demolition of underwater obstacles under assault conditions. There are things which, in lieu of such solutions, will sometimes work and therefore have to be used for the time being.

"There are partial solutions for the elimination of mines at the beach and the breaching of beach-exit barriers. There are several ways in which the wire on the beach can be destroyed just before the assault.

"The state of the whole art can only be called unsatisfactory; if these obstacles are going, in fact, to be encountered in quantity and cannot be avoided, the only alternative is enormously intensified effort. Assigning the project high priority and furnishing limitless funds will not solve the problem; personnel are needed. . . .

"Moreover, experience with the project thus far indicates that a much more close degree of co-ordination will be required than has been achieved thus far to give promise of early solutions, even to the most pressing problems."

In transmitting this report to the Chairman, NDRC, the Committee said:

"The directive which set February 15 as a pay-off day has conditioned all the work of the Committee, and all the work of the military and naval personnel at Fort Pierce. For the latter, it has meant taking things which were often in a preliminary research state and, skipping important research, passing them at once to at least a limited production stage. That possibly serious mistakes have occurred under these conditions seems not unlikely. It is certain that this process, far from accelerating research, has actually slowed it up; this would have been the case even without the possibly premature demonstration. For us it has meant that as soon as it became apparent we were not going to dream up something which would solve the problem at a single stroke, we could be helpful only in small and immediate ways. . . .

". . . We cannot, however, pretend that we have made a major contribution or one consistent with the amount of high-grade manpower we have tried to apply.

". . . War is a series of crises. If each time one looms, experimental establishments try to close their books, there will soon be no more books to close. It would be better to have a permanent sense of immediacy in such stations as Fort Pierce and, as pay-off days arise, to select well in advance those items which have by that time clearly shown that they warrant high priority processing. The alternative tried here has not accelerated the processing of such ready items; at the least, it has decelerated the study of other perhaps more promising items; and in the worst cases may have caused undesirable jumps in the research, steps over ground which may never be retraced until some other emergency reveals the lacunae in the existing information.

"It is recognized that there is little NDRC can do about this. It is questionable, however, whether we should again abet this sort of flurry."

The Committee expressed confidence in negotiations Admiral Furer was carrying on for a much more powerful Amphibious Research Center and a better experimental setup at Fort Pierce, and suggested that when that was effected NDRC should merely have a liaison representative at the station, who might be an appointee of OFS. To clear the decks for all these actions the Committee recommended that it be discharged. NDRC did not immediately concur with this recommendation. It asked that DOLOC continue until the proposed new Joint Army-Navy Experimental and Testing Board setup was well established.

This is the story of DOLOC, the story of a failure but not a fiasco. Indeed, some would not even say it was a failure. The Chairman received an encouraging letter, for example, on a very low day, August 28, 1944. This was from Warner:

"DOLOC was geared as an *ad hoc* committee to deliver results which could be applied immediately at the target date.

"DOLOC per se worked at the technical level, reported on a tactical level, accomplished no panaceas, contributed intangible guidance and moral support under rather hysterical conditions, and for the using Services on the target date it helped to evaluate the results with as much candor as the negatives demanded.

. . . .

"Since the fateful target date a number of DOLOC's technical considerations have been adopted, improved and standardized. . . . Within the Services the project has become stabilized with all the organization, channels of authority and equipment necessary to function. . . . I tend to agree with your impression that NDRC can furnish a technical service . . . but not with the original caliber of personnel or under the original project priority. . . . Thus, I believe NDRC should stay in the picture at the reduced level, that it should re-cut its cloth to fit the existing situation, and that by the readjustment there should be someone in Fort Pierce and in Washington who has the active responsibility and interest for improving JANET's lot through the available facilities of NDRC."

The new Joint Board was anxious to have a helper from NDRC. In September Burchard took Al Dietz to Fort Pierce as the first OFS appointee to JANET. The work of DOLOC effectively stopped when Dietz went into residence, and terminated officially a month later when Army and Navy concurred with the suggestion that the Committee be discharged.

Failure or not, this was the history of DOLOC. In it are lessons for those who heed.

WARTIME ALPHABET

GLOSSARY OF ABBREVIATIONS

A-2	Air Force Intelligence Branch
A-3	Air Force Branch in charge of operations
AA	Antiaircraft
AACS	Army Airways Communications System
AAF	Army Air Forces
AAORG	Antiaircraft Operations Research Group; a subdivision of ORG in the Navy
ABL-15	American British Laboratory of Division 15, NDRC; located in England
AC/S	Assistant Chief of Staff
AFPAC	Army Forces, Pacific
AGO	Adjutant General's Office
AGRL	Australian Group, Radiation Laboratory; headquartered at Sydney, Australia
AirORG	Air Operations Research Group; a subdivision of ORG
ALSOS	Code name for an Army-Navy-OSRD Intelligence Mission to Europe
AMP	Applied Mathematics Panel; a subdivision of OSRD
AN/TPS-10	Height-finding radar set known as Little Abner
APP	Applied Psychology Panel; a subdivision of OSRD
ASF	Army Service Forces
ASG	Advisory Specialist Group; experts in radar and countermeasures operating under Dr. Bowles's office
ASWORG	Antisubmarine Warfare Operations Research Group; forerunner of ORG
ATAD	Air Technical Analysis Division in the Navy
ATC	Air Transport Command
BBRL	British Branch, Radiation Laboratory; located in England
BCSO	British Commonwealth Scientific Office
BOQ	Bachelor Officers' Quarters
BuAer	Navy Bureau of Aeronautics; others were BuMed (Medicine and Surgery), BuOrd (Ordnance), BuPers (Personnel), and BuShips

CBI	China-Burma-India Theater of Operations
CIC	Combat Information Center
CINCLANT	Commander in Chief, Atlantic
CINCPAC	Commander in Chief, Pacific
CIOS	Combined Intelligence Objectives Subcommittee; headquartered in London
CMR	Committee on Medical Research
ComAirPac	Commander of (Navy) Air Forces in the Pacific
COMINCH	Commander in Chief
ComPhibLant	Commander Amphibious Forces, Atlantic
ComPhibsPac	Commander Amphibious Forces, Pacific
ComSubPac	Commander Submarines, Pacific
CPA	Central Pacific Area
CRD	Co-ordinator of (Navy) Research and Development
CSIR	Council for Scientific and Industrial Research (Australia)
CTD	Committee on Tropical Deterioration; a subdivision of OSRD
CWS	Chemical Warfare Service
DDT	dichloro-diphenyl-trichloro ethane; an insecticide
Division	An NDRC administrative unit. The Divisions were:

1 – Ballistics Research
2 – Structural Defense and Offense
3 – Rocket Ordnance
4 – Ordnance Accessories
5 – Guided Missiles
6 – Subsurface Warfare
7 – Fire Control
8 – Explosives
9 – Chemistry
10 – Absorbents and Aerosols
11 – Chemical Engineering
12 – Transportation Development
13 – Communications
14 – Radar
15 – Radio and Radar Countermeasures
16 – Optics and Camouflage
17 – Physics
18 – War Metallurgy
19 – Miscellaneous Weapons

| DOLOC | Committee on Demolition of Obstacles to Landing Operations |

DUKW	Code name for the amphibious 2½-ton truck
ERC	Enlisted Reserve Corps
ETO	European Theater of Operations
ETOUSA	U.S. Army in ETO; an administrative subdivision
FEA	Federal Economic Administration; a Government war agency
FEAF	Far East Air Force
FETU	Far Eastern Technical Unit; of CWS in the Southwest Pacific
FSC	Field Service Consultant; name applied to all field-service men of OFS
FSD	Field Service Division; proposed unit of the prospective National Science Foundation
G-1	Army General Staff Section responsible for personnel; others are G-2 (Intelligence), G-3 (Operations), etc.
GCI	Ground Control of Interception radar
GHQ	General Headquarters
GI	Literally — Government Issue; applied to an enlisted man
HE	High Explosive
HE/IB	Ratio of high explosive to incendiary bombs in a bombing load
HQ	Headquarters
HUSAFPOA	Headquarters U.S. Army Forces, Pacific Ocean Area
Husky	Code name for the invasion of Sicily
IB	Incendiary Bomb
I B M	International Business Machine
JANET	Joint Army-Navy Experimental and Testing Board
JCS	Joint Chiefs of Staff
JIC	Joint Intelligence Committee
JNW	Committee on New Weapons; under the JCS
JTG	Joint Target Group
LCC	Landing Craft, Control
LCI	Landing Craft, Infantry
LCM	Landing Craft, Mechanized
LCT	Landing Craft, Tanks
LCVP	Landing Craft, Vehicles and Personnel
LST	Landing Ship, Tanks

LVT	Landing Vehicle, Tracked; otherwise known as the Weasel
MEW	Microwave Early Warning radar
MID	Military Intelligence Division (Army)
MIDPAC	Army Forces in the Middle Pacific
MIS	Military Intelligence Section (Army)
M.I.T.	Massachusetts Institute of Technology
MTI	Moving Target Indicator
MTO	Mediterranean Theater of Operations
NALOC	Committee on Navigational Aids to Landing Operations
NavTechMisEu	Navy Technical Mission in Europe
NDD	New Developments Division; Special Staff Section of the Army which served as the major liaison channel for OFS
NDRC	National Defense Research Committee; a major subdivision of OSRD
NMP	Navigational Microfilm Projector; part of a radar inshore navigational system
N-P	Neuropsychiatric
NRF	National Research Foundation; proposed permanent scientific authority of the Government; suggested by Dr. Bush and under consideration by Congress
NSF	National Science Foundation; alternative name for NRF
OAD	Operations Analysis Division of the Army Air Forces
OFS	Office of Field Service; a major subdivision of OSRD
Olympic	Code name for the proposed invasion of Japan
ONI	Office of Naval Intelligence
OPD	(Army) Operations Division
OQMG	Office of the Quartermaster General
ORC	Operations Research Center; subdivision of ORG
ORG	(Navy) Operations Research Group
ORI	(Navy), Office of Research and Inventions
ORS	Operational Research Section; a term applied to both British and American groups. The field units of OAD with the various air forces carried this designation. It was also the name given to the OFS balanced team in Hawaii

ORS–POA	The Operational Research Section of OFS in General Richardson's headquarters at Oahu. Also known as ORS–CPA and ORS–MIDPAC under different organization of the Theater
OSRD	Office of Scientific Research and Development; a Government war agency
OSS	Office of Strategic Services; a Government war agency
OS/W	Office of the Secretary of War
Overlord	Code name for the invasion of Normandy
PacWarBd	Pacific Warfare Board
PBOSRD	Pacific Branch of OSRD; set up in Manila just before the end of the war
PhibORG	Amphibious Operations Research Group; a subdivision of ORG
POA	Pacific Ocean Areas; consolidation under Nimitz and Richardson of what had formerly been CPA and SPA
POE	Port of Embarkation
PPI	Plan Position Indicator
PR	Princes Risborough
PUS	Princeton University Station; research organization of Division 2, NDRC
PX	Post Exchange
QMC	Quartermaster Corps
RAF	(British) Royal Air Force
RCM	Radar countermeasures
RDD	(Army) Research and Development Division
RL	Radiation Laboratory; located at M.I.T.; the major activity of Division 14, NDRC
RPL	Radiophysics Laboratory at Sydney, Australia
RRL	Radio Research Laboratory; located at Harvard University; the major activity of Division 15, NDRC
R/S	Research Section; the name given to the OFS office in MacArthur's command
SCR-584	Signal Corps Radar 584; a mobile radar adapted to many uses
SGO	Surgeon General's Office
SHAEF	Supreme Headquarters, Allied Expeditionary Forces (in Europe)
SOP	Standard operating procedure

SORG	Submarine Operations Research Group; a subdivision of ORG
SPA	South Pacific Area
SpecORG	Subdivision of ORG established to deal with special problems such as suicide attacks
SPO	Scientific Personnel Office; a subdivision of OSRD
SWPA	Southwest Pacific Area
TIIC	Technical Industrial Intelligence Committee
TO	Table of Organization
Torch	Code name for the invasion of North Africa
UK	United Kingdom
USAFFE	U.S. Army Forces in the Far East
USNR	U.S. Naval Reserve; as distinguished from USN, meaning regular Navy
USSBS	United States Strategic Bombing Survey
V-1	Nazi buzz-bomb or robot plane
V-2	Nazi guided rocket weapon
V-E	Victory in Europe
VHF	Very high frequency
VIP	Very Important Person
V-J	Victory over Japan
VPR	Virtual PPI Reflectoscope; part of a radar system of inshore navigation
VT	Variable time; designation for a type of proximity fuze operated by a minute radio transmitting and receiving set; it could be set to detonate the bomb or shell at a fixed distance from its target
WAE	When actually employed; a type of Government employment in which the individual works for the Government only part of the time
WESPAC	Western Pacific; name applied to an administrative subdivision under AFPAC.
WOC	Without compensation; a type of Government employment
WPB	War Production Board; a Government war agency

PERSONNEL INDEX

SUBJECT INDEX